HANDBOOK
Injurious and Beneficial Mites Infesting Agri-horticultural Crops in India and their Management

HANDBOOK
Injurious and Beneficial Mites Infesting Agri-horticultural Crops in India and their Management

S.K. GUPTA, Ph.D, D.Sc.

(USERS Project, Department of Science and Technology, Govt. of India)

Retired Joint Director and Emeritus Scientist, Zoological Survey of India, Ministry of Environment and Forests, Govt. of India

NBI

Nature Books India

119, Jodhpur Garden, 2nd Floor

Kolkata - 700 045

CITATION

Gupta, S.K. 2012. *Handbook – Injurious and Beneficial Mites Infesting Agri-horticultural Crops in India and their Management* : 1-362 (including 20 colour plates). (Published by Nature Books India)

PUBLISHER

Nature Books India, 119, Jodhpur Garden, 2nd Floor, Kolkata - 700 045.

Published : March, 2012

ISBN 978-93-82258-00-1

Catalyzed and supported by the Department of Science & Technology under its "Utilization of Scientific Expertise of Retired Scientists Scheme"

PRICE
Indian Rs. 2450.00
Foreign : $ 175

Printed at M/s Power Printers, 2/8 A, Ansari Road, Darya Ganj, New Delhi - 110 002.

डा. एस. अय्यप्पन
सचिव एवं महानिदेशक
Dr. S. AYYAPPAN
SECRETARY & DIRECTOR GENERAL

भारत सरकार
कृषि अनुसंधान और शिक्षा विभाग एवं
भारतीय कृषि अनुसंधान परिषद
कृषि मंत्रालय, कृषि भवन, नई दिल्ली 110 114

GOVERNMENT OF INDIA
DEPARTMENT OF AGRICULTURAL RESEARCH & EDUCATION
AND
INDIAN COUNCIL OF AGRICULTURAL RESEARCH
MINISTRY OF AGRICULTURE. KRISHI BHAVAN. NEW DELHI 110 114
Tel.: 23382629; 23386711 Fax: 91-11-23384773
E-mail: dg.icar@nic.in

FOREWORD

Acarines, including mites and ticks, are of considerable economic importance in agriculture and public health aspects. Global efforts are on to study their diversity and impact on human welfare. Several species of mites, which are known to occur on plants have turned into major pests. One of the primary reasons behind this is the indiscriminate and injudicious uses of synthetic chemical pesticides in pest management program.

Out of over 1200 mite species known to occur on crops and stored products, there are at least 40 species of economically important pests and 30 species of potential predators. All these need indepth studies regarding both basic and applied prospects and in case of predators there is a need of conservation, augmentation and profitable utilization in biological control.

Due to the economical importance of mites, many papers on diverse aspects have been published along with some books for Indian plant mites but a compendium on mites of agri-horticultural crops, mushrooms, stored products etc. are available dealing with their documentation, bio-ecology, extent of damage etc. was needed. To bridge these gaps, Dr. S.K. Gupta, who has been awarded a financial grant by the Department of Science and Technology, Government of India under their USERS scheme, has prepared this ***Handbook. Injurious and Beneficial Mites infesting Agri-Horticultural crops in India and their management*** which deals with the basic and applied aspects of all mites of various types of crops, mushrooms and stored products. In addition, a general discussion on basic aspects like habits and habitats, study techniques, mite feeding and consequent damages, gall formation, malformation etc., mite pheromones and their uses in management, chemical, biological, biorational control, predators, parasites and pathogens of mites etc. have also been discussed. It also provides a list of mites on agri-horticultural crops in India, as well as keys to orders and families of mites occurring on these crops. I am sure, this Handbook, will be very helpful to the Entomologists, Acarologists, Researchers and Post Graduate students of India and abroad.

The effort of Dr. Gupta, the retired Joint Director, Zoological Survey of India, Kolkata and Former Project Co-ordinator of AICRP-Agricultural Acarology of the Indian Council of Agricultural Research, New Delhi deserves appreciation for bringing out this book.

(S. Ayyappan)

Dated the 7th June, 2011
New Delhi

AUTHOR'S PREFACE

Mites are microscopic to submicroscopic creatures, belong to phylum Arthropoda, class Arachnida and subclass Acari. Because of their minute size, they often remain unnoticed and become perceptible only when they do appreciable damages to various agri-horticultural crops registering substantial economic loss to the growers. The loss may be both qualitative and quantitative in nature and the extent of loss may be variable ranging from 5-70%, depending upon the type of the crop. In some rare cases they may even cause total crop failure when the population reaches to an uncontrollable level. However, the mite damage to crops is more due to injudicious uses of synthetic chemical pesticides which on one side invite human and environmental hazards and on the other side cause upsurge of pest population due to elimination of natural enemies. But not all mites are our enemies as there are many which occur on agri-horticultural crops which are our friends by acting as active predators of the pest species and thereby contribute substantially towards biological control. Thus, they become important component in Integrated Mite Management Programme (IMMP).

Though the investigation of mites on agri-horticultural crops in India started as early as 1868 when a plant feeding mite was recorded on tea but till the middle of past century (1964) only 65 species under 29 genera and 11 families were in record. The investigation of mite got fillip with the realization of the increasing importance of these mites and various Government agencies like Indian Council of Agricultural Research (ICAR), Ministry of Environment and Forests, Department of Science and Technology as well as several other organizations under various State Governments came forward by providing funds to undertake research on these mites both in basic and applied aspects. This led to bring out some notable publications like ChannaBasavanna (1966, 1981), Sadana (1985), Banerjee (1989), Gupta (1985, 1986, 1987, 2002, 2003, 2005), ChannaBasavanna & Viraktamath (Eds.) (1988, 1989), Mallik *et al.*, (2004) Srinivasa *et al.* (2004, 2004a), Sharma & Srinivasa (2004), Dhooria *et al.*, (2005), etc. Through all these a wealth of information on diverse aspects has been generated.

Despite all these, most of the available information is very much scattered and no consolidated book on injurious and beneficial mites of agri-horticultural crops in India is available. Further, Gupta (1985) in his Handbook on plant mites of India reported the occurrence of 557 species (including both phytophagous and predatory mites) known till then from India but the number has become doubled and no documentation of all those has been done till date. Hence, the Department of Science & Technology, Govt. of India, sanctioned a generous grant under its USERS project to this author for writing this handbook on the injurious and beneficial acarines of India and the present book, being the second one in the series, is the outcome of that.

This book deals with injurious and beneficial mites on crops like Cereals and Millets, Pulses, Fibre crops, Oil seeds, Plantation crops, Fruit trees, Vegetables, Medicinal - Aromatic - Dye-yielding - Spices- Condiments - Narcotic plants, Ornamentals, Weeds, Forests trees, Cash crops, Mushrooms, Stored products and Apiculture mites from India. Apart from that, some basic aspects like, Habits and Habitats, Study techniques, Mode of mite feeding and consequent damages, Management by various means, Malformation - Gall formation - Plant abnormalities, Resistance development and its consequent effects, Pheromones in mite control, Biology of predatory mites, Predator-prey interaction, Mite transmission of plant viruses, Parasites and pathogens of mites, etc. have also been dealt with. Besides, keys to important taxa of Agri-horticultural mites as well as a list of all known species from India and selected references are also given. Hopefully, the treasure of information given in this book will prove worthy to the agricultural entomologists, Acarologists, researchers, post graduate students and agricultural policy makers. This will develop awareness about menaces done by mites to crops and develop strategy to combat those.

The author records his sincerest gratitude to the Department of Science & Technology, Govt. of India for providing financial assistance without which this work would have been practically impossible to do. Sincere thanks are due to Dr. S. Dutta, Principal, Prof. Subir Dasgupta, Head and other faculty members of the Post Graduate Department of Zoology, Maulana Azad College, Kolkata for providing infrastructure facilities and constant encouragements. Several research students of the author like, Ms. Poulami Sarangi, Himani Biswas, Amrita Mukherjee, Ananya Das, Debalina Mandal, Pubali Mondal, Piyali Mujumdar, Dr. S. Podder, Dr. Indranil Roy, Soma Karmakar extended very valuable help and assistance throughout the project period and to all of them the author is highly indebted. Finally, the constant encouragement received from Swami Vishwamayananda, Asst. Secretary, Ramakrishna Mission Ashrama, Narendrapur and Dr. K. Karmakar, Bidhan Chandra Krishi Vishwavidyalaya, Kalyani are also acknowledged with grateful thanks. The author is highly grateful to Dr. S. Ayyappan, Director General, ICAR and Secretary to the Govt. of India, DARE, Krishi Bhavan, New Delhi for kindly writing the "Foreword" of this book which has enhanced its value. The last but not the least the moral support received from my daughter Ms. Nilanjana Gupta and technical support received from the numerous scientists all over the world by providing valuable literature on which this book is partly based, are also thankfully acknowledged.

Dr. S.K. Gupta

January 23, 2012

CONTENTS

1. INTRODUCTION

1.1 HABITS AND HABITATS

Almost any orchard or field crop or for that matter any plant is likely to be infested by mites which include spider mites, false spider mites, gall mites, predatory mites, erineum mites, rust mites, etc. Even, in forest canopies they are very abundant. The forest records indicate that the plant mites lived on the trees since Cretaceous period (Walter & Proctor, 1999).

The habits and habitats of plant mites are very diverse. Since majority of the plant mites are negatively phototrophic, the mites on plants are found on the undersurface of leaves either in colonies (Fam. Tetranychidae, Tenuipalpidae) or in solitary manners (majority of predatory mites, Tarsonemidae). Many of the mites especially the phytoseiid mites are seen in the angles formed by the veins with the leaf lamina. Some tetranychid mites (some *Oligonychus, Schizotetranychus, Eutetranychus* of the family Tetranychidae) may also be seen on the upper surface of leaves. Sometimes same leaf may be occupied by two species of mites, one on the dorsal surface of leaf (*Oligonychus mangiferus* on grape leaf) and another on the under surface of the same leaf (*Eotetranychus truncatus* on grape leaf). Many of the tenuipalpid mites are found on twigs, leaf petioles, fruit surface, besides both surfaces of leaves. The eriophyid mites normally occur either as vagrants on undersurface of leaves or, in flowers, leaf buds, on fruit surface or on galls, in inflorescence or in malformed and deformed plant parts. A large number of predatory mites occur on undersurface of leaves and some may be occupying tetranychid colonies or under surface of webs, having the capability to invade the webs. Many of the spider mites cover the colonies with webs, which may be light or dense, to protect themselves from their natural enemies as well as from vagaries of nature. Many of the predatory mites live within leaf domatia, where they get a protective shelter. A good number of mites, especially Phytoseiidae, Tydeidae, etc. may occur on twigs, stems or under barks.

The habits of plant inhabiting mites are also very diverse. Some are plant parasitic striking the individual plant cells with the stylet- like chelicerae and suck the plant sap producing various types of damage symptoms and consequently affecting yield. This provides the mites ready source of moisture. Plant parasitism has evolved repeatedly in different lineages of mites so that to-day most species of conifers, monocots, dicots, ferns are attacked by one or more species of mites (Helle & Sabelis, 1985). There are many predatory forms (Fam. Phytoseiidae, Ascidae, Anystidae, Stigmaeidae, etc.) which prey upon plant parasitic mites and thereby help in biological control. Among the two major groups of plant associated mites, one is the free living forms which include predaceous, phytophagous, fungivorous, coprophagous, saprophagous and phoretic forms, the other group the phytophagous forms include aerial species, that feed on plants both above ground and in the soil.

The predaceous forms are long legged, fast moving and have longer setae for invading the webbing of the tetranychid mites and feed upon adults, immatures and eggs of the phytophagous mites. In many predaceous mites, the chelicerae are styliform and palps are raptorial for capturing and sucking the body contents of the prey. Some have dentate chelicerae (Phytoseiidae, Ascidae).

Some of the phytophagous mites invade the storage houses, feed on the stored products and damage them so much so that they become useless for human consumption or for germination. Graminivorous mties feed on germ tissues of the grains and may damage the endosperm also. Many of the mites feed on dried fruits, stored debris, bulbs inflicting considerable economic loss.

Some plant mites are phoretic and they use other insects for dispersal as is seen in case of *Polyphagotarsonemus latus* using white flies for this purpose.

There are many plant mites which are fungus associated (e.g. some Oribatids. belonging to Oribatulidae, Camisiidae, acarids, etc.) which remain associated with the fungi grown on leaves and feed on fungal spores. Many mites seriously damage mushroom. They have pincer - like chelicerae, feed on fungal hyphae. Most of the mites occurring on tree trunks, branches, leaves, etc. are arboreal. The plant parasitic mites (Order Prostigmata) feed on fluids and for that they use modified stylet-like chelicerae to puncture the host cells and drain out the contents (Walter & Proctor, 1999). Phytophagy has arisen in seven clads of Prostigmata of which Eriophyoidea and Tetranychoidea are most important as well as in other clads like Erythraeidae, Eupodidae, Stigmaeidae, Tydeidae, Tarsonemidae.

The tarsonemid mites have evolved from mycophagous ancestors and have later adopted to plant parasitism (Lindquist, 1998, in Walter & Proctor, 1999). Eriophyids : the rust mites, gall mites or erinose mites have over 500 species from India belonging to Eriophyoidea (Families Phytoptidae, Diptilomiopidae, Eriophyidae). Most of these mites are tiny (less than 200 μ long) and worm-like with 2 pairs of legs. These are exclusively parasitic to plants belonging to monocots, dicots, conifers, ferns, etc. Many of those are host specific and migration is effected aerialy (Zhao & Amrine, 1997). They have tiny stylets enclosed in a U-shaped channel of the subcapitulum. Most eriophyids have apices of palp tarsi modified to form sucking pad with which they firmly attach their mouthparts with the leaf epidermis. The stylets thrust into host epidermal cells. Some eriophyids attach themselves on the leaf with anal suckers and then thrust the stylets into epidermal cells. Stylets do not form feeding tubes and they are withdrawn before cell fluid is sucked out (Oldfield & Michalska, 1996).

A large number of eriophyids make galls, erineum, deformities, big buds, witche's broom effect and attack stems, flowers but the roots are spared. In case of erineum mites, the mites live amidst hairs and thereby can get better protection from their natural enemies. The erinose leaf, if placed near electric light source, the mites will start emerging out as the hairs dry up. A large number of mites form galls and those have been separately dealt with in this book. The mechanism of galling is the insertion of plant tissues with stylets and injecting some chemical compounds into the plant cells which induce the surrounding cells to proliferate and that turn into galls. Varied types of galls (pouch type/finger-like/bead galls, nail-like, pocket-like) are produced by eriophyids. Some eriophyids are incriminated to transmit a number of plant viral diseases. Several eriophyids are known which cause russeting of leaves or blister of leaves. Some tenuipalpids and tarsonemids also induce gall-like growths.

As per Lindquist (1996), the current evidence suggest that eriophyid mites are closely related to tydeid mites and presumably plant feeding evolved from scavenging or fungus feeding leaf vagrants that were opportunistic leaf cell feeders (Walter & Proctor, 1999). The primitive form eriophyid species (*Pintasetacus*) cause galls on needles of Chilian species of Araucariaceae, that originated in Permian period, more than 250 million years ago (Boczek & Shevehenko, 1996, Walter & Proctor, 1999).

Some members of Earth Mites : Penthaleidae have evolved plant parasitic habit from fungivorous habit and have recently become very important pests especially of low growing herbs and pasture grass. *Halotydeus destructo*r is one such example which attacks broad leaf annuals and grasses and penetrate the flattened epithelial cells. This mite is a dark brown, orange or red with long red legs. Its immatures are normally spent in moss, algae and fungi growing on soil. Like *Halotydeus,* the *Penthaleus,* a related group, has also switched on to herbivory. These mites are brightly coloured and ornamented.

Tetranychids

These are exclusively parasites of vascular plants and many of those are economic pests of agri-horticulture and field crops and thus have received world attention. They stab the plant cells and suck out the contents causing various types of damages including necrosis, chlorosis, discolouration, premature leaf drop, fruit drop, etc. Like spiders, they spin webs to cover their colonies and hence the name spider mites. They live in colonies where mites of all stages may be seen and the colonies remain covered under webs giving them protection from desiccation and enemies. There are some which are highly polyphagous (*Tetranychus urticae* has over 900 hosts Walter & Proctor, 1999) and at the same time there are many which are highly host specific. As many as 1200 species under 70 genera are known worldwide (Bolland *et al.,* 1998).

Tenuipalpids

Tenuipalpidae, another important member of plant feeding mites, are known by over 600 species under 22 genera (Evans *et al.*, 1993) and are exclusively phytophagous and occur on leaves (both surfaces), twigs, petioles, fruits and flowers.

Tuckerellids

Tuckerellidae, another member of Tetranychoidea, are most ornate and long, having serrate posterior setae and palmate dorsal setae. Some are important pests of citrus, conifers, grasses, etc.

The tetranychoid mites have evolved phytophagy from predaceous ancestors. The other groups of plant mites having agri-horticultural importance are the predatory groups belonging to Order Mesostigmata (Fam. Phytoseiidae, Ascidae), Order Prostigmata (Anystidae, Cheyletidae, Cunaxidae, Bdellidae, Stigmaeidae, Tydeidae, Raphignathidae). Some of these are very common on plants while others are somewhat rare and infrequently met with. Many of these species have importance in biological control, especially those belonging to Phytoseiidae and hence have well explored and well studied.

Weed mites

Many of the mites habour weeds in the crop field. Some of the members are temporary inhabitants, occupy only when their primary hosts are not available and some are permanent settlers. Some of those are predators while there are many which are phytophagous and act as important biocontrol agents for obnoxious or poisonous weeds (eg. parthenium by *T. urticae*).

Some oribatids are used in biocontrol of aquatic weeds (eg. water hyacinth, *Eichhornia crassipes*) by oribatid mite *Orthogalumna terrebrantis*).

Fruit feeders

There are many fallen fruits under the process of decaying, which get colonized by mites of those some are predators, some are phytophagous, some are fungivorous, some are coprophagous and there are some which are phoretic coming in fruits through the invading insects. Some tydeids, tarsonemids invade fig fruit and may scavenge or are fungivorous.

Flower inhabiting

Many of the mites are flower inhabitants and visit from one flower to another and thereby help in pollination. Humming bird-associated mites are one of the well studied flower inhabiting mites. Mites under Ascidae include some of the flower inhabiting mites like *Proctolaelaps* which feed on pollen or nectar in inflorescence and may act as phoretic on nitidulid beetles that pollinate the palm trees (Naskrecki

& Colwell, 1995). The members of the genus *Neocypholaelaps* (Fam. Ameroseiidae) are feeders of pollen and nectars and use bees for transport. The mites under Oribatid group (Scheloribatidae, Haplozetidae) are also common in flowers.

Foliar Predatory Prostigmatid mites

Among the prostigmatid predatory mites living on leaves, the common ones are Anystidae, Cheyletidae, Cunaxidae, Bdellidae, Stigmaeidae, Raphignathidae and Tydeidae. Most predatory prostigmatid mites are either yellowish orange or bright red (Stigmaeidae, Cunaxidae, Bdellidae) and some tydeids are blackish or greenish may be with spots. Anystids are yellowish or reddish, make very fast whirling movement and fall down on the ground as soon as disturbed. Cheyletids are yellowish, ambush predators and are inhabitants of juncture of petioles and leaf blades. Some members of Cunaxids are also ambush predators. The palps are either well armed to capture the prey or are thrown forward to snap-trap prey against the snout. The anystid mites stab the insect prey with mouthparts and paralyse them with a toxin before they feed upon them. Some nymphs and adults of the genus *Charletonia* (Erythraeidae) feed on eggs of butterflies. *Balaustium*, also an erythraeid mite, predates on mites and insects. The members of Stigmaeidae are also active predators feeding upon all stages of phytophagous mites, though they have preference for eggs.

Foliar Mesostigmata

Among Mesostigmata, the members of the family Phytoseiidae are not only abundant but are also diverse. There are about 2300 described species from the world and there are some which are of paramount importance in biological control and therefore have invited attention of world acarologists and entomologists. They have several advantages as bio control agents as they are abundant, have good searching ability, show seasonal synchrony with plant feeding mites and can sustain on other food like pollen, honey, nectar in absence of normal prey.

Among Mesostigmata, Ascid mites like *Lasioseius, Proctolaelaps, Blattisocius* are also often found on leaves and are good predators especially in paddy ecosystem.

Mites in leaf domatia

Many of the mites live in leaf domatia or leaf tomenta where they get safe shelter and can protect themselves from inhospitable weather conditions. Some of the leaf domatia are in the form of pits sunken deep within leaf lamina. Igloo- like domes arise from the surface or pocket-like sheets of tissues and that connect the veins. Mites will be invariably available in the tuft domatia and in more elaborate pits, pockets, pouches and domes. The other inhabitants of domatia are thrips, bugs, and scale insects. The fungivores are common inhabitants of leaf domatia in humid climate. Predatory mites are common inhabitants of the leaf domatia and they benefit the plants by reducing the load of plant feeding mites. Other leaf domatia are considered as defense against herbivores and removal of those domatia will increase the plant feeding mite population. The predatory mites get preferential benefit from leaf domatia as they get protected places for oviposition and moulting.

Oribatid mites on leaf

In humid forest, several hundred oribatid mites may be seen in the leaf. The arboreal oribatids show distant sexual dimorphism. These mites prefer leaves with smooth surface. The leaves/fruits when attacked by parasitic fungi, huge fungal growth occurs and mites belonging to oribatids, tydeids, astigmatids are attracted and build up huge population.

Tarsonemids

Most species of tarsonemids are fungivorous, occur in protected areas in fruits and leaves while some members (*Dendroptus*) are predators feeding on eriophyid eggs, *Daidalotarsonemus* are abundant on stems and trunks.

Moss mites

Oribatid members of the families Camisiidae, Carabodidae, Ceratozetidae, Crotoniidae, Galumnidae, Liacaridae, Oribatulidae, Damaeidae, Phthiracaridae are commonly found associated with moss and lichens which grow as epicorticolous moss and lichens on tree trunks. These mites graze on lichens, algae, fungi. Members of *Humerobates, Diapterobates* are particularly common on twigs, branches and buds (Walter & Proctor, 1999).

Fungal sporocarps

The mite fauna which dominate this habitat are Astigmata and Mesostigmata. Most mesostigmatids found in bracket fungi are mycetophiles that feed as predators on the insects, mites and nematodes which inhabit decaying sporocarps but Ameroseiide and Ascidae are fungivorous. One of the commonest groups of astigmatid mites on fleshy fungi are histiostomatids feeding on bacteria/yeasts. Oribatids on fungal sporocarps show evidence for feeding specificity (Walter & Proctor, 1999).

Under bark mite fauna

Under bark provides a good habitat for mite fauna and they are more abundant in the decomposed portion of trunk or in the beetle galleries or in association with wood boring insects. Mites belonging to Astigmata, Mesostigmata, Prostigmata are the prominent fauna. Many of the Mesostigmatids are predators of mites and insects; some are phoretic on beetles (Walter & Proctor, 1999).

1.2 TECHNIQUES

Collection

Since the mites have diversified habitats, there are different methods for collection of different groups of mites which are mentioned below in brief :

Hand picking : Though it is most strenuous but yet it is profitable as a rich and varied collection of plant mites can be obtained by this method. The infested leaves are examined in the field itself under 10 x lens and mites are picked up with a fine sable hair brush moistened with ethyl alcohol (75%). Better results are obtained if the infested leaves are brought to the laboratory in a polythene bag after tightly closing the bag with rubber band and examined under stereobinocular microscope. For better collection of tenuipalpids, tydeids, this will be a more suitable method. However, it is equally important to identify the host plant by a plant taxonomist. For tetranychid and tarsonemid mites, the collection of male specimens is most essential as otherwise identification of species becomes a difficult task. For eriophyid mite collection, one should look into plant galls and plant deformities and herberea of host plants are to be maintained. In this case, the dry infested plant parts are to be treated in chloral hydrate-water media so as to bring the mites to their original shape. The eriophyids which occur as vagrants, may be collected by examining the leaves directly under stereobinocular microscope. The equipments which are needed for collection are hand lens, vials (5 cm x 1.25 cm), paper envelope, polythene bags, fine brush (series-o), forceps, scalpel, field note book and a pencil. It is most essential to record in the field itself the colouration of mite, habitat, habits, type of injury caused to plant and associated predators, if any.

Sweeping : Low herbaceous plants, grass land, etc when swept by a fine net (a type commonly used for insect collection), a large number of mites will be collected on the inner surface of the net wall and later those can be picked up with a sable hair brush.

Beating : A white enamel tray with a cotton pad at the inner surface is kept and the plant part or twig or flowers from where the mites are to be collected are beaten with a wooden rod. This will cause dislodgement of the mites from the plant parts and will fall on the cotton pad and consequently will get entangled. Later, those are picked up with a brush. Small tydeid mites which are otherwise difficult to collect, can be collected at ease. Often, collecting the anystid mites becomes difficult because those make very fast whirling movement as soon as touched or the habitat where they occur is disturbed. The best way to collect those is to beat the plant part/twig over an open umbrella. All those anystids, some bdellids, cunaxids and phytoseiids will fall on the open umbrella and from there those can be collected with a fine brush moistened with alcohol.

Aspirating : A Singer type aspirator (Singer, 1964) is quite convenient for collection of plant mites as it helps to collect the mites directly from the habitat to the collection tube.

Brushing Method : This is done in mite brushing machine which is somewhat modified from the one used by Henderson & McBurnie (1943) and later used by many including the present author (Gupta *et al.*, 1975). This is a very handy machine, made of two contra rotating brushes operated by a 6 volt battery. The leaf to be brushed is held between the brushes. The mites get dislodged and fall on a plastic disc below the brushes. The plastic disc is kept smeared with vaseline and the mites will fall on the disc and will get stuck up there. Later, those are picked up with a brush. The infested leaves should be moved forward and backward several times to ensure thorough dislodgement of all the mites from the leaves. The leaf should be brushed holding the leaf one time at petiole and on another time the apical tip alternately. This method is also used for estimating the population of mites as the plastic disc is divided into sectors and counting the mites from different sectors is done depending upon population level of mites.

Flotation Method : The leaves after plucking from the field are put in a glass jar containing water and a pinch of detergent (Teepol) and then the jar is vigorously shaken. As a result, the mites get dislodged. It is then filtered and the residue which is left contains the mite specimens. It is then washed in a watch glass by alcohol dropped through a dropper and then examined.

Scrapping and Teasing : Infested plant parts like inflorescence or buds when teased with needle, the mites come out and then are collected.

Galls which are gently opened are put into an open glass jar and the latter is kept in an airy room away from direct sunlight. As the galls gradually dry up, the mites come out from the galls and start crawling on inside wall of jar. The inside wall is wiped with glycerol up to 5 cm below the mouth of the jar to avoid the escape of mite. Later, previously warmed chloropicric acid is poured over the dried plant part and the cylinder is vigorously shaken. The plant material is allowed to settle and the liquid containing mites is poured off into a suitable container and then stored.

The vagrant eriophyids are best collected by wrapping the infested plant parts into a tissue paper and stored in an envelope. The mites are subsequently recovered by simmering the plant parts with Keifer's preparatory solution which is made of:-

Resorcinol	-	50 gms
Diglycolic acid	-	20 gms
Glycerol	-	25 ml
Iodine	-	enough to produce a desired colour
Water	-	10 cc.

When the mites are warmed in this solution, they get expanded, cleared and become suitable for slide preparation. In case of leaf vagrants, the infested plant parts are put into a vial (10 cm x 2.5 cm) and the liquid (a thin sorbitol syrup in 25% solution of isopropyl alcohol + iodine crystals) is put into it after returning to the laboratory. Data are written on outside wall of the tube.

Heat treatment : A good number of plant mites can also be collected by subjecting the plant material to heat treatment in a modified Tullgren's funnel. An electric bulb (40 w) will be enough to do complete extraction. The mites are collected in a receiver containing a preservative (75% alcohol) and fitted with stem of the funnel.

Preservation

(i) The plant mites are best preserved in 70-80% ethyl alcohol. A few drops of glycerine may be added to avoid drying of specimens.

(ii) Oudeman's fluid: Alcohol - 87 parts, glycerol - 5 parts, glacial acetic acid - 8 parts. In this preservative the mites are preserved with their appendages stretched and that helps in better orientation of specimens.

(iii) For eriophyids, the infested plant parts may be wrapped up in tissue paper and dried for storing indefinitely.

(iv) AGA solution : Isopropyl alcohol - 70% or ethyl alcohol - 8 parts, glacial acetic acid - 1 part, glycerine - 1 part and sorbitol - 300 gms to the one gallon of the above.

(v) According to Jeppson *et al.* (1975), for eriophyids, thin sorbitol syrup in 25% solution of isopropyl alcohol may be used. For this, 25% alcohol solution is made first and then sorbitol solution is added allowing the sugar to dissolve until fluid becomes thick syrup. Small amount of iodine crystals are added to prevent mould. The preservative is to be kept in laboratory and poured into a vial containing plant parts. Recovering mites from dry infested plant parts consists of placing small amount of these parts, galls, etc. in a cavity slide, putting a drop of preparatory medium and examining with transmitted light. Gentle heating may be required to obtain better clarity of specimens.

Clearing

Gutierrez (1985) suggested for tetranychids the use of clearing agent (lactic acid + lignin pink as indicated by Evans & Browning 1955. (*Ann. Mag Nat. Hist.*, 8(12): 631-635). Lactic acid inflates the body. Lignin pink makes the specimen translucid, enabling to make it clearly visible under the microscope. The specimens from the collection vial should be put into a glass cupel (4 cm^3) with a flat bottom. About 8-10 drops of stained lactic acid are then added. The cupel is heated after placing on an electric slide warmer (40-60°C). Alcohol quickly evaporates and clearing generally lasts 1-2 hrs.

For dark specimens, it should be immersed in Andre's fluid (water - 30 cm^3, chloral hydrate - 40 g, glacial acetic acid - 30 cm^3).

Mounting

Temporary mounting : The specimen is mounted in a cavity slide. A drop of lactic acid is placed in the cavity and the mite is pushed in the cavity into the liquid with a fine needle. A small piece of cover slip is put over the cavity and if there is not enough lactic acid, some quantity of lactic acid may be added from the edges. It is then warmed by putting it over an electric slide warmer and when sufficient clarity has been achieved, it is then examined under stereobinocular microscope. By this method, mite can be cleared without damaging the specimen. In the absence of electric slide warmer, the temporary mounted slide can also be kept on a 40 watts electric bulb for a few seconds and as soon as the lactic acid fumes start coming out, it is removed and examined under stereobinocular microscope. If proper clearing has not been achieved or proper orientation of body parts has not been achieved, those can be done easily because this specimen is mounted in temporary mounting medium.

The temporary mounted slide with sealing by euparal may be transformed into a semi permanent preparation and can be kept for 2-3 years.

Permanent mounting : The mounting media which are used for mites are as below :

Hoyers' medium

Distilled water	-	50 cm^3
Gum arabic	-	30 gms
Chloral hydrate	-	200 gms.
Glycerol	-	16 cm^3

The ingredients are to be mixed in above sequence with a stirring rod. It is required to heat the liquid slowly at 50°C to accelerate dissolution of gum arabic. Use of purified gum in fine powder form will simplify the process and in that case filtration may not be needed.

With cavity slide also this permanent mounting may be used and in that case square cover glass may be used. Slides should be heated on electric slide warmer for a day to remove air bubble, better clearing and orientation. With simple slide, the round cover glass may be used. After the slides get dried, the permanent slide should be ringed with Euparal because the medium is hygroscopic. For humid climate, this medium is unsuitable. Each slide should have two labels, one for giving collection data (location, host plant, date of collection, name of collector) and the other giving identity of the specimen with sex. The former label should be on right hand side and the latter on the left. The slides should be kept flat and stored in dark dry place (Gutierrez, 1985).

The other mounting medium is Heinze's medium (Evans & Till, 1979). Its composition is : polyvinyl alcohol - 10 gms, distilled water 40-60 ml, lactic acid - 35 ml, glycerol - 10 ml, phenol - 1% aqueous soln. - 25 ml, chloral hydrate - 100 gms. The ingredients are to be mixed in the sequence as mentioned. Both living as well as preserved specimens can be mounted directly in this medium. If necessary, the specimen can be remounted by removing the cover slip by immersing the slide in water overnight. In tropical humid climate, this medium also may not be very suitable as after a few months the medium shrinks and the specimen gets distorted. It should be borne in mind that if more than one specimen is available, as far as possible, the specimen should be mounted both dorsally and ventrally, so as to have both the views and morphological parts of both the sides are visible. For tetranychid mites, since the examination of the male aedeagus is a must, the male should be mounted laterally so that the aedeagus becomes visible.

Recovery of specimens and Remounting

If the mounting medium gets dried up and the specimens get distorted, it can be recovered by soaking the slide in warm water. When the cover glass gets loosened, it is removed by keeping the slide under stereobinocular and gently pushing off the coverslip with a needle. Later, the specimen is treated with lactic acid and gently heated. The specimen will get its normal shape and then mounted in permanent mounting medium.

For eriophyid mites, Jeppson *et al.* (1975) suggested use of Kono's medium. It involves mounting in two stages. The primary medium is made of chloral hydrate - 100 gms, glycerine - 10 gms, water - 50 ml and Conc. Hcl - 1 cc. Mites are gently cooked in Kono's preparatory mixture and when cleared, they are needled over into a wash of Hoyer's and to the final slide. Final slide should not be heated. For eriophyids, there is another mounting medium i.e. formaldehyde medium consisting of following ingredients: sorbitol - 3 gms, gum arabic powder - 1 gm, iodine crystal - 0.02 gm and 4% formalin solution - 5 c.c. These materials are allowed to dissolve with agitation for 24 hours or more and then following ingredients are added - chloral hydrate crystal - 14 gm, glycerine - 20 drops, potassium iodide 0.1 gm or 0.2 gm, formalin solution (4%) may be added further, if necessary. While preparing slide, 2 drops of formalin medium is put in the cavity of a slide and the mites are needled into it. A drop of Hcl solution. and a drop of phenol solution may be added into it. The slide is then gently heated on hot plate set below boiling point of water till a gentle boiling is reached. Later, it is transferred to a drop of fresh formalin medium to wash and to a drop of medium on a final slide. Some support to cover slip may be given by putting small broken pieces of coverslips or kapkok fibers to prevent crushing of mites.

Rearing

The different methods used for plant mite rearing are discussed in brief :

Leaf Disk Culture : Helle & Overmeer (1985) proposed the leaf disk culture technique in which the detached bean leaf (*Phaseolus vulgaris*) or castor leaf (*Ricinus communis*) with a short piece of petiole is pressed firmly with ventral leaf surface facing upward on a wad of wet cotton pad contained in a small Petridish. Any holes occurring between the margin of the leaf and the cotton wool are filled up by pulling the cotton wool up and pressing it against the leaf. This is to prevent the escape of mites. After some days, the leaf will take root and then the leaf culture may last for several weeks. Instead of using ordinary tap water, if nutrient solution is used, then the detached bean leaf culture may last for a longer period. The nutrient solution may contain 213 mg KnO_3, 127 mg $MgSo_4$, $7H_2O$, 141 mg KH_2Po_4, 5 mg $(NH_4)_2$ So_4 and 186 mg NH_4No_3 per litre of tap water (Helle, 1962, *Planteziekten* 68 : 155-195). The nutrient solution should be used during the first time only when the cotton wool is used for the first time. Thereafter, ordinary tap water may be used. If the leaves become thickly populated, then the mites can be transferred to fresh detached leaf culture. A large number of tetranychid mites can be reared using this technique.

The most convenient method is to confine the mites into an isolated leaf in small cages of Huffaker's type (Huffaker, 1948) as details given in Evans *et al.*, (1961). Phytophagous mites feeding on plants can be reared in cells cutting circles out of the centre of small felt disc. These felt washers are fastened to the leaves with waterproof glue and covered with glass or cellophane.

Mites can also be cultured in seedlings kept in pots. Petroleum jelly is applied around the base of the stem to prevent escape of mites.

A most common method is to rear on excised leaf instead of on whole leaf and keeping the same in Petridish (5 cm dia) over a cotton pad or sponge sheet kept supersaturated with water and having water all around the excised leaf to prevent escape of mites. Leaf is periodically changed as and when dried. Water is to be added daily to maintain a film of water all round the excised leaf. Many oligophagous and monophagous mites can be reared on leaf disc or detached leaves on their host plants. There are many advantages in this method as because it can be directly examined by keeping the Petridish under binocular microscope. Also, mass production of homogenous species population can be produced by this method. The mated adult females are released on the excised leaves and kept there for 24 hours to allow them to lay eggs and study of life cycle can be initiated from the freshly laid eggs. These cultures on excised leaves can be maintained under controlled conditions also by putting the Petridishes in BOD incubators and in case of mass multiplication, several stocks can be maintained. Care is to be taken that no predator or any other alien spices contaminate the culture.

Rearing in closed cells : Rearing in plexiglass cells is recommended for the species which migrate from the leaf (eg. *Bryobia*) or where the excised leaf culture is not feasible (in case of leathery textured leaf). As per Helle & Overmeer (1985), this method can be adapted as a piece of plexiglass (thickness 5-10mm) is taken, one or more circular holes of dia 5-15 mm are made, in such a way that these holes fit within the outline of the leaf lamina. A plate of plexiglass of the same size forms the base of the construction. On this base plate, 3 layers of thicked moistened filter paper are laid, on which the leaf is placed. The plexiglass with holes is then placed carefully on the leaf. The whole structure is kept together tightly with rubber bands. The cells are closed with cover slips which can be fixed by sticky tape. When necessary, the cover slips can be opened by removing the tape to manipulate the mites. Though this method is good but for a mass scale multiplication this technique may not be suitable.

Rearing on plants : The potted host plants with 2 primary leaves are taken. The plants are artificially infested with the mites. The plants get seriously infested within a short period. In case of heavy infestation, the replacement of fresh plant is needed. If needed, the plants may be encircled with a mosquito net to avoid entry of unwanted organisms and especially predators. By this method, a continuous supply of a large numbers of mites is possible. The mites can be collected from the infested potted plants by tapping the leaves over a white enamle tray and picking them up with a fine brush.

For mites that have to be reared on plants like asparagus or conifers, that can be done on branches of that plant kept in a glass beaker.

Rearing of Phytoseiid predators : Not all phytoseiids are obligate predators. There are many which can thrive upon pollen of different plants, honey, nectar, etc. However, rearing predators on pollen has advantage as they can be handled easily. Pollen can be easily collected and can be stored in refrigerator for more than a year. Maintaining high humidity is required (70% R.H.) enabling the eggs to hatch. In order to maintain phytoseiid colonies of same age, the eggs can be transferred with a fine brush to a new rearing unit. The old colonies may be destroyed.

Rearing on artificial arena : McMurtry & Scriven (1965 : *J. Econ. Ent.*, **58** : 282-284) developed a method in which mites were reared in an arena. This consists of 15x15 cm piece of construction paper sprayed with black paint and laid on 1.5 cm thick 16x16 cm piece of foam plastic saturated with water. The foam plastic is put in a 20x20 cake pan filled with water. Strips of tissue paper are stretched round the periphery of the construction paper, to act as barrier and prevent escape of mites.

Overmeer *et al.* (1982: *Z. Angew Ento.*, **93** : 1-11) modified this technique and used 8x15 cm tile of plastic, 5 mm thick. A thicker piece of foam plastic (3 cm) was used so that it could hold more water. The surface of foam plastic was equal to that of the tile. Four short strips of tissue paper, 7 cm wide, stretched along four edges of the tile and folded in such a way so that 1.5 cm of the periphery of the tile is covered by the tissue paper and rest of the strip hangs down in water contained in a tray so that the tissue paper remains wet. A rectangle of the sticky substance is given above the edge of the tile which acts as extra barrier. For food, either the spider mite infested leaf can be kept on the substrate or the spider mites can be brushed into the arena. Many species of phytoseiids can be reared by using this technique. The phytoseiids feeding on pollen as well as the obligate predators can be kept in the arena.

Detached leaf culture : A detached leaf is taken and put on a wet sponge in a Petridish with water. Phytoseiid mites along with their prey can be easily reared on such detached leaves. Those leaves which can remain fresh for a longer period will be better for culture. For this, bean leaf can be used. *Phytoseiulus persimilis* can be easily reared on such detached leaf. Care is to be taken to provide the suitable prey for culturing the phytoseiid mites. Different phytoseiids may have different prey preference. A wad of cotton may be put encircling the leaf disc to act as barrier.

Rearing predatory mites in cages : Sometimes closed cages are used where the mite is kept confined and in that case the risk of loosing the mite is practically nil. Tanigoshi *et al.* (1975 : *Ann. Ento. Soc. Am.*, **71** : 313- 316) took 2 cardboard ice-cream cartoons (4.5 cm height and 8.5 cm dia). The bottoms of the cartoons were removed and a piece of fibreglass window screen was fitted between the cartoons. The cartoons were fastened bottom to bottom. In each of the 2 lids of ice-cream cartoons a hole of diameter 2.5 cm was cut and covered with parachute cloth. Lima bean infested with spider mite was put within upper chamber of rearing unit and phytoseiid mite was inoculated into this chamber. After 3 days, this unit was infested and fresh infested Lima been was put in the upper chamber. The prey and predatory mites show tendency to move to the upper chamber through the fibre glass window and the old leaves of the lower chamber are discarded.

Rearing in potted plants : Mallik *et al.* (1999 : *J. Acarol.*, **15** : 15-17) reared the predatory mite *Neoseiulus longispinosus* on bean leaves artificially infested with *T. urticae* grown in pots and releasing predatory mites when it attained 9, 12 and 18 leaflets stage, 12, 21 and 33 days after sowing, respectively. But releasing at 9 leaflet stage was most appropriate. *Neoseiules longispinosus* was released 9 days after release of spider mite; the predator population reached a peak of 17.48 mites per leaflet in 12 days. Releasing predator at later stage, did not appear to be effective. The total time from sowing bean leaves to harvesting of predators was 33 days. The authors reported that the batch of 15 plants which occupied 1.5m^2 area in the glass house yielded 4714.2 predators. According to the requirement of predator, the size of glass house and number of French bean plants can be raised.

Yao & Chant (1982 : *Internat. J. Acarol.*, **8** : 205-209) developed a technique for confining mites for population studies in the laboratory. They used a fine resistance wire (CHROMEL A, size 26, 0.5 mm in diameter) with a temperature of 54°C generated by a low voltage electric current. The wire was bound around the edge of plastic circle (Perplex) on which the experimental arena was rested. A round hole of 5cm diameter was made in the middle of the perplex to receive a round copper pipe. The perplex ring was used to support a bean leaf on paper arena and also to serve as insulator between the wire and copper pipe. The lower end of the copper pipe was inserted into water with temperature kept constant (19-21°C). The temperature of the perplex ring increased with contact of hot wire. The cooling water was in a large container where the inflow of water was allowed to enter continuously and outflow of water was allowed to leave from the container at the same time and rate.

A separate plastic disc with hole in the middle (1 cm dia) was placed horizentally inside the copper plate to support a piece of foam on which a bean leaf was put to serve as experimental arena which can be kept green for several days and the paper arena can also be kept moist for a long period. The moist paper arena helped both the predator and the prey species to drink water without drowning on it. The effective temperature of 54°C of the hot wire helped to confine the mites.

According to the authors, this method was effective to confine both predators and tetranychids in the experimental arena. When the mite moved so close to the wire made a retreat immediately from the heated wire around the edge of the arena and this method was successful to confine the mites in the arena because of this reason. The accidental mortality was small. Krishnamoorthy (1990 : *Acarology Newsl.*, **17** & **18** : 28-29) developed a self watering device used for phytoseiid rearing programme. The self watering device consisted of two components. 1) A squeeze bottle which served as a tank and (ii) and a support with both ends open. The tank was a squeeze bottle (1 lit capacity) and a support was made up of plastic cylinder. A small hole was provided nearer to one of the open ends and an inverted V-shaped cut at the other end. The support was fixed to the open end of the tank and the joint was sealed to form a device. After filling, the tank was inverted by tightly holding a palm on the open end of the squeeze bottle to avoid spillage and placed inside rust free aluminum tray (25 X 23 X 3.8 cm) containing water. The palm was then removed so that the device could stand on the tray. Mite rearing units made out of Petri dishes (0.5 cm dia) were arranged on the tray. This self watering device automatically watered the tray for 40 days at laboratory room temperature of 26 ± 2°C. The rearing units used in this study were of such size so that it could be examined under stereobinocular microscope. Tripod stand can be provided to prevent accidental falling of tank.

Sampling Methods

There are several methods for sampling of mites and some of those are mentioned below :

Direct counting : This method though time consuming but is more or less accurate. The infested leaves are collected from the field and then examined under stereobinocular microscope and counted mite population. Since some mites move very fast, the counting directly like this may prove erroneous as there may be a chance to count the same mite more than once. Sabelis (1985) suggested to keep the infested leaf at 5°C to make mites immovable before counting or to "Sper Hold" hair spray immediately after sampling (Jones & Parrella, 1984, *J. Econ. Ent.*, **77** : 75-79).

Imprint Method : The infested leaf is kept in between two blotting papers or mimeographed paper and a wooden roller is passed to and fro over the mimeographed paper so as to crush the mites (both adults, immatures and eggs). Normally each stage leaves behind a particular colour stain on the blotting paper and then by counting the stains, an estimation of population can be made.

However, confusion may arise if the leaf is infested by more than one species of tetranychid mite because the stains left by them may not be easy to distinguish. Further, if the infestation is very heavy, the stains will coalesce and in that case the population counting from imprints may be inaccurate.

Brushing machine

This has been discussed under collection.

Washing Method

Already discussed under collection.

Beating method

This method has been discussed for collection purpose. In this method, often difficulty is faced with the *Tetranychus* species which can not be easily dislodged as they are covered under heavy webbing. The beating of twig can also be dome on a piece of white cloth or white paper and from the dislodged mites a rough estimate of the population can be made.

Among all the methods, the dislodgement of mites by mite brushing method appears to be more accurate as well as convenient. Since it is battery operated, it can be taken to field for population estimation.

Sampling frequency

This will depend upon interval between successive sample dates which is proportional to the time constant of population growth which equals the inverse of the intrinsic rate of increase (r_m^{-1} day) (Sabelis, 1985). Potentially, spider mite population doubles in 2-4 days but at low night temperatures, the influence of predators and unstable age distributions, time intervals of one week is generally sufficient to record two fold increase in spider mite population. Population modes of spider mites -taking into account abiotic factors and are free of assumptions regarding age distribution could be extremely useful to determining time intervals between successive sample dates (Croft *et al.* 1976, *Env. & Entomol.*, **5** : 227-234, Helle & Sabelis, 1985)

Sample size

It will depend upon the distribution of mites in the area to be sampled. It is essential first to have a quantitative notion of the effects of distribution on sample size. This will be done in an imaginary experiment using a population whose size and distribution are known.

Stratified sampling

Sabelis (1985) suggested the following in this regard and the same is given here as such to help the future worker. In case of random sampling, the number of mites found in the sampled are, x, is binomially distributed with parameters p (=the probability of sampling a mite) and q(=1-p) An estimate of X is then

$\bar{X} = x/p.$

Which is unbiased with variance

$Var(\bar{X}) = Xq/p$

And coefficient of variation

$C = (var(\bar{X})^{1/2}/X = (q/(Xp))^{1/2}$ .... (1)

Rearranging this equation gives

$p = (1+(XC^2)^{-1}$ ....(2)

C = level of precision and p can be re-interpreted as the fraction of leaf area to be sampled given total population size X and the level of precision C. The lower the value of C, the higher p and thus larger the sample size required.

In case of patchy population, then var ($\bar{X}$) will exceed Xq/p and p will be underestimated by equation (2). If the population of European Red mite is distributed over apple leaves according to negative bionomial distribution with parameters X/L and k, then the fraction p can be shown to be equal to :-

$p = \frac{}{C^2}\left(\frac{1}{X} + \frac{1}{kL} + \frac{1}{} + \frac{...}{}\right)$...............................(3)

where L = total number of sampling units (leaves) available in total (leaf area). If k tends to infinity, then the negative binomial approaches the Poisson distribution assumed in deriving equation (2). In that case, equation (2) and (3) are very similar indeed.

According to Sabelis (1985) k is to be linearly related to the mean density of European red mite per apple leaf, with slope 0.536 and intercept 0.09. Hence, when the mean density of mites is 0.5, X = 1500, L=3000 (leaves/tree) and C=0.25, then p of equation (3) equals 0.0256, which corresponds to a sample of ca 75 leaves. When the mean density is 5 mites per leaf and X = 15000, then the required sample size is 9 leaves. Clearly, these sample sizes are two three times larger than those calculated basing on equation (2) and assuming poisson distribution.

Gupta *et al.* (1975) (*Acarologia*, **17** : 489-492) in their work on development of sampling technique for estimating population of *T. neocaledonicus* infesting brinjal, had considered 1, 2, 3, 4, 6 and 8 sq. cm leaf areas and compared their precision and efficiency and it was found that 1cm^2 sample size was the most efficient in this regard. Comparison of population of three portions of plant canopy (basal, middle and upper), indicated no significant difference. Fifty three leaves per field were found to be minimum number of sample required to determine the population density of this mite in this field. So it was summarized that the population of *T. neocaledonicus* can be estimated from 53 leaves plucked at random from field and counting the mites from 1 sq. cm area from lower surface plucked from any where on the lower, middle, top canopies of the plant.

Techniques for toxicological tests

As per Helle & Overmeer (1985) there are many test methods for toxicological experiments and some of those are as below :

Topical application : Harrison (1961 : *N.Z.J. Sci.*, **4** : 534-539) developed this technique. As reported by Sabelis (1985), in this method, each adult female mite is tested by expelling the insecticidal contents of a capillary over its ventral or dorsal surface. The mite is held in position on the fine end of the glass tube by suction. Capillary is self-filling with kerosene in which the toxicant is dissolved. The capillary is a minute calibrated volume, approximately 0.0005 µl, being $1/40^{th}$ body weight of adult female mite. Batches of 10 treated mites are collected under CO_2 anaesthesia in small perplex cages. Each perplex cage with treated mites is held on bean leaf allowing mite to feed on bean leaf. Mortality is counted after 24 hours. This method is highly accurate.

Slide Dep. Method : Helle & Overmeer (1985) describes this method as:- A small piece of double sided Scotch tape is pressed on their dorsum. The slide is dipped into a toxicant solution and then gently agitated. It is then taken out and put over an absorbent material for about 15 minutes so as to drain out excess material. Slides with mites are stored in incubator at 20-25^{0}C with high RH (> 90%). After 24 hours, the mortality is checked. Mites responding to prodding with a brush are considered to be alive.

This method was modified by Cranham (1974 : *Ann. Appl. Biol.*, **78** : 99-111). In this method, instead of dipping the slide in toxicant solution, it was spread with the toxicant by putting it under Potter's Tower. This method is very convenient and relatively accurate.

Adult leaf disc test

In this, the leaves are either dipped or sprayed by a spray tower to produce leaf residues. Discs are cut from the leaves and placed on wet cotton pad. The adult female mites are transferred to each disc, having 3 replicates for each treatment and the control. Mortality is counted after every 24 hours interval.

Ovicidal tests

The adult females are released on leaves placed on an excised leaf kept on wet cotton pad allowing the females to lay eggs. After 1 day, the females are removed leaving only the eggs. Then the eggs kept in excised leaves are sprayed under Potter's tower and such leaves are kept on cotton pad in a tray under controlled temperature of 25^{0}C and RH of 85% preferably under long day photoperiod. Such sprayed leaves are examined after 4-5 days to see if eggs hatched. If the Potter's tower is unavailable, the leaves with eggs may be dipped in the test liquid. The excised leaves with eggs may also be dipped into pesticidal solution for 5 seconds, agitated gently and then the leaf is kept for 7 days to see hatching of eggs.

Preparation for Electron Microscopic studies

SEM studies : The specimens are fixed in 0.2 M sodium phosphate buffer (pH 7.4) containing 4% glutaraldehyde (EM graded) overnight at 4^0C and rinsed it for 3 times with buffer. Post fixation is done in 1% osmium tetra-oxide in phosphate buffer for 2 hours at room temperature. Dehydration is done through graded ethanol series followed by drying through critical point method. Dried specimen is coated with gold and mounted on specimen stub (Chillar *et al.*, 2007).

TEM studies : Before the specimen is fixed for TEM studies, it is necessary to pierce the specimen carefully with a tiny sharp insect pin. The middle part of body in nymph and caudal portion in case of adults are to be pierced. Specimen is fixed in 2.5% glutaraldehyde in 0.1 M phosphate buffer (pH 7.4) for 2-4 hours. The specimen is washed several times in pure 0.2 M phosphate buffer or in 6.85% sucrose in 0.1 M phosphate buffer. It is then fixed in 0.1 M phosphate buffer containing 1-2% osmium tetra-oxide and 8.5% sucrose overnight. After dehydrating in alcohol acetone series, the specimen is embedded in an araldite mixture. Ultra-thin sections are cut on ultra microtome. Few sections may be stained in toluidene blue and observed under light optical microscope. Uranyl acetate and lead citrate are used for TEM stains (Chillar *et al.*, 2007).

Preparation for histological studies

Chillar *et al.* (2007) described the different steps involved for preparation of histological studies and those are briefly mentioned below as such.

(i) **Collection of Material** : The damaged leaves showing different degrees of damages as well as healthy leaves are cut in 4-5 mm length.

(ii) **Fixation** : Formalin-aceto-alcohol (FAA) (Formalin- 35% 5 parts, galcial acitic acid 5 parts and 70% ethanol (90 parts) are generally used as it penetrates the plant also. Materials are immersed in FAA for 24 hours before conserving them in 70% ethanol for further processing.

(iii) **Dehydration :**

a) Bath 1 : Water : 90% ethanol + Tertiary butanol (30 : 50 : 20), the material is kept in this for 12 hrs.

b) Bath 2 : Water : 90% ethanol + Tertiary butanol (15 : 50 : 35).

c) Bath 3 : Water : 90% ethanol + Tertiary butanol (5 : 40 : 55).

d) Bath 4 : 90% ethanol + Tertiary butanol (25 : 75).

e) Bath 5 : Tertiary butanol (100).

The material is to be kept in each bath from 2nd to 5th bath. After the last bath, material should be transferred to pure TBA for 12 hours with two changes in the solvent.

(iv) **Paraffin infiltration :** After dehydration, wax flex are added to the material in equal proportion. The mixture is left at 20⁰C for 5 hours, then at 40⁰C for 12 hrs and finally at 60⁰C for 2 hrs in an oven. The leaf bits should be at the bottom of the liquid. At the end of the process the supernatant liquid is to be decanted, pure liquid is added and it is left at 60⁰C for 2 hrs. The last step is to be repeated thrice.

(v) **Embedding :** It can be done in small paper vessel on a water bath. The vessel is to be smeared with glycerine and then the molten wax is poured at 60⁰C. The specimens are removed from container with the help of warmed forceps and placed in blocks. The material may be properly oriented. Leaf bits should be at the middle of the block. The blocks are cooled in cold water.

(vi) **Sectioning :** It is done through microtome. Blocks are trimmed, then mounted on a small piece of wooden leg. The surface of the object holder is covered with molten wax and is allowed to set in. With the help of heated spatula, the mounted object is to be fixed on holder and is oriented in such a way that the sides are in horizontal position in relation to knife. The sections of 10-15 μm thickness are cut serially using rotary wheel at room temperature. Sections are placed on slide smeared with adhesive (glycerine 15 ml, gelatin - 1 g, phenol - 2 g in 10 ml water) (Chillar *et al.*, 2007).

(vii) **De-paraffination and staining :**

Wax is removed by xylol and slides are dehydrated.

Rehydration is then done in the following sequence :

Xylol (2 changes), xylol + Butanol (50 : 50), Pure butanol, butanol ethanol (50 : 50), ethanol-96%, ethanol-80%, ethanol-70% and ethanol-50%. Staining is done in the same manner as explained in case of anatomical studies.

Preparation for anatomical studies

Specimen is dissected in isotonic sucrose soution. For ultra structural studies, electron microscopic preparation is to be made. To study the internal organs, it is considered better to remove the anterior portion of body to allow better penetration of fixative. After primary fixation, the specimen should be post fixed with 1.4% osmium tetra-oxide in 0.45 M sucrose for 1.5 hr. before dehydrating them in graded series of ethanol and propylene oxide and embedded in wax. For highly sclerotized mites, ester wax should be used.

Semi thin sections can be stained with Stevenel's blue and such sections are usually contrasted with uranyl acetate and lead citrate.

Counting

Per square cm Counting : In this method, the phytophagous mites are counted but it is not suitable for eriophyids. A mite infested leaf is taken and on that transparent sheet having squares traced from a graph paper is superimposed. Mites are counted from some selected squares putting the leaf and the transparent sheet under binocular microscope. A tally counter, if used, will be better. If the mites are present on both the surfaces, the counting should be done from both the surfaces as well as if the population is to be counted from all the three canopies (top, middle, bottom). This method will be suitable if the distribution of mite population is uniform.

Bud mite counting : Buds of citrus or other plants are often infested with mites. The buds are plucked, opened under stereobinocular microscrope and the mites are counted from there.

In case of eriophyid mites, the infested leaves are immersed in methanol/ethanol /acetone/glycerol (10: 1) for 3-4 hours. The leaves are gently spread on glass slide and mites are counted (Janardhan *et al.*, 1972, *Madras Agr, J.*, **59** : 437; Chillar *et al.*, 2007).

Counting by photographs : As per Sircom (2000, *Exp. Appl. Acarol.*, 51-61; Chillar *et al.*, 2007), a camera with a macrolens, orange filter and data back system may be used for photographic symptoms of plant mites. For rapid and accurate photography, an aluminium frame is attached to the camera with a plexiglass bracket to hold the leaf.

Bioassay

Petridish Method (Dry film technique) : A Petridish is taken and in that one ml of the pesticide/acaricide solution is placed on bottom of Petridish. It is then closed and the solution is swirled briefly in upright and inverted positions. The dishes are then opened and put under a fan for air drying. Known number of mites are released in each dish and then the Petridish is closed with the mites inside. Thereafter, the mortality is counted after 24 hours.

Impregnated Paper Bioassay : In this method the mites are exposed to pesticide in special paper chamber which is made of two pieces of Whatman No. 1 (42.5 mm dia) filter paper. One filter paper is moulded to create 2 mm deep and 33 mm dia depression. Second filter paper is unmoulded and is used as chamber lid. Papers are secured by using glue between two squares of glass (75 x 75 x 4mm), in centre of which a 35mm diameter hole is drilled. Each filter paper is treated with known dose of acaricide solution. Control dishes are treated with only solvent solution. Known number of mites are released in each dish before closing them tightly and mortality is counted after 24 hours (Chillar *et al.*, 2007).

1.3 ANATOMICAL FEATURES OF MITES OF AGRI-HORTICULTURAL IMPORTANCE

The mites of agri-horticultural importance belong to two major groups, viz. Phytophagus including Tetranychidae, Tenuipalpidae, Tarsonemidae, Tuckerellidae and Eriophyoidea and predatory (Phytoseiidae, Ascidae, Anystidae, Bdellidae, Calegonellidae, Camerobiidae, Cheyletidae, Cunaxidae, Erythraeidae, Eupodidae, Raphignathidae, Stigmaeidae, Tydeidae). Since the anatomical features of all families have been dealt with in detail in Gupta (1985, 1986, 2002, 2003), in this only salient anatomical features are mentioned of Acari as a hole.

Body Size (Shape & Coloration) : Most of the plant associated mites are small, size varies from 200-300 microns (in Eriophyidae) and as big as Erythraeidae, Bdellidae, Anystidae and Cunaxidae where size may be 500-600 microns. Body is mostly soft, may be bright reddish, yellowish, greenish, often with stipplings or patches. Bodies are mostly ovoid or round excepting eriophyoids which are elongated, worm-like.

Segmentation : The segmentation is obscure in most of the mites except in Tarsonemina where segmentation is shown by a number of overlapping shields. The anterior is composed of precheliceral segment (segment - I), cheliceral segment (segment - II), pedipalpal segment bearing pedipalp (segment - III) and is followed by 4 leg bearing segments (segment - IV - VII). The number of segments which form the rest of the body is not known in the absence of adequate embryological evidence.

Cuticle : It is secreted by epidermis and is differentiated into 4 strata, *viz.* tectostracum (Cerotegumen), epiostracum (Epicuticle), ectostracum (Exocuticle) and hypostracum (Endocuticle) (Vitzthum, 1940-43). The epidermis is also responsible for production of setae which are of diverse shape, size and function and are important taxonomic characters at generic and sub generic levels. Some setae have optically active chitin, being birefringent or anisotropic and the other type lacks active chitin and is isotropic. The former is the characteristic of Achtinochaeta (includes orders Astigmata, Prostigmata, Cryptostigmata) and the latter group includes orders Mesostigmata, Metastigmata and Tetrastigmata. The former type of setae are "eupathidia", "famulli". Some setae are transversly striated, some setae called solenidia are of various shapes, pyriform, clavate have no basal bulb.

Gnathosoma (Capitulum) : This includes precheliceral, cheliceral and pedipalpal segments and is articulated with idiosoma by synarthrodial membrane. Gnathosoma is often enclosed with camerostome. Tectum forms the roof of the gnathoma and pedipalpal coxae form the lateral walls, which fuse dorsally with tectum and ventral extension of coxae form the floor. Mouth lies between and below the chelicerae. The venter of gnathosoma in nymphs and adults of Mesostigmata bears 4 pairs of setae. Mouth is bordered dorsally by an upper lip (labrum) and ventrally by a pair of lateral lips. Gnathosoma bears various numbers of dorsal and ventral setae.

Chelicerae : It is the feeding organ and in majority cases it is chelate. Chelicera of Astigmata and Prostigmata are 3 segmented, consisting of small basal part (homologous with trochanter of other appendages), a large compound segment (may be formed by femur, genu, tibia, tarsus) and a short movable digit. The chelicerae exhibit considerable variety in form as a result of their adaptation for different feeding habits. In Tetranychidae, these are needle-like, in Phytoseiidae they are dentate for capturing prey, in Stigmaeidae, these are stylet-like. Movable digit of male chelicerae in Mesostigmata bears a process (spermatophoral process) which is used for transferring spermatophore.

Pedipalpi : Pedipalpal coxae fuse to form gnathosomal base. The remaining segments of pedipalp are movably articulated to the body of gnathosoma anterolaterally to form sensory appendages which may be modified for grasping food. Palp 6 segmented in Mesostigmata (Coxa, trochanter, femur, genu, tibia, tarsus) in Prostigmata and in Astigmata, it is 5 segmented. Due to fusion of one or more segments, may sometimes reduce the number of segments. In Cunaxidae, Cheyletidae, they are modified for raptorial purpose. In Tetranychidae, they take part in producing silk web for covering their colonies. In some Prostigmata, the distal segments are provided with spur-like setae and in others form thumb-claw complex.

Idiosoma : The idiosoma may be oval, subcircular, rounded or elongated and worm-like. A furrow sometimes demarcates the propodosoma and hysterosoma, the latter part is again distinguished into metapodosoma (from base of II pair of legs upto base of IV pair of legs) and opisthosoma (from base of IV pair of legs upto posterior tip of body). Among Prostigmata, Tarsonemina possess a number of overlapping dorsal shields. The sclerotization of idiosoma may be of varying degrees. The dorsal surface of Mesostigmata may have a single shield or may have more than one. The setae on dorsal surface of idiosoma are arranged in transverse rows following definite patterns in different taxa and their relative size, length, position, relative distances among themselves, nature of setae as rod like, simple, serrate, palmate, filiform, fan-like, spatulate, knobbed etc. help in separating taxonomic categories.

Ventrally, the sites of the attachment of ambulatory appendages, anus, genital openings in adults are also of great taxonomic importance. In Mesostigmata, the sternites of podosoma are represented by a tritosternum. The coxae of each pair of legs in Actinochaeta are fused with their sternite to form coxisternum, so the first movable segment of leg is trochanter. The anus is placed medioventrally, near hind end of body and in Mesostigmata it is surrounded by sclerotized anal shield. Anal openings are closed by a pair of valves.

The genital opening is variously positioned. In females of Anactinochaeta, it is in the form of transverse slit located between IV coxae. In Mesostigmata, it is protected by one or more shields. The genital opening in male is in intercoxal region. The leg segments include coxae, trochanter, femur, genu, tibia, tarsus, pre-tarsus. Legs may terminate in claws and empodium. The number of claws may vary from

1-3. Empodium may be pad-like, may bear empodial claw and tenent hairs. In Mesostigmata, leg I is longer than others and may act as sensory appendage and may lack ambulacrum.

Though as a rule, the larvae have 3 pairs of legs while nymphs and adults have 4 pairs of legs but there are certain exceptions as eriophyid mites or gall mites have 2 pairs of legs in all stages of development while *Larvacarus* (Fam. Tenuipalpidae) and Podapolipidae have 3 pairs of legs in all stages of development. Besides locomotion, legs help in clasping or capturing prey organism or may be used for phoretic purpose, detecting prey, etc.

Sense Organ : Various types of setae are present acting as sense organs. A simple erect seta, trichobothrium occurs on legs or on idiosoma performing tactile function. In Prostigmata, specialized sensory organ called Pseudostigmata are present. That is also present in Cryptostigmata. Pseudostigmatid organ lies in distinct cavity, called Pseudostigmata. The body setae may be simple, serrate, filiform, palmate, etc. In some Mesostigmata, photoreceptive organs are present in pulvillus of the 1st pair of legs. Eyes when present occur on propodosoma and are never faceted. Each consists of circular differentiated area in cuticle, the lens often replaced by darkish pigment. Maximum of 2 pairs of eyes are present. In Anystidae, a hemispherical protuberance lying under an anterior projection (naso) of propodosoma is present. One of the two pairs of eyes may be lost or represented by tubercles (Tetranychidae). The scar-like markings of the integument, referred to as lyriform organs, are also considered to be sensory organs.

1.4 BIOLOGICAL ASPECTS OF PLANT FEEDING AND PREDATORY MITES AND EFFECT OF ENVIORNMENTAL FACTORS

Life Cycle

The plant mites in general show arrhenotokous type of reproduction where the fertilized females produce offsprings of both sexes and the unfertilized females produce only the males. Theyletoky is also seen in some plant mites where the parthenogenetically produced offsprings are all females and the males are unknown.

Mating is generally accomplished immediately after emergence. In many tarsonemids, the males are seen carrying the pharate females so that the males can mate immediately as soon as the females emerge. In tetranychids, the male crawls down the posterior end of the female and arches its abdomen upwards to accomplish copulation. Male holds the female with the forelegs. In phytoseiid mites, the male introduces the spermatophore by the specialized process present on the movable cheliceral digit. The amount of spermatozoa introduced during copulation determines the sex ratio. The development cycle includes one or more active stages. In many Mesostigmata (Phytoseiidae, Ascidae), there are 4 active stages as larva, protonymph, deutonymph, adult. However, there may be another active stage in between deutonymph and adult called tritonymph. In some tetranychids, the males do not show deutonymphal stage and moult directly to adults from protonymphal stage. In Prostigmata, the number of active stages varies. In Tarsonemidae, only 2 active stages are seen *viz.* larva and adult. In Erythraeidae, the larval stage is followed by a single nymphal stage. In Tetranychidae, female passes through 2 nymphal stages. In between each stage, there is a brief inactive or resting stage when they do not feed, remain covered with a waxy coating and that stage is called quiescent. In some families of Prostigmata, e.g. Tydeidae, Bdellidae etc., the larva is followed by 3 nymphal stages. In Eriophyidae, there are 2 active stages, the first stage and second stage nymphs. However, in some eriophyids, the life cycle is complicated as two types of females are produced, the deutogyne adapted for hibernation and start reproduction in the next season, and the other type is protogyne which reproduces throughout summer and spring and dies with the advent of winter. Thus, a case of alteration of generation is exhibited. The presence of two different types of structural forms within females is called deuterogyne. The deutogyne hibernate in the crevices and other shelters in previous years wood on plants. The term protogyne applies only to adults. The deutogynes become active in late winter, leave their hibernating sites and infest the buds and look for suitable location for feeding and breeding. They produce protogyne and the same is repeated till early May when deutogynes begin to appear among protogynes. The deutogynes travel and enter into crevices of stem upto 15 cm and by middle of July when the leaves begin to fall, those deutogynes which reach the hibernation sites survive while the protogynes perish with the fall of leaves. Winter rain and frost recondition the deutogynes for making active in following spring (Baker & Wharton, 1952).

In many Astigmatid mites, optional hypopial stage (non-feeding active/inactive stage) occurs between protonymph and tritonymph. This stage is for withstanding unfavourable condition and also for dispersal. The oviposition rate, sex ratio, etc. are variable in different groups of Acari.

Effect of environmental factors

Most of the plant feeding mites show a definite seasonal cycle. Temperate species often enters into diapause to survive during extreme cold but diapose is absent in tropical species. The temperature regime also influences the rate of multiplication and development period. With the rise in ambient temperature, the tetranychid mites multiply rapidly and a huge population is build up during late April to early June but with the onset of rain, the population is adversely affected and in many cases they are completely washed out. But the population reappears in post monsoon period though during this time the growth is not that fast as is seen during summer. The population remains at low level during winter months or may be absent. The seasonal cycle of tenuipalpid mites also follows the same pattern as is seen in tetranychids. The eriophyids also show well marked seasonality. The effect of weather factors on population fluctuation has been studied for several mites and some of the information has been given in the following chapters under crop pests.

The mites show various seasonal adaptations to survive the unfavourable weather conditions. The rate of development with varying temperatures has been studied for many economically important species of both phytophagous and predatory groups and on that basis several mathematical expressions have been produced. Temperature also has important role with fecundity. Fecundity is moderately high at higher temperature and declines at lower temperature. Food, moisture, age of species and host plant also influence fecundity.

The spider mites enter diapause either at egg stage, (many members of *Petrobia, Panonychus* show this type of diapause) while the diapausing at adult female stage is shown by some members of *Tetranychus, Eotetranychus.* The diapausing and non-diapausing stages often show difference in colouration, anatomical features, behaviour, etc. The photoperiod has important role in causing diapause. Apart from day length, temperature, quality of food plant may also indirectly influence diapause.

Temperature apart from food scarcity has also an important part to play in dispersal of species. The temperature with RH is one of the important factors in development of many tetranychid mites. The optimum temperatures for development vary with the species. It may be 25-28^0 C in *Panonychus ulmi,* 21-24^0 C in *Bryobia.* However, the average is 27-30^0 C. The tolerance level of upper limits of temperatures is also available in different species as well as in different stages of the same species.

Humidity

The humidity alone or humidity with temperature influence mite development. Mites show a phenomenon of humidity preference like that of temperature. They have a tendency to congregate within a narrow range of humidity. High RH may interfere with mite feeding by preventing loss of moisture from the body by evaporation through the cuticle. Hot dry weather is conducive to rapid development and high population level of spider mite. Body colouration has important role as because the dark coloured specimens absorb more sunlight which raises the body temperature and help to get rid of excess moisture in the body. In desert, light colour apparently helps in reflecting sun rays and thus saves from excessive evaporation.

The eriophyids which are on the undersurface of leaves are related to the presence of high RH.

Many of the mites show special features for moisture conservation and maintaining water balance. Some of those features are waxy coating on epicuticle which prevents water loss. The spiracle closing mechanism also regulates water loss. Majority of mites have optimal range of moisture in which a given species thrives. Mortality may be caused at extremely high moisture content. The survival is directly related to extremely high humidity condition as because at high humidity the bacterial, fungal, viral infections may be spread. Therefore, for each species there are certain limits of temperature and humidity within which they can live.

Rainfall and Wind

Heavy rain with strong wind is highly detrimental for mite population. The eriophyids which dwell within concealed places like buds, galls, etc. are not affected so much but the others which are leaf dwellings suffer most. The shade trees often provide protection to mite population. Though the mobile stages of mites may be washed with rain but the eggs of red spider mites remain unaffected as they remain firmly attached on the leaf surface. Though very strong wind often may damage the population but relatively less strong wind often helps the spider mites in dispersal and to settle in a new crop field.

Light

The light is an essential ecological factor for many biological processes. Red spider mites dwelling on upper leaf surface or exposed parts of the plant show positive response towards light but those living on undersurface do not show this behavior.

Light influences egg laying and ovipositional rhythm of tea red spider mite, *Oligonychus coffeae*. A change in light regime either from light to darkness or vice-versa influences oviposition. Mites also show sensitivity to lights of different wave lengths. The egg hatching shows relationship with different light colouration. Mites are not equally active during all 24 hours of the day. Some are diurnal and some are nocturnal, some prefer dawn (matinal) and others prefer dusk (crepuscular). Regularly occurring daily cycles of light and darkness exert a profound influence on the behavior and metabolism of mites. Complex ecological adaptations are known to be under the control of photoperiodism (environmental rhythm of light and darkness). Seasonal variation of colour and structure, feeding, breeding, etc. are also under the control of photoperiodism.

Host Plants

Mites show extreme variations with regard to development, fecundity, longevity with host plants and a volume of works has been done by several workers especially with regard to the economically important species. The texture, vestiture, nutritional values of host plants influence the feeding of mites. The biochemical factors of host plant also influence mite feeding and development. Nitrogen content of plant has been reported to influence oviposition as higher fecundity was associated with higher nitrogen content. Various anatomical characters of plants also have influence on mite feeding and development. In general, high fertilizer rate and excess of soluble elements like magnesium, calcium are conducive to mite development. The eriophyid bud mites prefer terminal buds with plant growth substances.

Effect of agricultural practicles

This aspect has a very important part to play in development of mite population. During the last few decades the mite problem has become alarming and for that the agricultural practices have important role. The use of high yielding varieties, excess irrigation and excess nitrogenous fertilizers induce rapid mite multiplication and that leads to mite outbreak. Removal of weeds also has varying effect on population build up, because weeds harbour the predators which are eliminated with the removal of weeds and that in turn, disbalances the natural balance. Introduction of new crop variety alters the intensity of mite infestation. Effect of monoculture also favours mite infestation as it provides food on continuous basis which enables quick build up. Red mites on apple enhances its population with pruning.

Effect of natural enemies

This is one of the most important controlling factors in population build up of mites. Mite outbreaks in some seasons takes place due to absence of regulatory factors like absence of natural enemies. Hence, conservation of natural enemies in the field is of utmost importance as in some cases they themselves can keep the pest population below economic injury level without application of pesticides. The important mite predators have been discussed in subsequent chapter.

Spatial distribution

The distribution of mites on leaves may be random or may be patchy or aggregated in some parts of leaves. The two parameters expressions that the "variance" and "Mean" are commonly used to determine spatial distributions. When the variance is more than mean, it indicates that the distribution pattern is aggregate and both the factors are equal, it indicates random distribution. The distribution of mites on plant canopies is also variable as some prefer top young leaves, some prefer the leaves of middle canopies while the others prefer matured leaves of bottom canopy. Even within leaves, majority prefer lower surface of leaves but some are there which will be found only on the upper surface (*Oligonychus mangiferus* on mango). Thus, the spatial distribution pattern has some importance in deciding the control strategy. Besides, the sampling strategy will also depend upon the distribution pattern of mites on leaves.

Webbing

Many spider mites secrete silken web to cover their colonies. This provides protection from natural enemies, vagaries of nature and also the mites protect them from toxic effects of pesticides. Members of the family Bdellidae, Camerobiidae and Cheyletidae cover their eggs with webs (Gerson, 1985). Tenuipalpids and *Aponychus* mites also cover their eggs with webs. The main function of covering eggs with webs is to protect them from predators. The webbing also influences the hatching percentage of eggs as has been seen in *T. urticae*. The web is also associated with courtship purpose. The web serves as physical contact with male and female prior to mating as well as pheromone substrate or carrier. The reports are also there where it has been recorded that the strands of the webs have been used during fight among males to pull out the competiting males. Therefore, the male which spins more fast silk, wins (Gerson, 1985).

Colonization and host plant effect

The webs are also used as lifelines and dispersal by blowing off from the host plant (e.g. *T. urticae, Oligonychus unguis*). As the dispersing female has to settle down to a new host and to start feeding, it spins webs and so also do the newly emerged immatures and thereby the plant becomes densely covered with webs. The eggs are laid either below or on the webs. The better is the host, more is the silk production. Feeding may not determine webbing as starving female also spins webs. Many mites spin webs throughout their lives.

Webbing at light

The light has some effect on spinning web as more web is spun under diurnal light condition as mites kept in dark, spun reduced webbing. However, exposure to continuous light will also reduce webbing because of imbalance.

Webbing and interspecific competition

The reports are there that the heavily spinning mite like *Tetranychus* does not allow other mites to settle on that leaf and so replaces it. *Bryobia*, a non-spinning spider mite was displaced by *Tetranychus*, as the former could not traverse the leaf surface webbed by the latter.

Webbing and natural enemies

Web reduces efficiency of general phytoseiid predators as they become entangled in web and also their searching ability is affected. Some phytoseiids ever avoid those leaves which are heavily covered with webs. However, the specialized predators like *Phytoseiulus persimilis* can effectively move on the webs and place its eggs on webs.

Webbing and acaricides

The webbing provides a protective canopy to the mite colonies and prevents reaching the spray droplets. Many of the mites show spindown effect when insecticide is sprayed. Pesticides like synthetic pyrethroids show such spindown effect and that may be one of the reasons why mite outbreak takes place after application of synthetic pyrethroids (Gerson, 1985).

1.5 GENERAL MODE OF FEEDING OF PHYTOPHAGOUS MITES ON HOST PLANTS AND DAMAGE SYMPTOMS

Normally the plant feeding mites feed on lower surface of leaves but there are some which feed on both the surfaces. During feeding, the mites penetrate the leaves by their stylet-like chelicerae and suck out the cell contents. Depth of penetration of tissues depends upon length of stylets, feeding time, population density, host plant anatomical features, etc. Low density of spider mite may damage the spongy mesophyll tissue but higher densities of population may damage the palisade parenchyma. During mite feeding, they cause three types of injuries, viz. Mechanical injury, Physical injury and Chemical injury.

Mechanical injury : The piercing of plant tissues by stylet like chelicerae injures the epidermal and mesophyll layers which cause water loss and that reduces the chlorophyll metabolism. This, in-turn, affects the growth of the plant. Besides, the damaged cells loose contact as a result of which, the normal cell functioning is reduced and that also affects the plant growth. In addition, while feeding, the mites inject the saliva in plant cells which causes degeneration of plant cells due to proteolytic enzymes present in it. Due to mechanical injuries, the photosynthetic enzymes are influenced which change the pathway of carbon and CO_2 intake. All these damage the starch synthesis. Some mites also inject plant hormone- like substances causing differential cell growth leading to malformation, gall formation, deformation, etc. Many eriophyids and some tetranychids also inject viruses causing a number of plant viral diseases.

Physical injury : The mite feeding affects transpiration rate due to loss of protective covering and disturbances in stomatal openings. This causes hydrolysis of protein into amino acid and starch into soluble sugar. These provide a better nutrition to plant feeding mites and that accelerates their multiplication.

Chemical injury : The mite feeding changes the concentration of inorganic compounds (NPK) and organic compounds (carbohydrate, phenolics, etc) and due to these the photosynthesis is affected.

General type of damage symptoms

Due to mite feeding, as mentioned above, two types of damage symptoms are produced, the direct and indirect. The former may be of two types, visible and non-visible. The visible symptoms are discolouration of leaves, russeting of leaves/ fruits, erineum and gall formation, curling/crinkling of leaves, deformation, malformation, premature defoliation, fruit drop, etc. The non-visible symptoms are reduction of leaf size, reduction in number of leaves/fruits/flowers per plant, shortening of shoots, damage in storage quality of fruits, etc. All these different kinds of damages are discussed in detail in mite attack on different types of crops in subsequent chapters.

Typical mite feeding symptoms are small light coloured punctures and those on prolonged exposure develop into irregularly shaped greyish or whitish spots which later turn bronzy. Some mite feeding causes leaf curling. Necrosis may also occur in leaves/growing tips. Sometimes feeding causes leaf burning, discolouration, defoliation. Mite feeding also causes abscesses. Often high density attack of mites makes the leaves brittle and fall off as soon as touched (*Bryobia praetiosa* on pear). Sometimes leaves become blackened (*Tetraniychus pacificus* on pear). However, when this same species feeds on other hosts, produce different types of damage symptoms. Most of the tetranychid mites produce the damage symptoms described above. All these damages cause retardation of plant growth, affect yield, reduce quality and quantity of fruits and flowers and finally cause economic loss to the growers.

The Tenuipalpid mites mostly attack lower surface of leaves as well as twigs, fruits, petioles and due to feeding causes browning and drying of leaves, premature leaf and fruit drop, scarring on fruit surface and affecting quality of fruits (*Brevipalpus* spp.). Sometimes these mites produce sunken spots on leaves. Some *Brevipalpus* species produce yellow areas on upper surface and brown on lower surface. Large chlorotic spots with concentric rings of chestnut coloured resinous substance are often produced on leaves by the private mite. Ring spots are also formed on fruits and twigs. Later, those spots erupt to produce scaling of bark that resembles scaly bark psorosis. Sometimes leprosies is caused by toxin injected by this mite during feeding process (Jeppson *et al.*, 1975). Some *Brevipalpus* produce gall-like symptoms along main stem of the seedlings. The galls are woody, appear like axils and no leaves develop on axils.

B. phoenicis and *B. californicus* are associated with ring spotting of grape fruit in Texas. Leprosis-like spots appear when the population is high (Jeppson *et al.*, 1975). *Tenuipalpus punicae* causes heavy defoliation. *Dolichotetranychus floridanus* attacks pineapple and invite fungi and bacteria on the feeding sites causing bud rot (Pritchard and Baker, 1958). *Raoiella indica* attacks date palm producing sticky yellowish/reddish spots on leaves.

Tarsonemid mites produce various types of damage symptoms which include crinkling/curling of leaves, rottening of stems, (*P. latus* on chilli), injury to young plants, rottening of fruits (*Steneotarsonemus ananas* on pineapple), producing brown crater-like depressions (*Steneotarsonemus bancrofti* on sugarcane); distortion of leaves (*S. furcatus* on maranta leaves), distortion, stunting, mortality of leaves/flowers (*S. laticeps* on bulbs), production of roughened wrinkled appearance on upper surface of cyclamen, irregular folding and fluting of leaf margin, bulging or blistering of veins (*Steneotarsonemus pallidus* on cyclamen).

In case of Eriophyid mites, the feeding injuries are extremely diverse like production of galls (*Aceria pongamiae* on *Pongamia glabra*); erineum formation (*Aceria lycopersici* on brinjal); velvety erineum on litchi (by *Aceria litchii*), warty patches (*Aceria clerodendronis* on *Clerodendron inerme*), blistering of leaves (*Eriophyes pyri* on pear),cup shaped depressions (*Aceria holopteleae* on *Holoptelea integrifolia*), russeting of leaves (*Phyllocoptruta oleivora* on Citrus), silvering of leaves (*Eriophyes pyri* on pear), big bud (*Aceria sheldoni* on Citrus), witche's broom effect (*Paraphytoptus rhamniphagus* on *Rhamnus purshiana*), vegetative and floral malformation (*Aceria mangiferae* on mango), Red Berry disease (*Aceria essigi* on *Rubas laciniatus*), Dry Berry disease (on loganberry by *Phyllocoptes gracilis*), Tight rolling of leaves(*Aceria granati* on pomegranate), Drying of bulbs (*Aceria tulipae* on bulb), Curling of leaves(*Aceria infectoriae* on *Ficus infectoria*) (Jeppson *et al.*, 1975). Apart from these, eriophid mites cause a number of viral diseases to plants which have been dealt with in a separate chapter in this book.

1.6 MAJOR GROUPS OF INJURIOUS PLANT FEEDING MITES AND BENEFICIAL PREDATORY MITES

A. INJURIOUS PLANT FEEDING MITES

The plant feeding mites belong to five major groups which are Tetranychidae, Tenuipalpidae, Tarsonemidae, Eriophyoidea, Tuckerellidae and details of those are given below :

Tetranychidae Donnadieu : These mites are popularly called spider mites because of the fact that these mites like spiders can spin webs to cover their colonies for getting protection from natural enemies and also to protect themselves from pesticides. These are soft bodied, variously coloured, colony forming, mostly live on undersurface of leaves and sometimes on upper surface as well. Their sizes vary from 5-6 mm long.

Chelicerae movable, stylet-like, set in stylophore, is formed by fusion of cheliceral bases. Palpi – 4 segmented, with strong claws. Propodosoma with 3-4 pairs of setae; hysterosoma with 8-13 pairs of setae. Tarsi of legs I-II with duplex setae. Genital portion of female with characteristic wrinkles, tenent hairs present on tarsal claw. Empodium well developed, reduced or absent, with or without tenent hairs. Aedeagus of male is characteristic of family, and is of great use in separating the species. In subfamily Bryobiinae, there are 3 pairs of anal setae while in Tetranychinae there are 2 pairs of anal setae.

These mites are exclusively plant feeders and many of these are important crop pests. Some members are important bio control agents of water hyacinth. Little over 101 species are known from India under 2 subfamilies, 6 tribes and 18 genera against over 1200 species from the world. Some members are host specific while there are many which are polyphagous. The reproduction is by both arrhenotoky and thelytoky. The life stages include egg, larva, protonymph, deutonymph and adult. The life cycles in details and damage symptoms caused by different species are discussed under the chapter Mite pests of various crops. Various anatomical features, characters of taxonomic importance, keys to different Indian species are dealt with in detail in Gupta (1985) and Gupta & Gupta (1994).

Tenuipalpidae Berlese : These mites are popularly called false spider mites as because they look like spider mites but unlike them do not spin webs. These are variously coloured mostly bright, reddish, flat, pear shaped, slow moving and occur in colonies on undersurface of leaves especially along veins,also on twigs, buds, fruits, galls and petioles. Meyer (1979) reported 504 species in 21 genera from the world. Some species feed on bark. Many are agricultural and horticultural pests. Since their population often remains in field below economic injury level, they do not cause economic damage in most cases.

Chelicerae stylet - like, recurved and arise from eversible stylophore, palpus simple lacking claws on penultimate segment. Propodosoma bears 3 pairs of setae, hysterosoma bears 1-3 pairs of dorsocentrals, 1 pair of humeral, 5-7 pairs of dorsolaterals, there may be 1-4 pairs of dorsosubcentral hysterosomal or some may be lacking these. Ventral metapodosoma with 2 pairs of setae but their number may vary. There may or may not be distinct ventral and genital plates. Dorsum is provided with ornamentation in the form of striations, reticulations and rarely it is smooth. The tenent hairs on empodium present on lateral claws. These are also exclusively plant suckers but unlike spider mites they do not cause severe economic damage in many cases, barring a few. Gupta (1985) discussed the morphological characters which are used for taxonomic identities of the genera and species. From India the number of species known is 54 (Gupta, 1985) under 10 genera and since then some more species have been added. He also discussed the morphological characters of taxonomic importance and provided keys to Indian genera and species. Jeppson *et al.* (1975) considered 15 genera under this family and discussed characters of taxonomic importance. Presently, about 600 species are known from the world.

The injurious tenuipalpid mites from India are discussed under different crop pests in subsequent chapters.

Tarsonemidae Kramer : These are tiny, glossy mites, found on undersurface of leaves as well as in association with fungus. Males often carry with their chelicerae the female deutonymphs.

Body rounded, gnathosoma with minute palpi lying closely appressed laterally. Chelae tiny and stylet-like. Stigma of female opens behind gnathosoma, male without stigma. Empodium without membranous flap-like organ attached to claw. Leg IV in female ending in terminal and sub terminal whip-like setae. Gupta (1985) discussed the various morphological characters used in taxonomy of this group as well as provided keys to Indian genera and species known till that time. Jeppson *et al.*(1975) elaborately discussed the anatomical characters of this family. Many are polyphagous, while some have restricted host range.

The life stages are egg - larva - quiescent pupal stage - adult. The pupal stage is sessile and the larval integument appears inflated or floated with the cuticle tightly structured. Transformation of adult takes place within the larval skin through successive stages of withdrawing the appendages from the old integument. The pupal skin splits dorsally at the completion of transformation to the adult and the mature adult emerges. The colour varies according to food intake and hence body colour is not a reliable character (Jeppson *et al.*, 1975). Presnetly, as many as 730 species are known from the world.

Tuckerellidae Baker & Pritchard : These are somewhat rare group of plant mites and are tropical and sub tropical in occurrence. The host range of these mites are also restricted.

The dorsal chaetotaxy is very distinctive of this family with 4 pairs of palmate propodosomal setae and 36 pairs of dorsal palmate hysterosomal setae as well as 5 or 6 pairs of flagellate setae caudally. Palpus elongate with thumb - claw complex. Genito-anal region of female is distinctive.

Only one genus *Tuckerella* Womersley is known under this family and 3 species under this genus are known from India.

Eriophyoidae Nalepa : These mites are popularly known as gall mites or bud mites or rust mites or erineum mites. They look entirely different from all other mites because of worm-like appearance, having minute body (about 200 microns long), practically invisible in naked eye and have only 2 pairs of legs in all stages of development.

Minute, elongated, worm-like mites, having 2 pairs of legs in all stages including adults, placed anteriorly. Body divided into short Cephalothorax, covered over dorsally and on the sides by the cephalothorasic shield and a longer tapering abdomen with annulation which may or may not show dorsoventral differentiation. Rostrum anteriorly projecting or down curved with needle-like or lancet-like chelicerae. Genital opening transverse. Body setation is reduced to minimum. Gupta (1985) discussed in detail the morphological characters of taxonomic importance as well as keys to sub-families, tribes, genera and species known from India. Jeppson *et al.* (1975) also discussed the anatomical characters and provided keys to the known taxonomic categories. Gupta & Gupta (1999) reported 448 species under 96 genera as the known eriophyoid fauna from India. Presently over 500 species are known from India against over 4000 from the world.

There are 2 active stages. The first stage nymph and second stage nymph. However, in some eriophyids, the life cycle is somewhat complicated as there are 2 types of females, the deutogyne adapted for hibernation and start reproduction in the next session, while the other type is protogyne which generally reproduces throughout the summer and spring and dies with the advent of winter. In this case an alteration of generation is exhibited. The presence of two different structural forms of females within a species is called deuterogyne. Protogyne and deutogyne apply only to adults. The first and second stage of deuterogynous species does not indicate whether they will produce protogyne, deutogyne or male. The deutogynes hibernate in crevices and other shelters in previous year's wood on plants. They become active in late winter, come out of hibernation site in search of suitable location for feeding and breeding. They produce protogyne and the same is repeated till early May when the deutogynes begin to appear amongst the protogynes. The deutogynes travel and enter into crevices of the stem upto 15 cm or more and by middle of July when the leaves begin to fall, those deutogynes which reach the hibernation sites survive while the protogynes perish with the fall of leaves. The deutogynes after reaching hibernation sites become dormant and partially dry up. Winter rain and frost recondition the deutogynes for making them active in the following spring (Baker & Wharton, 1952; Gupta, 1985).

Penthaleidae Oudemans : These are commonly called grain mites. These are small, soft bodied, without external peritremes and with the trachea originating at base of chelicerae. Rhagidial organ (solenidia) lie flat in specialized areas on tarsus I and II, tarsal claws hooked, empodia pad-like having radiating hairs. Anterior medium portion of propodosoma bears tubercle with a pair of setae (Jeppson *et al.*, 1975).

These mites infest small grains, grasses, legumes, vegetables, ornamental flowers, cotton, peanut and various woods. The infected field appears greyish or silvery due to destruction of chlorophyll because of mite feeding. Tips of leaves give a scorchy appearance. Grain yield and forage are reduced. The life cycle passes through egg - larva - protonymph - deutonymph and adult. The eggs may be of two different types, winter eggs having short incubation period and aestivating eggs, having extended incubation period. The length of life cycle varies with weather condition (Jeppson *et al.*, 1975).

The economically important species like *Penthaleus major* (Duges), the winter grain mite and *Halotydeus destructor* Berlese, red-legged earth mite, are serious pests of many crops. The infestation causes bleaching of leaves, followed by silvering, drying and scorching of leaves. Seedlings are often killed.

Acaridae : The mites of this family especially some belonging to *Rhizoglyphus, Tyrophagus* and *Caloglyphus* often do damage to vegetables, flowers, bulbs, roots and tubers. *Rhizoglyphus echinopus* (F. & R.) is the most serious pest of potato, dahlia, etc. *Caloglyphus* also sometimes damages grains, nuts, fruits. *Tyrophagus* mites are encountered in leaf sheaths of grasses, cereals or in plants damaged by phytophagous insects and mites. *Tyrophagus dimidiatus* is found on leaf sheaths damaged by tarsonemid or on grasses and cereals damaged by fruit fly (*Oscinella frit*) (Jeppson *et al.*, 1975).

Oribatid Mites : Some of the oribatid mites are known to damage plant parts like roots, leaves, bulbs causing reasonable economic loss. Some of the members belong to *Camisia, Humerobates, Perlohomannia, Orthogalumna,* etc. They sometimes feed on algae grown on bark of fruit trees and occasionally may become harmful.

Tydeidae Kramer : Some of the members of this family are plant feeders (eg. *Tydeus californicus* (Banks), *Lorryia formosa* Cooreman) but many are fungal feeders, some feed on honeydew and others are predators. This family is included under predatory mites in this book.

B. BENEFICIAL PREDATORY MITES

Order : PROSTIGMATA

Anystidae Oudemans : These are large, orange or yellow, very fast moving, making whirling movement on undersurface of leaves and occasionally on upper surface as well.

Long legged, fast moving, predaceous in habit having legs arranged radially. Idiosoma short or broad or longer than broad, integument striated. Prodorsal shield may or may not be present. Naso with a pair of sensilla, normally present on anterior margin of propodosoma, latter also bears 1 or 2 pairs of eyes, Chelicera with hook-like chela distally, with 1 or 2 claws, which may be combed/toothed, empodium claw-like or brush- like or bell-like, genital suckers absent (Meyer & Ueckermann, 1987).

Some of these mites are good predators of both insects and mites. Their prey consumption rate is very high(872.6 females of *T.urticae* per predator (*Anystis agilis*) in life time. The insects on which it feeds include thrips, aphids, leaf hoppers, Lucerne fleas, etc. Reports are also there to feed on tick larvae. Gerson & Smiley (1990) suggested conservation of this predatory mite for profitable utilization in bio-control. A total of 9 species under 3 genera are known from India (Gupta, 2002).

Bdellidae Duges : These mites are brightly coloured, fast moving, popularly called Snout mites and are good predators.

Medium sized with finely striated integument. Subcutaneous shields may be present on propodosoma. Gnathosoma cone-like, formed by elongate chelate chelicerae, one or more setae present on chelicerae. Ventral hypostome with 2, 6 or 7 pairs of ventrolateral setae and 2 pairs of setae on lateral lips. Palpi 5 segmented, tracheal opening near cheliceral bases. Idiosoma with two pairs of sensillae present on pseudostigmatid organ, 2, 4 or 5 eyes present. Legs 8 segmented. Rayed, pad-like pulvillus. Genital tracheae, when present, well developed.

These mites are voracious predators of good number of mites and insects. Its insect preys include Lucerne flea, a pest of pasture in Australia, Lucerne aphids, on eggs and crawlers of armoured scales and mite like *Bryobia praetiosa* (Gerson & Smiley, 1990). Their consumption rate also is good. However, their frequency of availability in the field is little less and therefore, its potentiality as bio-control agent is doubtful.

As many as 14 species, under 6 genera and 4 subfamilies are known from India (Gupta, 2002). Recently, Roy and Saha (2010: *Jour Asia-Pacific. Ent.*, **12** : 121-126) described a new species under *Bdellodes*.

Camerobiidae McGregor : Members of this family have long stilted legs, weak palpi in ventrally directed gnathosoma having looped peritreme.

The species of the genus *Neophyllobius* feed on crawlers of armoured scales as well as various plant inhabiting mites. It also feeds on eriophyids and tenuipalpids. Since the population of this predatory mite is rather scarce, their importance as bio control agents is doubtful (Gerson & Smiley, 1990).

Caligonellidae Grandjean : Small mites, tree living, reddish, cheliceral basal segments fused with each other in mid-line forming a conical stylophore. Palp 5 segments. Palp tarsus as long as tibial claw, slender, cylindrical, arising from distal half of palp tibia with specialized seta present apically. Idiosoma integument finely striated or with dorsal plates, eyes 1-2 paired. Coxa I & II and III & IV forming two groups. Pretarsus with 2 claws having tenent hairs.

The predatory nature of this group needs to be exploited. Some members of this family have been recorded on cherry tree, under bark (Krantz ,1978). Not much is known about their economic importance.

Cheyletidae Leach : These mites have prominent thumb-claw complex, M-shaped peritreme, palp tarsus with sickle-like and comb-like setae, body setae of diverse shape(rod-like, palmate, serrate, pectinate, lanceolate, fan-like, etc.) palp tarsus with claws and often with teeth, number and size of dorsal plates, nature of tarsal claws, number of teeth on palp claw, nature of sensilla on palp tarsus, structure of peritreme vary in different genera and form important taxonomic characters.

The free living mites are predaceous, feed on micro-arthropods, acarid mites, collembola, etc. They are also abundant on granaries. Many species feed on armoured scales, in stored product ecosystem. The predatory cheyletid mite, *Cheyletus eruditus*, prefers temperature range of 20 - 25^{0C} and 70% to 80% RH (Gerson & Smiley, 1990). Gupta (2002) reported occurrence of 15 species under 10 genera from India associated with plants.

Cunaxidae Thor : Chelicerae separated, hinged at base and move over gnathosoma in a scissors-like fashion. Ventrally hypostome with 6-7 pairs of setae. Genital plate in female without internal setae. Genital aperture with 2-3 pairs of acetabula. Palp segment terminates in a claw, some segments bear strong spines. Tarsal empodium claw-like with 4 raylets, claws lack ventrolateral hairs. Body usually soft, also may be strongly sclerotized, with or without ventral shields. Eyes may or may not be present.

These are yellow, red or brown, fast runners, occur on diverse crops and many other habitats and feed on mites as well as insects. Some cunaxids are known to fasten their prey with silken threads, excreted through their mouthparts. *Cunaxa capreolus* feeds on *Eutetranychus orientalis* and a generation is completed in about 4 weeks time. Average prey consumption during development was 230 booklice or 472 spider mites. Some feed on scale insects, some on eriophyids (Gerson & Smiley, 1990).

Gupta (2002) reported the occurrence of 21 species under 5 genera and 2 subfamilies from India.

Erythraeidae Robineau-Desvoidy : Reddish mite, heteromorphic, lack urstigmata, parasitic on arthropods at larval stage and free living as predators during nymphal and adult stages. A shallow furrow separates the propodosoma from hysterosoma. Cristia Metopica with 2 sensory areas. Chelicerae unsegmaned, stylet-like, toothed distally. Genital suckers absent.

Some of the members like *Balaustium, Erythraeus, Bochartia Sphaerolophus* occasionally are good predators. They feed on many arthropods (including moths and scale insects, psyllids) and mites *Panonychus ulmi* (Gerson & Smiley, 1990).

Gupta (2002; Roy *et al.*, 2008) reported 17 species under 6 genera and 4 subfamilies known from India.

Eupodidae Koch : Yellowish white, medium sized mites, pear shaped, flat, fast moving, highly fragile. Propodosoma and hysterosoma may be separated by a suture, skin soft, finely striated, weakly haired, pseudostigmata with weakly differentiated sensory seta, Femur IV of *Eupodes* is much thicker than other leg femurs, used for jumping purpose. Palpi with 4 movable segments, chelicerae with modified chela.

Some of the members of this family are pests of mushroom (*Linopodes antennaepes* Banks) damaging mushroom. They are found on mushroom beds. They are also found on moss and under leaves.

Only 2 species of this family under 1 genus are known from India (Gupta, 2002).

Raphignathidae Kramer : Small reddish mites, no suture between propodosoma and hysterosoma. Number of shields varies. Area between shields striated. Eye 1-2 pairs, propodosoma without sensory setae. Palp tarsus moderately long, located ventrally, each tarsus with 2 claws and rayed pulvillus. Chela stylet-like for piercing purpose, coxae either contiguous or separated into groups. Genital suckers absent.

These mites are predators, mostly of eggs. However, their numbers in field are very few and hence their effectiveness as predator is uncertain.

Gupta (2002) reported the occurrence of 3 species under 2 genera known from India and thereafter one more species has been added (Roy *et al.*, 2006, *Entomon.*, **31** : 360-313).

Stigmaeidae Oudemans : Members of this family can be distinguished by absence of peritreme, podocephalic canal may lead from base of gnathosoma to coxae II, dorsum of idiosoma nude or completely covered by 2 shields or partly covered by 2 or more shields, dorsal body setae vary from 13-14 pairs. Chelicerae free, may be partly fused in some genera, palpal thumb claw complex present and consisting of tibial claw, with a setae-like or claw-like accessory claw at the base and a palp tarsus. Single pair of anogenital plate present covering the genital and anal vestibule.

These are yellow, ovoid or elongate mites, very frequently occur in crops and ornamental plants and some are very important predators (Species of *Agistemus, Zetzellia, Stigmaeus, Eryngiopus*)

They effectively feed on tetranychids, tenuipalpids, eriophyids and can exert profitable control. They feed on eggs, immature stages and adults of the prey. *Agistemus exsertus* consumes 60 eggs/day or 45 immatures/day (Gerson & Smiley 1990).

A total of 26 species under 6 genera are known from India (Gupta, 2002; Roy *et al.*, 2010, *Entomon* 34: 175-180).

Tydeidae Kramer : Small or tiny mites, 250-500 microns long, weak or nonsclerotized body. Palp 4 segmented, palp tarsus with 5 setae, a solenidion may be present ventrally or terminally, palp with 1 or 2 simple setae, chelicerae with needle-like unopposed chela. Dorsal setae 3 pairs P_1, P_2, P_3 besides a pair of sensillary setae on the propodosoma. Hysterosomal setae in 5 transverse rows of 4 setae each or in $4^1/_2$ rows. Dorsal setae may be of diverse shape, simple, serrate, club shaped, lanceolate, etc. Striation pattern of dorsum is of important taxonomic character for separation of genera and species (Gupta, 2002).

Many of these mites are egg feeders, some feed on eriophyids, (Schruff, 1972, OEPP/EPPO Bull., **3** : 51-55), nematodes (Santos *et al.*, 1981, *Ecology*, **62** : 664-669), soft scales, *Saissetia oleae* (Gerson & Smiley, 1990). Apart from being predators, they serve as food of other predators and can also clean up after honeydew producers, thereby reducing damage attributable to sooty mould (Gerson & Smiley, 1990).

From India 22 species under 5 genera are known (Gupta, 2002; Roy *et al.*, 2009, *JBNHS*, **106** : 83-85).

Order : MESOSTIGMATA

Phytoseiidae Berlese : Palp tarsus with 2 tined apotele, chelicerae chelate, undifferentiated hypostomal setae, a smooth or indistinctly serrate tectum, an entire or transversely divided dorsal shield.

Free living, dorsal shield entire on all but on one, *Macroseius biscutatus* where it is divided (Chant & McMurtry, 2007), 200-600 microns long, idiosoma of adult female with 38 or fewer pairs of setae, (of a total of 43 pairs of setae) known to occur in the family; dorsal shield with 23 or fewer pairs of setae (of a total of 28 possible pairs of setae), caudoventral area of female with 10 or fewer pairs of setae, paraventral setae (z_1) absent, never with more than 1 pair of setae on R_1 series or 2 pairs of setae on r series and never with setae in the UR series, palpal claw 2 tined, corniculae slender, proximal, parallel, blade-like, tritosternum well developed with 2 lacinae, both digits of chelicherae well developed, dentition variable, peritrematal shield in most species fused anteriorly with dorsal shield, free or fused posteriorly with exopodal plate, male with spermatophoral process, macrosetae on leg IV may or may not be present (Chant & McMurtry, 2007).

These are well distributed throughout the world, occur on all types of vegetations, many are very important predators of plant feeding mites, scale insects, thrips, aphids, nematodes, etc. and are considered as one of the best known predators of Acari. They are voracious feeders and because of these advantages, this group has attracted attention of acarologists and entomologists and efforts are being made globally to utilize these mites in biological control programme. Several species have attained commercial status, being commercially mass multiplied and sold to farmers like chemical pesticides. Efforts are on to develop resistant strains to many acaricides for better utilization of these mites and some resistant strains have already been developed. Global attempts are being made to promote use of phytoseiid mites in pest management programme.

So far as India is concerned, Phytoseiidae is one of the best worked out groups as evident from the fact that a total of 203 species under 20 genera and 3 subfamilies are known presently as compared to 2280 (+) known from the world (Gupta, 2003; Roy *et al.*, 2008; Roy and Saha, 2010). Gupta (1986, 2003) discussed all the species known from India giving descriptions, illustrations, keys, etc. of all the taxa. Chant & McMurtry (2007) provided new classification bringing about a lot of changes in the generic concept. Some of the most promising phytoseiid predators identified from India are *Neoseiulus longispinosus, Euseius alstoniae, Euseius ovalis, Euseius finlandicus, Amblyseius largoensis, Transeius tetranychivorus, Amblyseius channabasavannai, Euseius coccineae,* etc.

Family Ascidae Voigts & Oudemans : Tritosternum present, Chaetotaxy of trochanter, femur and genu 2-5-6, chelicerae with spermatophoral process. Anal, ventrianal, hologastric or holoventral shields in adults not fused with dorsal shield, posterior coxae without setigerous spurs in both sexes. Dorsum with holodorsal or schizodorsal shield. Corniculae horn-like, dorsal shield strongly sclerotized. Hypostome grooved in both sexes with 5-7 rows of denticles. Adult with distinct podonotal or opisthonotal shields.

This family includes many species which occur on plants and are useful predators of plant feeding mites. A large number of members of this family occur in stored products and either feed on acarids or are phoretic. They are also known to feed on nematodes (Gerson & Smiley, 1990).

Plant associated ascids from India are 9 species under 5 genera (Gupta, 2002).

1.7 MANAGEMENT OF MITE PESTS WITH CHEMICALS

Before going to the management aspect of plant feeding mites, it is essential to know why the mite problem has become so serious globally.

Reasons for mite pest outbreak

The reasons which are assigned to for pest outbreak are :

a. Random and indiscriminate use of chlorinated hydrocarbons which eliminate natural enemies of pest mites, leading to rapid multiplication of pests.

b. Development of pest resistance due to uses of sub lethal doses of organophosphoric compounds, carbamets, etc. and often due to resurgence problem caused by injudicious use of synthetic pesticides especially pyrethroids.

c. Use of high yielding crop varieties, adapting improved agricultural practices and excess irrigation which make the crops more nutritive and that lead to more mite multiplication.

d. Insufficient coverage of pesticides with the habitat of plant feeding mites.

e. Many of the mites which were earlier innocuous or of little importance have assumed the status of major pests now throughout the world.

The nature of chemical control of mites is extremely dynamic because several elements are involved. Among these, the mention may be made of the susceptibility of various developmental stages of the species to pesticides, the effect of these pesticides on the performance of host plant and its yield, elimination of competitive mite and insect species and suppressive action on natural enemies and all these are of prime importance.

Factors governing effictiveness of pesticides

a. Pesticides effect on various developmental stages of the pest mite

b. Mite activity and distribution of pest population on host plant

c. Source of re-infestation

d. Pesticide resistance problem

e. Mode of spraying to ensure proper foliage covering

f. Weather factors before and after application of pesticides

Decision regarding selection of pesticides

a. The primary toxicity of pesticides to eggs

b. Toxicity on mobile stages

c. Toxicity on both eggs and mobile stages and its predators

d. Time of application

In case the crop is heavily infested, it is desirable to choose such pesticides which are effective against most of the motile stages (larva, nymph and adult stages).

Relation of plant growth and mite activity

The effectiveness of pesticides will vary during the plant growth. The rapid expansion of the young leaves may diminish the effectiveness of the pesticides because the newly emerging leaves will be free from toxicant deposits and hence mites can grow there rapidly.

Distribution pattern of pest population and source of re-infestation

These two are very important factors and will have decisive role on effectiveness of pesticides. Hence, before application of pesticides it is needed to have information on these aspects. The source of re-infestation is very much essential as often the mites move to alternate hosts when the crop season is off and re-infest the next season's crops.

Resistance and foliage covering

The development of resistance is dependent upon the type of chemical used and its frequency. While spraying, it is needed to see that the application of pesticides provides good coverage of foliage and that will depend upon the type of the sprayer and the skill of the person who is spraying. The systemic acaricides, ovicides which penetrate through the leaf or have toxic vapour action do not require complete coverage of the leaves.

Weather condition

This is another factor which will decide the success of pesticidal action. Heavy rain shortly after spraying, low humidity and hot scorchy sun during spraying have significant detrimental effect.

Choice of acaricides

The host plant, presence of predators/parasites and other beneficials on the crops are important points to be considered before spraying.

Specific acaricides

These include those which are effective on mites, some of these are :

Dicofol : It is very effective, have high initial toxicity, prolonged residual action, ovicidal action and relatively safe to natural enemies especially predatory mites. In some cases resistance may develop, if used repeatedly.

Sulphur : This inorganic acaricide is very effective against spider mites, false spider mites and eriophyids. It acts through vapour and contact action. The prevailing temperature is very important as it is less effective below 20° C and show phytotoxicity. Its efficiency increases with particle size, the smaller the particle size, more is the efficiency. Sulphur is more effective against larvae.

Acaro-insecticides

Ethion : It is one of the most effective insecticides found successful against mites. It is nonsystemic but has trans-laminar action against mites. It is effective against all groups of plant feeding mites. Repeated application may develop resistance problem.

Carbofuran : It is also widely used against mites.

Some other acaro-insectides which have been tested during the last 50 years and found promising against mites are endosulfan, monocrotophos, phosphamidon, dimethoate, carbophenothion, chlorfenvinphos, chlorpyriphos, fenthion, malathion, oxydemeton methyl, phosalone, quinalphos, cypermethrin, fenvalerate, fenpropathrin, deltamethrin, permethrin, binapacryl, chlorfenson, bromoprophylate, methomyl, oxythioquinox.

The use of some of the above named pesticides is still in vogue and performance of those has been indicated while dealing with mite pests of different crops in the subsequent chapters.

Recently, many new pesticides have come in the market and some of those have been found to be quite effective against many of the mite pests. Mention is made of some of those :

Fenpyroximate : (5% SC) Trade name Danitron, Meteor, Acaban. It shows contact activity and is effective on all stages of *T. urticae* and *P. citri*. Larvae are more susceptible to other stages.

Avermectin : (Trade name Vertimec 1.8 EC.) It is a macroliddi-saccharide derived from *Streptomyces avermectins*, produced during fermentation process. It is active at low dosage 4.5–22.5g ai/ha. Recommended dosage is 9 g. ai/ha. for mites, for insects (Catterpillar, grubs) the recommended dose is 10-50g. ai/ha.

Thiourea : (Trade name Polo, Pegasus 50% EC, 250 SC, 500 SC) it is effective against tetranychid, tarsonemid and eriophyid mites. The recommended dose is 250–450 g. ai/ha.

Sulphur Ester Propergite : (Trade name Omite, Comite, Ornamite, Uniroyal, DO 14 ENT 27226) : Formulations include Omite 20 EC, 30 WP, 57 EC, 68 EC, 570 EW (Emulsion in water), 720 EC.

Spirodiclofen Tetraonic acid derivatives : (Trade name Oberon 240 S)

Spiromesifen : (24% SC) Envidor

Flucycloxuron (insect growth regulator) (Andalin) : It is active against eggs, pre-imaginal stages of mite pests of the genera *Panonychus* and *Tetranychus* as well as eriophyids.

Pyridaben (Pyridazinones)(trade name Nexter R) : Highly active against all developing stages of mites.

The other modern pesticides are : Acephate (75%SP), Lannate 12.5 SL, Megister (Fenazaquin 10 EC), Mitex -S 80% WP, Flubendiamide 24% + Thiacloprid 24% - 480SC (W/V), Hexithiazox 0.005% (Maiden 5%), Imidacloprid 200 SL, Carbendazim, CHA2062, Sedna 5% SC Cyhexatin, Amitraz, Bifenthirin, Buprofin, Diafenthiuron, etc.

Many of these pesticides have been used against different species of mites in the recent years (*Source: Abstract Int. Symp-cum-Workshop in Acarlogy, 8–10 April 2010 BCKV*, Kalyani) and some are indeed good for effective management of mite pests.

The results of various experiments done in field and laboratory levels against diverse mite pests are mentioned in the subsequent chapters dealing with mite pests of crops.

Management of mite pest of crops with botanical Pesticides and Biorationals

A large number of plant species, about 2,50,000, are known to possess secondary metabolites' which are biologically active and 10,000 of those have been chemically identified. The plants produce secondary metabolites for their own defence system and recently some attempts are being made globally to utilize those in pest management. The advantages of these are safe to natural enemies and pollinators, environmental friendly, cause no human hazards and involve least cost. There is no risk of developing resistance or causing resurgence. These secondary metabolites are not uniformly placed in plants and are also present in varying proportions. Many of these plant based pesticides having properties like antifeedant, repellent, development deterrent, oviposition inhibitor besides having toxic effect causing mortality. Only 1% or less of the botanical pesticides have been critically evaluated as pesticides indicating a huge scope of further research in this area.

The plant species which have already shown great promise in control of mites are given below :

Acorus calamus : The rhizome extract of this plant has acaricidal effect against spider mites(see also chapter dealing with pests of crops). Maitra & Gupta (2006) reported 75% mortality of *Tetranychus macfarlanei* on Ashwagandha.

Allium sativum : The active compound from garlic extract has pesticidal property against mite. Allitin is the toxicant present in it. Gupta *et al.* (2007) reported 46.66%, 66.66%, 86.66%, 93.33% and 100% at 1% conc. and 53.33%, 73.33%, 100% at 1.5% conc. after 24, 48, 72, 96, 120 hrs, respectively, against *Brevipalpus phoenicis* in case of former and 24 hrs., 48 hrs. and 72 hrs., in case of latter.

Anona squamosa : The extract of custard apple leaf/seed also has acaricidal effect.Anonaine is the toxicant present in this plant. Maitra & Gupta (2006) recorded 100% mortality against *T. macfarlanei* and *B. euphorbiae* with custard apple seed extract.

Azadirachta indica : This is one of the most effective and widely used plant species, the extract of which is used as botanical pesticides against many plant feeding mites. Leaf extract (aqueous/methanol), NSKE, neem oil have all been found promising against mites. It has toxicant, antifeedant, growth inhibitor and repellent actions. Azadirachtin is the active compound having the pesticidal property. Neem kernel powder can also be used as pesticide. Neem products have been used by many persons on various mite pests and some of those have been referred to in the subsequent chapters. Several agro chemical companies have introduced different formulations of neem based products. Some of the commercially available neem based products are Replin, Alchook, Nimbion, Neemark, Nimbocinol, Margosan, etc. It is effective against different species of spider mites registering 60-80%mortality. Maitra & Gupta (2006) reported 100%mortality of *Petrobia harti* on *Oxalis corniculata* using neem leaf extract and also got 100% mortality of *Bravipalpus californicus* on mentha using neem leaf extract.

***Chrysanthemum cenerariaefolium* (Pyrethrins) :** Its extract is also an effective pesticide on mites. Its active ingredients are pyrethin I, Cenerin I. and Jasmolin I. It is a contact miticide. It is formulated as dust, emulsion. Since naturally occurring pyrethin is photo unstable, a number of synthetic pyrethrins have been already produced, the names of which have been mentioned earlier. The effectiveness of synthetic pyrethins have been discussed in the subsequent chapters under crop pests.

***Derris elliptica* :** Derris powder which is produced by drying and powdering of roots of this plant has acaricidal property and is used for de-ticking.

***Madhuca indica* :** The oil of this plant has acaricidal property against sucking mite pests.

***Melia azadirach* :** The extract of this plant has also been found to have acaricidal property against different mites. The active compounds are Meliantriol I (present in seed oil) and azadirachtin.

***Nicotiana tabacum* :** Since earlier days its decoction is used in pest management. The active compounds are non-nicotine and neo nicotine or anabasin. It is non systemic in action and also has slight stomach and contact actions. Tobacco decoction is produced by boiling 1kg of tobacco waste in 10 litres of water for an hour. Soap powder may be added to increase its effectiveness. Nicotine sulphate also has been used in earlier days for pest control.

***Pongamia glabra* :** Pongamia oil is widely used in mite control. Its active compound is Karanjin, having antifeedant and toxicant activities. Kumaran *et al.*, 2007 (*J. Acarol.*, **17** : 105-107) recorded 45.20 % and 31.63% reduction in population of *T. urticae* in I and II trials giving cost benefit ratios as 1 : 2.94 when pongamia oil was applied @ 20 ml/litre.

***Vitex negundo* :** This is one of the most common botanical pesticides which is prepared from leaf extract of this plant. The active components are Viticosteron-E, ecdysone, iridoides . It inhibits development and also has toxic effect. The results of various trials with this plant extract have been discussed in subsequent chapters under mite pests of crops. It is effective against *T. urticae* infesting various crops. Nishinda extract 3% registered 13%, 80%, 93% mortality of *T. urticae* infesting Aswangadha while the corresponding mortality was 73%, 87%, 100% at 5% conc. (Karmakar *et al.*, 2009). Some botanical pesticides act as anti juvenile hormone. Topical application of these compounds caused shortening of lifecycle which led to reduced feeding and hence less damage. *Ageratum houstanianum* is one such plant.

Botanical Oils : Pongamia oil (3 – 5%) and Mahua oil (4 -5%)are known to cause mortality of 90% of *T. urticae, O. indicus,* and also have ovicidal action. Eucalyptus oil 0.3 – 0.6 % caused higher mortality of *T. urticae.* Sesamum oil was found to be very toxic to *O. indicus* causing 100% mortality at 3%. It also has oviposition deterrence. However, it is toxic to phytoseiid mites. (Srinivasa and Mallik, 2010). Neem oil 60 EC (30 ml/L) gave 49.21% reduction of *T. urticae* when neem oil was used giving cost benefit ratio of 1 : 3.31.

Seed Extracts : Aqueous extracts of Pongamia @ 4-5%, Mahogany @ 8-15%, and Anona @ 10-20% caused 79%, 78%, 69% mortality of *T. urticae* adults, respectively after 72 hours. Rhizome extract of *Acorus calamus* @10 -20% was found better in deterring both *T urticae* and *O. indicus* females from laying eggs. The methanol extract of *V. negundo* had shown better acaricidal effects than its leaf extracts causing 80-84% mortality @ 4-10% conc. when tested against *T. urticae* and *O. indicus.*

Extracts of *V. penduncularis, Cinnamomum camphora, C. zeylanicum, C. tamala* and *Clerodendron inerme* had shown acaricidal properties in their barks as well as leaves. Manjunatha *et al.* (2008). (*Nat. Symp. Pl. Prot. Bangalore*). Extracts of these plants also affected egg laying. Methanol extract was better over aqueous extract. The extracts of *Jatropha curcus, J. multiveda, J. gosypifolia* leaves and bark extracts had acaricidal properties. (Srinivasa & Mallik, 2010)

Since work done on uses of botanical pesticides against mites in India is not much, it will be better if more emphasis is laid on exploration of plant extracts, dosage fixation, purification, identifying of molecular structures, commercial productions, etc. It is more likely that in future these will take the place of synthetic chemical pesticides, which do more harm than good to us.

Ram tulsi *(Ocimum grattisimum)* : Maitra and Gupta (2006) recoded 100% mortality of *Petrobia harti* and *Brevipalpus euphorbiae* with leaf extract of this plant. Gupta *et al.*, (2007) reported 6.66%, 13.33%, 20.00%, 40%, 40% at 1% and 20%, 26.66%, 33.33%, 46.66%, 66.56% at 1.5% conc. after 24,48,72,96 & 120 hrs, respectively against *Brevipalpus phoenicis* on Vasak (*Justicia adhatoda*).

Swet Chita (*Plumbago zeylanica*) : Maitra and Gutpa (2006) recorded 50%, 75% mortality of *Brevipalpus californicus* and *B. euphorbiae,* after 24 and 72 hrs., respectively on mentha and 100% mortality of *B.euphorbiae* on host Vasak after 72 hrs.

Mentha *(Mentha arvensis)* : Maitra and Gupta (2006) recorded 100% mortality of *T. macfarlanei* after 24 hrs. on Ashwagandha. Gupta *et al.*, (2007) reported 53.33%,

66.66%, 86.6%, and 100% at 1% conc. and 66.66% 88.66%, 93.33%, and 100% at 1.5% conc. against *B. phoenicis* infesting Vasak.

Sarpagandha *(Rauvolfia serpentina)* : Maitra & Gupta (2006) recorded 100% mortality of *B. euphorbiae* on Vasak with leaf extract of this plant.

Ashwagandha *(Withenia somnifera)* : 100% mortality of *B. euphorbiae* infesting Vasak was recorded with Ashwagandha leaf extract after 24 hrs. (Maitra and Gupta, 2006).

Turmeric *(Curcuma longa)* : The rhizome extract of turmeric registered mortality of 100% of *P. harti* and *T. macfarlanei* on *Oxalis* and Ashwagandha respectively (Maitra & Gupta, 2006)

Chilli *(Capsicum annnuum):* 100% mortality was achieved in case of *B. euphorbiae* on Vasak with chilli paste solution (Maitra & Gupta, 2006) after 24 hrs.

Marigold *(Tagetes patula)* : Gupta *et al.* (2007) recoded 26.66%, 40.00%, 46.66%, 60.00%, and 86.66% at 1% and 33.33%, 46.66%, 53.33%, 66.66% and 93.33% at 1.5% Conc. After 24, 48, 72, 96, 120 hours, respectively against *B. phoenicis* infesting Vasak.

Custard Apple *(Anona sqamosa)* : Gupta *et al.* (2007) recorded 0%, 6.66%, 13.33%, 26.66%, 26.66%, at 1% conc. and 00.00%, 20.00%, 26.66%, 33.33% and 40% at 1.5% conc. on *B. phoenicis* infesting Vasak after 24, 48, 72, 96 & 120 hrs., respectively.

Ritha *(Sapindus mukurossi)* : Gupta *et al.* (2007) reported 26.66%, 46.66%, 66.66%, 66.66% and 93.33% at 1% and 46.66% 53.33%, 66.66%, 86.66% and 100% at 1.5% conc. after 24, 48, 72, 96 and 120 hrs., respectively on *B. phoenicis* infesting Vasak.

NSKE : Karmakar *et al.*, (2009) recorded 60%, 80%, 80%, 100% mortality with this after 24, 48, 72 and 96 hours, respectively in case of *T. urticae* infesting Ashwagandha.

Neem *(Azadirachta indica)* : The methanol extract of leaves of this plant was tested against *T. urticae* and *Transeius tetranychivorus* and the result indicated mortality of *T. urticae* as 60.25%, 72.5%, 58.75%, 56.25% and 51.25% at 5%, 4%, 3%, 2% and 1%, respectively and the corresponding mortality of *Transeius tetranychivorus* was 66.25%, 55%, 23.75%, 21.22% and 13.75%, respectively. (Yathiraj & Jagadish, 1999). The other workers who got good results with neem formulations are Selvanarayanan (1999), Umamaheswari *et al.*(1999).

Clerodendrum inerme : The extract of this plant when tested against *T. urticae* and *Transeius tetranychivorus*, revealed mortality of 63.75%, 55.00%, 37.50%, 28.75% and 6.25% in case of *T. urticae* at 5%, 4%, 3%, 2%, 1%, respectively, while the corresponding figures for *T. tetranychivorus* were 3.75%, 2.5%, 2.5%, 1.25%, 1.25% respectively, at 5%, 4%, 3%, 2%, 1%, respectively (Yathiraj & Jagadish, 1999).

Datura repens : The mortality achieved with leaf extract of this plant in case of *T. urticae* was respectively 65%, 58.75%, 62.50%, 37.50% and 17.5% at 5%, 4%, 3%,

2% and 1%, respectively and the corresponding figures for *Transeius tetranychivorus* were 48.75%, 27.5%, 27.5% 21.25%, and 18.75%, respectively (Yathiraj & Jagadish, 1999)

Eucalyptus globulus : Yathiraj & Jagadish (1999) reported 38.75%, 38.75%, 38.75%, 42.50%, and 21.25% mortality of *T. urticae* and 13.75%, 12.50%, 12.5%, 10.0% and 6.25% mortality of *Transeius tetranychivorus* at 5%, 4%, 3%, 2% and 1%, respectively in both cases.

Leucas aspera : Yathiraj & Jagadish (1999) reported 65.00%, 47.5%, 37.5%, 27.50% and 16.25% for *T. urticae* and 41.25% , 36.25%, 35%, 35%, 18.75% in case of *Transeius tetranychivorus* both at 5%,4%, 3%, 2% and 1%, respectively using leaf extract of this plant.

Vitex negundo : Yathiraj and Jagadish (1999, *J.Acar.* 15:40:43) reported 41.25%, 41%, 31.25%, 26.25%, 13.75% for *T. urticae* and 57.50%, 58.75%, 45.00%, 45.00% and 43.75% for *Transeius tetranychivorus* at 5%, 4%, 3%, 2% and 1%, respectively.

Hossein *et al.* (2010) evaluated the toxicity of essential oils of *Ruta graveolens* and *Ferula gummosa* against *T. urticae* and reported that both gave mortality which increased with increasing dosage. Mortality was 82.05% at 73.4 µl/L with *R. graveolens* while galbalum oil gave 37.84% killing after 24 hours. Hence, the former oil is more toxic. Essential oil obtained from *Mentha pulegium* and *Cinnamomum zeylanicum* when tried against *T. urticae* could give 100% mortality at 24 hours at 100 µl/L and the other one gave 83% mortality (Mozaffari *et al.*, 2010).

Biorationals

Some works have already been initiated with the use of biorationals in mite control. Patil and Nandihalli (2007) in an experiment conducted against eggs and adults of *T. macfarlanei* reported mortalities as below :

Biorationals	On Eggs (in percent)	Adults (in percent)	
		48 hours	72 hours
Fish Oil Rosin soap 5%	5.18	1.67	9.36
Cow urine + water (1.6%)	5.18	0.00	11.22
Earthworm wash + water (1.5%)	5.18	0.00	11.33
Garlic Kerosene extract (2%)	8.60	1.67	14.92
Chilli Kerosene extract (2%)	8.60	0.00	15.03
Garlic aqueous extract (2%)	6.84	0.00	3.70
Chilli aqueous extract (2%)	6.84	0.00	1.85
Chilli garlic aqueous extract (2%)	10.35	3.33	13.07
Chilli garlic kerosene extract (2%)	10.35	6.67	18.85
Black peper seed extract (2%)	10.35	3.33	5.56

The above table indicates that the biorational approach of mite control will also be effective if more thorough investigations are made.

Mineral Hydrocarbon oils

In the present days, several tests are being done in mite pest control by using petroleum oils. The use of these oils induces no resistance problem and exerts excellent control without affecting natural enemies present in the field. The action by which these oils kill the mites is by clogging the spiracles and these mites die due to suffocation. This forms a part of organic farming. Excellent control of European Red Mite (ERM) *Panonychus ulmi* on apple could be done with Orchex-796, Orchol-13 and Mak@1% conc. each within 30 days of spraying. Bharadwaj and Bharadwaj (2010) conducted an experiment with some mineral oils for control of ERM on apple and achieved quite satisfactory result for its control. The results are given below :

Oils	Conc.	7 days	30 days	Conc.	7 days	30 days
Orchol-13	1%	96.00	91.40	0.5%	84.1	81.2
Orchex796	1%	94.2	92.56	0.5%	80.4	76.4
Mak all season	1%	93.6	91.52	0.5%	80.4	72.4
HP Summer oil	1%	90.0	86.2	0.5%	74.3	68.3
Servo all season oil	1%	89.0	82.2	0.5%	71.1	70.7
Control		0	.0		0	0

The above results indicate the promise of mineral oil in mite control. Northover (1998: Proc. Spray. Oils Beyond 2000, Sustainable Pest and Disease Management, Sydney NSW, Australia, pp. 402-408), reported spraying of stylet spray oil giving 87% mortality of eggs and 93% of mobiles in case of ERM on Canadian grapes. Delaying the application of oil spray on apple from green tip to full bloom significantly provided better control of ERM (Eslick *et al.*, 1998, NSW, Australia, pp. 402-496).

1.8 RESISTANCE DEVELOPMENT IN MITES AND CONSEQUENT PROBLEM THEREOF IN MITE MANAGEMENT

On one hand the different pesticides especially the modern synthetic chemical pesticides are used to control mite pests for saving our crop and on the other hand the mite pests are also making endeavours to evolve mechanism of resisting the chemicals. Some members of the mite population succeed to withstand those which they do by genetic modification while the others who are susceptible to this chemicals, fail to do so and hence perish. In this way, a constant struggle is going on in nature. Some succeed in developing resistance, do degrade or detoxify the toxic chemicals by enzymatic action consequent upon developing resistant genes. This leads to development of resistance in due course of time.

The resistance can be defined as : Development of an ability in a strain of pests to tolerate doses of toxicant which would prove lethal to the majority of the individuals in a normal population of the same species (WHO, 1957) or resistance marks a genetic change in response to selection (Crow, 1960) or by toxicants may impair control in the field (Sawick, 1987) or a change in sensitivity of population which is reflected in the repeated failure of a product to achieve the expected level of control when used according to the label recommendation for that pest species (Ruscoe, 1987).

Status of pesticidal resistance in mites

The resistance to acaricides was first observed by Compton and Kearns in 2-spotted spider mite against ammonium potassium selenosulfide in 1937. Resistance to TEPP became evident in 1949. In Europe, the resistance to organophosphoric acaricides was noticed in 1950. *Panonychus citri* was found resistant to Schradan in1958. Subsequently, the resistance to acaricides, insecticides, oil by mites became global problem.

Factors affecting resistance development

As per Saini (undated) the factors affecting resistance development are :

1. The frequency of resistant gene present in the population
2. Nature of genes
3. Intensity of selection pressure
4. Rate of multiplication of species

Succeeding generations of the pest therefore have increasingly higher proportions of resistant individuals and resistant population may persist for many generations in the field, even after the cessation of particular pesticidal pressure. A mean increase of LD_{50} value occurs and that, in turn, invites both human and environmental hazards.

Resistant population may develop by changes in behavior like avoidance of treated surface. The detoxifying enzymes have important role in development of resistance.

The main factors influencing selection of resistance are :

1. Genetic
2. Bioecological
3. Operational

Development of pesticide resistance

1. Change in target sites
2. Increased rate of detoxicification
3. Decreased rates of uptakes and mite effective storage mechanism

Most resistance to pesticides is inherited in a typically Mendelian fashion but in some cases it can be due to biochemical and genetic characteristics.

Mites can develop resistance within very short time even within 4 years of use of a certain pesticide and often develop high degree of cross resistance also. Most tetranychid mites reproduce by arrhenotokous parthenogenesis. Haplo-diploid sex determination has particular implication in genetic variability. There is a basic similarity in development of resistance in mites and insects.

Management of pesticide resistance

There are many scientific, economic, social and political constraints in managing pesticide resistance and solving those in a complex problem. Due to genetic, reproductive, behavioral, ecological and operational factors, development of resistance differs among different species and also among members of same population. The resistance management therefore involves reducing allied frequency, reducing dominance and reducing fitness of resistant genotypes.

Tactice for prevention and management of pesticide resistance

1. Variation in dose or rate of pesticides
2. Frequency of application
3. Local rather than area wise
4. Treatment on economic threshold
5. Use of less persistent pesticides
6. Life stages of pest
7. Using mixture of pesticides having different mode of action
8. Alteration in sequence of pesticide application
9. Use of appropriate pesticide formulation
10. Use of synergits
11. Exploring resistant biotypes of target pest becoming more susceptible to other control measures
12. Pesticides selectivity through use of systemic insecticides
13. Conservation and use of natural enemies.
14. Relying on other methods of control (cultural/biological/botanical)

Some of the future strategies in pesticide resistance management according to Saini (undated) are :

1. Better understanding of resistance mechanism

2. Discovering new target pesticide development
3. Use of biotechnology techniques
4. Use of simulation modeling in prediction
5. Resistance monitoring

Aspects of resistance in mites

Tetranychcus urticae showns OP resistance and also, in addition, other species of spider mites show this. Insensitive AchEs have been demonstrated in red form of *T. urtice,* in *T. pacificus,* in *T. kanzawai* and *Panonychus citri.* In *T. urticae,* there is evidence that OP resistance in different populations is due to insensitive AchEs which has been given in 2 ways.

1. Biochemically
2. By genetic means i.e. by investigation to determine whether the major genes from different populations are allelic. Helle and Overmeer (1973: *Ann. Rev. Ent.,* **18** : 97-120) strongly suggested that resistance demonstrated in both *T. urticae* and *T. pacificus* concern mutations at homologus foci.

Another type of OP resistance in *T. urticae* is based on an increase in detoxification capacity. This results from increased carboxy - esterase and phosphatase activities as was first shown by Matsumara and Voss (1964: *J. Econ. Ent.,* **57** : 911-917) in a strain from USA. The resistance was monogenetic. Kuwahara *et al.* (1981 *Appl. Ent. Zool.,* **17** : 82-91) demonstrated the presence of similar detoxifying mechanism in two OP resistant strains of *T. kanzawai.* A combination of insensitive target with an increased faculty for detoxification can result in very high resistant levels. A detoxification mechanism would improve the effect on AchE sensitivity.

AchE is not the most common OP resistant mechanism in phytoseiid mites. The resistance to azinophos-methyl by *Neoseiulus fallacis* is based on detoxification by means of a glutathione - transferase (Helle, 1984, *Acarology,* **VI**(1) : 122-131) and in *Phytoseiulus persimilis* resistant to OP compound resulted from increased activity of glutathione transferase also. Resistance to tetradifon as ovicide has also been demonstrated.

Dicofol resistance is based on a recessive gene with a moderate level of resistance. Binapacnyl resisatance of *P. ulmi* has also been demonstrated by Cranham (1982: *Ann. Appl. Biol.,* 100 : 11-23) in England. Helle (1984) is of opinion that there exists several separate genes each causing a rather specific resistance, but so far no gene with a wider resistance spectrum has been noticed. Most of the genes are dominant excepting a gene for dicofol persistence and a major gene for OP resistance are recessive. Spider mites, however exhibit a male haploidy and in the male there is an immediate result on selection of mutants, irrespective of the fact whether those mutations are dominant or recessive. Recessive, resistance is more common in spider mites than in other taxa with diploid sexes.

Selection, Mutation and Migration

Helle (1984) provided excellent discussion on this aspect and the interested readers may look into that chapter for the detail. The author concluded that:

1. Mutation for parathion - insensitive AchE did not occur in 3150000 alleles tested. The mutations rate at 95% confidence levels is less than 9.5×10^{-7}
2. Migration of mites in long term laboratory experiments makes a definite impact, inspite of stringent measures to prevent contamination.
3. Investigators are generally not aware of the impact of migration and are inclined to underestimate the chances of contamination.

Resistance and Fitness

The interested readers are suggested to go through the discussion under this topic by Helle (1984). Jeyarani *et al.* (2010) reported wide spread development of acaricide resistance in *T. urticae* which is a polyphagous species. The study revealed that Lc_{50} value was concordant at F-7 and F-8 generations for dicofol with LC_{50} value of 2.20 ppm, F-8, F-9 for propergite and Fenazaqiun with LC_{50} values of 22.30 and 6.31 ppm, respectively and LC_{50} values of this population were stabilized after 10 generations. Higher resistance level was detected at all places, may be because of its frequent use.

Cho *et al.* (1995: *Korean J. Appl Ent.*, **31** : 40-45) contributed on monitoring of acaricide resistance in the field collected population of *T. urticae.*

Sheeba *et al.* (2010) while working on acaricide resistance of mites reported LC_{50} values of profenophos and abamectin which were 0.114 and 0.032 ppm respectively. LT_{50} values of profenophos were 2.39 and 2.07 hrs. for 0.50, and 1.0 ppm and of abamectin were 6.62, 4.28, and 2.04 hours for 0.05, 0.1 and 0.2 ppm, respectively. Abamectin 0.0144% effected population reduction to the level of 99.59% with low nut damage grade but abamectin 0.0144% was moderately toxic to predatory mites. Profenophos and abamectin at higher doses were toxic to honey bees.

Life time of Acaricides

Due to absence of resistance gene or resistant gene is too scarce, resistance does not develop inspite of repeated pesticidal application for a very long period. If the resistant gene occurs at a high measurable frequency (10^{-7} or 10^{-8}) and if those genes occurred regularly, distributed over populations infesting crops on earth, then a monitoring system could be developed to predict the development of resistance. But this is not the case (Helle, 1984). The author is of opinion that a number of defined resistant strains could be established involving the different resistant types, to screen new materials for cross resistance. But this has never been done though it will benefit to both producers and consumers.

Sugeetha *et al.*, (2007: *J. Acarol.*, **17** : 57-60) studied development of insecticide résistance in *N. longispinosus*. The peak in the survival of *N. longispinosus* was observed in 24th generation, finally stability in resistance was observed from 42nd generation. In case of dicofol, LC_{50} value increased from 0.867 to 20.533 ppm. Highest LC_{50} of 20.533 was recorded during 40th generation which was equivalent to 20.59 folds resistance. In case of both monocrotophos and dicofol, the resistance of *N. longispinosus*, the median lethal concentration decreased from 5th and 10th generations. The decrease was upto 15.46% in 5th generation and 43.39% reduction. In 5th - 10th generation. In dicofol, the decrease was upto 82.75% in 5th generation, 91.23% reduction in 10th generation.

Shaila & Mallik (2007: *J Acarol.*, **17** : 51-53) evaluated resistance levels for 6 chemicals in *Neoseiulus longispinosus*. The level of resistance to different compounds varied significantly among the population of *N. longispinosus*. Field level population developed lower level of resistance compared to polyhouse population.

Sugeetha *et al.* (2007: *J. Acarol.*, **17** : 61-62) studied biochemical parameters of insecticide resistant strains of *N. longispinosus* and reported that development of resistance to monocrotophos did not enhance the fecundity of *N. longispinosus* though initially increased and in dicofol it reduced fecundity during initial stage and later increased during 30th generation. The development period was shorter in resistant population than in susceptible strain.

1.9 BIOLOGICAL CONTROL

The plant feeding mites have several natural enemies including predators and pathogens while Pathogens and Parasites have been discussed in separate chapter, the present chapter will deal only with predators.

Predators : The predators of plant feeding mites include predatory mites, predatory insects and spiders.

Predatory insects : The groups of insects reported to be quite effective predators are as follows:-

Order : Coleoptera : Members of the genus *Stethorus* (fam. Coccinellidae) are exclusive spider mite predators. Some of the promising ones with their rate of feeding is given below :

Coccinellidae	Name of predator	Rate of Comsumption	Name of prey	Reference
	Stethorus punctillum Weise	40 mites/day 20 mites/day	*T. urticae* *P. ulmi*	Huffaker & McMurtry (1970)
	Stethorus vinsoni	Adult 18-20/day	Tetranychids	do
	S. picipes Cassey	291-372/day	*P. ulmi*	do
	S. bifidus	40-60/day	*P. ulmi*	do
	S. gilvifrons Muls.	27-47/day	*T. urticae*	do
	S. japonicus Kamiya	771/day	*P. citri* eggs	do
	S. picipes	247-486/day	*P. citri*	do
	S. sexmaculalus	468/day	*T. urticae*	
	S .picipes	161-221/day	*T. urticae*	do
	S. punctillum Weise	-	*O. punicae*	
	S. keralicus Kapur		*R. macfarlanei*	Nagesha Chandra & Channa Basavanna, (1983 *Acar. Newsl.*, **13** : 3), Puttaswami & Rangaswamy (1976 *Curr. Sci.*, **5** : 27-28.) reported biology of this predator on *R. macfarlanei*

Mohanasundaram & Karuppuchamy (1987: *Curr Sci.*, **56** : 845-846) reported that *Stethorus pauperculus* as predator of *O. indicus* on sorghum in Tamil Nadu.

Puttaswamy & Channa Basavanna (1977: *Mysore J. Agr. Sci.*) studied its biology. Jose *et al.* (1989) reported that its larvae had consumed 251.56 eggs in life time.

Staphylinidae	Name of predator	Name of prey	Reference
	Scymnus gracilis	*O. indicus*	As cited in Huffaker
	Jauravia sp.	Tetranychids	& McMurtry (1970)
	Oligota abdominalis Say	Spider Mites	
	Oligota flavicornis Boisd	Tetranychids	
	O. oviformis (Casey)	Spider mites	
	O. pygmaea Sol.	Spider mites	

Deepak *et al.*, 1995, 1995a also studied biology of *Oligota oviformis* on *T. urticae* and reported duration of different development stages. Deepak *et al.* 1995 also studied feeding potentiality of *O. oviformis* with regard, to its different developmental stages.

Order : Neuroptera

Chrysopidae	Name of predator	Name of prey	Reference
	Chrysoperla carnea (Stephens)	Spider mites, false spider mites and tarsonemids	Huffaker & McMurtry (1970)
	C. septempunctata Wesm.	Tetranychids	
	C. vulgaris Schneider	Tetranychids	
Hemerobiidae	*Hemerobius humulinus* L	*P. ulmi*	
	H. lutecens Fab.	*P. ulmi*	

Micromus timidus is an important predator of *T.urticae* in Orissa besides aphids and white flies. Its life cycle and duration of different developmental stages was studied by Bhagat & Patnaik (1989: *Progress. Acarology*, **2** : 381-384). It is also a good predator of tea mites (Narayanan *et al.*, 1967: *Agr. Ent. Rev.* ICAR: 205-246.

Coniopterygidae	Name of predator	Name of Prey	Reference
	Coniopteryx vicina Hagen	*P. ulmi*	Huffaker & McMurtry (1970)
	C. pineticola End.	*P. ulmi*	do

Order Hemiptera

Anthocoride	Name of predator	Name of Prey	Reference
	Anthocoris musculus Say	*P. ulmi*	Huffaker & McMurtry (1970)
	A. nemorum (L.)	*P. ulmi*	
	Orius minutus L.	*P. ulmi*	
	Anthocoris sp.	*Tetranychus* sp.	
Miridae	*Belpharidopterus angulatus* (Fall.)	*P. ulmi*	
	Campylomma verbasci (Mey.-D)	*P. ulmi*	
Nabidae	*Nabis apterus* Fab.	Spider Mites	
Lygaeidae	*Geocoris* sp.	*T. urticae*	

Order Thysanoptera

	Name of predator	Name of prey	Reference
Thripidae	*Scolothrips sexmaculatus* (Perg.)	*T. urticae* *E. banksi*	Huffaker & McMurtry (1970)
	S. longicornis Priesner	*T. urticae*	
	S. indicus	*T. urticae*	
Phlaeothripidae	*Cryptothrips nigripes* Reuter	*T. urticae*	Huffaker & McMurtry (1970)
	Haplothrips faurei Hood	*P. ulmi*	
Aelothripidae	*Aelothrips melaleucus* Haliday	*T. urticae*	Huffaker & McMurtry (1970)

Jayanti & Verghese (2007: *J. Acarol.*, **16** : 139-141) studied impact of *Amblyseius* on *Scirtothrips dorsalis* on pomegrenate.

Order Diptera

Cecidomyidae	Name of predator	Name of prey	Reference
	Arthrocnodax occidentalis Felt	*P. oleivora*	Huffaker & McMurtry (1970)
	Feltiella sp.	Feeds on eggs and immature stages of *Tetranychus* spp., consume 9-12 eggs/day, its peak population coincided with that of prey	
Fam Syrphidae	Syrphid larvae	*T. urticae, P. ulmi*	Huffaker & McMurtry (1970)

Sub Class : ARANEAE (Spiders)

These are important bio controlling agents of plant feeding mites and are distributed throughout the world. The members of Argiopidae, Thereidiidae, Lycosidae, Linyphiidae are effective predators of spider mites.

The effectiveness of predators will depend upon rate of consumption of prey, functional and numerical responses, host specificity, searching ability and seasonal synchrony. Many of the OP compounds, carbamates and chlorinated hydrocarbons destroy the natural enemies and therefore the application of pesticides should be done judiciously so that predator population is not affected.

Predatory Mites

A large number of mites are known to feed upon the palnt feeding mites and thereby keep the population of pest species under check. The predatory mites for biological control are mentioned below :

Family : Phytoseiidae

As mentioned earlier, this group of predatory mites has received maximum attention globally because of being foremost important and therefore was most explored and exploited and works on diverse aspects have been undertaken.

These mites feed besides plant feeding mites, the other soft bodied insects like aphids, thrips, mealy bugs, scale insects, etc.

Out of 203 species so far known from India, 20 species have been found to feed actively on phytophagous mites. All these species are listed giving the stage of mite species on which they were found feeding. The phytoseiid mites have several advantages over other predatory mites as :

1. High fecundity
2. Abundant occurrence
3. Good searching capacity
4. Good dispersal rate
5. Adaptability to different ecological niches.
6. High degree of prey specificity

The important phytoseiid predatory species from India are :

Predator	Prey consumed	Stages of	Host plant	Locality
Euseius finlandicus	*Oligonychus coffeae*	All stages	Tea	NE India
E. delhiensis	*Eutetranychus orientalis*	Nymph, eggs	Citrus	Cosmopolitan
E. alstoniae	*E. orientalis*	Nymph, eggs	Citrus	W.B., Punjab
E. coccineae	*P. citri*	Eggs	Mulberry	W. Bengal
Amblyseius largoensis	*Brevipalpus deleoni* *Aceria litchii*	All stages	Tea, Litchi	Assam, W. Bengal
A. channabasavannai	*Raoiella indica*	Larvae, nymph	Arecanut	Kerala
A. herbicolus	*O.coffeae*, *Aceria litchii*, *B.phoenicis*	All stages	Tea, litchi, citrus	Kerala, NE India, W.B., Punjab
A. aerialis	*P.citri*	Eggs	Citrus	Assam

Predator	Prey consumed	Stages of	Host plant	Locality
Neoseiulus longispinosus	*Oligonychus oryzae* *Schizotetranychus andropogoni*	All stages Do	Paddy	W. Bengal
	Schizotetranychus andropogoni	All stages	Paddy	W.B., Punjab
N. indicus	*Petrobia latens*	Eggs	Wheat	Punjab
Transeius tetranychivorus	*T. ludeni*	All stages	Beans	S. India
Transeius tetranychivorus	*R. indica*	Egg, nymph	Arecanut	Kerala
Paraphytoseius multidentatus	*Aceria lycopersici*	All stages	Brinjal	cosmopolitan
Gynaeseius ricini	*T. urticae*	All stages	Ornamental plants	Sikkim
Scapulaseius syzygii	*Aceria litchii*	All stages	Litchi	W. Bengal
	S. andropogoni	on paddy		
E. concordis	Tetranychids	All stages	--	Karnataka
Typhlodromus homalii	*O. coffeae*	Eggs	Tea	Tamil Nadu
Typhlodromus rickeri	*Tetranychus* sp.	Eggs	Ornamental plants	W. Bengal
Phytoseius kapuri	*Eotetranychus* sp.	Eggs, nymphs	Ornamental plants	W. Bengal
Euseius ovalis	Tetranychids, *Bemisia tabaci*	All stages, nymphs	Chilli,	Cosmopolitan
E. finlandicus	*Brevipalpus phoenicis*	Adults	Citrus	Punjab
Amblyseius herbicoloides	*T. neocaledonicus*, *T. ludeni*	Larvae, protonymps deutonymphs		Kerala

Gupta (1985, 1986, 2003) reviewed the work done in bio-ecology feeding potentiality, predator-prey interaction, effect of pesticides, etc. on some of the promising phytoseiid predators known from India and the interested readers may refer those works to have a summarized information in these aspects.

In addition to the indigenous species, some exotic species were also attempted to release for biological control of mite pests and, of those, mention may be made of *Phytoseiulus persimilis* which is one of the most successful predators of phytoseiid mites for controlling spider mites.

It was introduced at Bangalore from Switzerland by Commonwealth Institute of Biological Control for trial against *Raoiella indica, Tetranychus* sp, *Oligonychus* sp. Unfortunately, it could not survive in the field during monsoon months when the population of *R. indica* was very low. It was again introduced exporting from England for control of *Oligonychus indicus* and *R. indica* but that attempt did not achieve success, though its introduction in many other parts of the world found to be highly successful.

Manjunatha *et al.* (1999: *J.Acarol.*, **14** : 16-21) developed mass multiplication technique of *E. ovalis* and Nangia & ChannaBasavanna (1999, *J. Acarol.*, **13** : 45-48) conducted experiment on release of *Transeius tetranychivorus* on *T. ludeni.*

Among the non-phytoseiid mite predators, the following species appear to be of some promise though due to poor abundance in the field, their success as efficient bio-controlling agent appears to be doubtful. The promising predators are:-

Anystidae	*Anystis baccarum* Linn.	Important predator of tetranychids in Jammu and Kashmir (Gupta, 2002)
	Tencateia sp.	It feeds on *Aleurocanthus rugosa, Dialeurodes pallida, Tricentrus gibbosulus, Membrothrips garuda,* all are betelvine pests. (Gupta, 2002).
Cheyletidae	*Cheletogenes ornatus* (C&F)	It feeds on *Aceria mangiferae* the mango bud mite.
	Cheyletus eruditus (Schrank)	Feeds on *E. orientalis* on citrus in Punjab.
	C. malaccensis Oud.	Feeds on *Schizotetranychus andropogoni* on paddy.
Cunaxidae	*Cunaxa capreolus* (Berlese)	This probably feeds on *T. neocaledonicus* (Gupta, 2002).
	Cunaxa setirostris (Hermann)	Feeds on *Eutetranychus orientalis* on citrus in Punjab, *Oligonychus iseilemae* on coconut in Kerala, *O. mangiferus* on mango (Gupta, 2002)
	Neocunaxoides sp.	Feeds on *D. floridanus.* The effects of temperature and RH on this was studied (Das *et al.*, 1987)
Stigmaeidae	*Agistemus fleschneri* Summers	Feeds on *Brevipalpus obovatus* infesting guava in West Bengal, *Aceria mangiferae* on mango in Manipur (Gupta, 2002)

	Agistemus herbarius Kuznetzov & Wainstein	Feeds on eggs of *O. mangiferus* and *T, urticae* on grape vines in J.K. (Gupta, 2002)
	Agistemus macrommatus Gonzalez-Rodriguez	Feeds on *T. ludeni* infesting cowpea in Uttar Pradesh (Arbabi & Singh, 1990) also, *T. neocaledonicus* infesting *Calotropis* in Lakshadweep (Gupta, 2002).
	Agistemus industani Gonzalez-Rodriguez	Rai *et al.* (1999) studied predatory behaviour using *T. ludeni* as its prey on mulberry plant at Varanasi. Rai & Singh (1999: *J. Acarol.*, **14** : 4-7) studied its biology and reported its voracious feeding on eggs of *T. ludeni* (Gupta, 2002)
	Agistemus sp.	Feeds on adults of a spider mite in Punjab, *Aceria litchii* in West Bengal. (Singh *et al.*, 1989, *Prog. Acar.*, **2** : 361-367)
	Eryngiopus coimbatorensis Gupta & David	Voraciously feeds on *Melanopsis glomerata* on sugarcane (Gupta, 2002)
Erythraeidae	*Bochartia* sp.	Parasitized jassids (Ghai and Ahmed 1975, *Ent. Newsl.*, IARI, **5** : 29-30
Tydeidae	*Pronematus elongatus* Baker	Feeds on grape vine mites in J & K (Gupta, 2002)
	Pronematus fleschneri Baker	Feeds on *T. neocaledonicus* on brinjal in W. Bengal
Acaridae	*Caloglyphus* sp.	Feeds on early instar nymphs of Locust.
	Sancassania sp.	Feeds on eggs of sugarcane white grub.
	Tyrophagus putrescentiae (Schrank)	Feeds on nematode, *Meloidogyne javanica*, in Haryana (Gupta, 2002)
Mochlozetidae	*Unguizetes clavatus* Aoki	Feeds on Betelvine pests like *Aleurocanthus rugosa, Dialeurodes pallida, Tricentrus gibbosulus*

1.10 PHEROMONES IN MITES AND THEIR USES IN MITE MANAGEMENT

Pheromones are the semiochemicals which are released by a species and when the same is perceived by members of the same species incite some behavioral changes. The behavioral changes are favourable to the success of that species, e.g. Sex pheromones. Pheromones regulate many biological fuctions. Thus, the pheromones help in chemical communication among members of the same species. Sonenshine (1984 : *Acarology*, **VI** : 100-106) provided an excellent review on this aspect and the present account given here is mostly based on that.

Alarm Pheromones : *Tyrophagus putrescentiae* is known to release this pheromone. This compound also acts as allomones for repelling other species.

Assembly Pheromones : This is a widely distributed acarine pheromone and has been reported in Ticks. This pheromone probably serves to hold acarine population at sites where possibility of getting sexual partner is certain or where likelihood of getting an appropriate host plant is more probable or environmental condition is more favourable for their survival.

Aggregation-attachment pheromone : This pheromone occurs only in ticks (*Amblyomma* sp.) and are produced by feeding males. They attract both males and females.

Sex pheromone : The pheromone attracts both sexes for mating purpose.

Sex attractant pheromone : These pheromones attract the members from a distance (upto 8-9 cm) and have been found in Ticks (Sonenshine, 1984). This attractant excides feeding males, causing them to detach and orient to the emitting females. The most widely used compound is DCP, recorded in 8 species of hard ticks (Sonenshine, 1984).

Arrestant Sex pheromones : Phytoseiid females, both adults and immatures, produce this pheromone. The males move around female deutonymphs with their appendages in touch with that and mates with that as soon as the adult female emerges. Similar phenomenon is also seen in spider mites where the males guard the female deutonymphs and do not allow other mites to mate with it. Often they fight among themselves to have possession of the female (Sonenshine, 1984).

Contact Sex Pheromones : This pheromone, together with normal ambulatory movements, provides the essential components regulating mating behaviour in ticks.

Control of Acari by natural compound

Lures : In case of *Amblyomma maculatum* aggregation pheromone with an insecticide, isobenzan when used was found effective. The ticks were attracted with the pheromone bait and then were killed by the insecticide. The pheromone if applied to the specific feeding site will be more effective. However, so far this pheromone has not yet been commercially utilized.

Confusant : This has been used in ticks. The objective is to confuse the organism and this is done by spreading the pheromone everywhere in the host body. By this method the mating can be reduced considerably. This pheromone when used in combination with acaricide can substantially reduce the tick population on livestock. This is yet to be used commercially.

Antagonists : In this technique, the production of pheromone is prevented and thus the sex pheromone activity is reduced. To achieve success of this, a fair knowledge of pheromone biosynthesis, secretory activity and receptor physiology is needed and in fact, that is utterly lacking in case of Acari. Significant reductions in mating were also observed when pheromone impregnated molecular sieve dust was used in place of gelatin microcapsules. This in combination with acaricides will be suitable for tick control in livestock. Commercial exploitation of this technique is yet to be done (Sonenshine, 1984).

Masking agents : In this method, masking the presence of pheromone emiting females and suppressing the male courtship behaviour are done. This has been effectively done in *Hyalomma anatolicum excavatum* (Sonenshine, 1984).

Assembly and arrestant pheromone : In this strategy the long lasting interspecific pheromones plus insecticides may be useful for control of ticks especially in those cases where application of chemical pesticides has limitations (Sonenshine, 1984).

Repellent : This techniques involves protecting stored products from attack of stored product mites by using filter paper discs impregnated with plant oils adjacent to a food product (moist dog food). A complete protection could be achieved when applied at 0.5% concentration.

All the above examples for utilizing pheromones in Acarine control involve ticks but hardly any work worthy to mention on mites pest control has been done and this shows a big gap in our knowledge and hence needs attention of the future workers. It may be mentioned that a good amount of success has been achieved in pheromonal control of insect pests and a few of those are commercially used. Therefore, there is a good scope of work on use of pheromone in mite pest control.

Effect of Kairomones

Indulatha & Mallik (2007) reported that almost $^{3}/_{4}$th of starved predators showed positive response by moving towards the arm of Olfactometer saturated with volatiles from infected leaves and $^{1}/_{4}{}^{th}$ had shown negative response. This study showed that *N. longispinosus* perceived Kairomones emitted during feeding by spider mites as was observed in case of *P. persimiles* (Sabelis & Baan (1983, *Ent. Exp. Appl.*, **33** : 303-314).

1.11 EFFECTS OF PESTICIDES ON PREDATORY MITES

Rai *et al.* (1995) reported toxicity of different pesticides on *Euseius alstoniae* and those were in descending order as fluvalinate>monocrotophos>dicofol>methyl-o-demeton>tetradifon>quinalphos>triazophos>ethion>wettable sulphur>replin>neemark>NSKE.

Rather *et al.* (2007: *J. Acarol.*, **17** : 72-73) reported thar Azadirachtin (0.5%) and ATSO spray oil (0.75%) proved comparatively safer to predatory mites while Clofentezine (0.05%) significantly reduced predator mite population.

Yathiraj & Jagadish (1999: *J. Acarol.*, **15** : 40-43) reported that the extracts of *Azadirachta indica, Clerodendrun inerme* and *Eucalyptus globulus* were toxic to predators.

1.12 BIOLOGY OF PREDATORY MITES/PREDATOR-PREY INTERACTION/FIELD RELEASE/MASS MULTIPLICATION

Chandrasekharappa *et al.* 1995 studied biology of *N. longispinosus* using *T. ludeni* as food at 20, 25, 30 and 35°C. The development of eggs to adult took 99.0 ±11.46 and 95.33± 8.33 hours, respectively at higher temperature. At 20°C the mortality was high and at 30°C, none reached maturity. The authors studied feeding potentiality of this predatory mite as well as of *T. tetranychivorus* mite and reported that higher temperatures and higher humidity induced increased feeding potentiality of both the species (Chandrasekharappa *et al.*, 1995a). Jagadish *et al.* (1999: *J. Acrol.*, **15** : 32-35) studied effect of temperature on development of *Euseius concordis*. The development was shortened at higher temperature (35°C) - 66.80 ± 1.4 hours and was prolonged at lower temperature (20°C) - 120.48± 1.0 hours. The optimum temperature for development was 25-27°C.

Nageshachandra *et al.* (1999: *J. Acarol.*, **15** : 36-39) reported relative preference of food in descending order for *E. concordis* which was castor pollen/castor pollen + *T. neocaledonicus* + *Brevipalpus phoenicis, Raoiella indica* + *Aculus* sp.

Manjunatha and Puttaswamy (1993: *J. Insects Sci. and its Application,* **14** : 611-614) studied development of *N. longispinosus* as influenced by castor pollen and its interaction with *Oligonychus indicus*. Sadanandan & Ramani (2010) studied developmental biology at 27±1°C and mentioned the duration of different stages as well as total developmental period.

Nangia & ChannaBasavanna (1995) conducted experiment regarding field release of *T. tetranychivorus* on *T. ludeni* population and reported that plants receiving predators 5 days after release of prey were free of both mites species by the end of fifth week, whereas the plants receiving predators with a time gap of 10 days, became free of both species at the end of 7th week. In either case the predator effectively suppressed prey population in course of time. Nangia & ChannaBasavanna (1995b) studied interaction between *T. tetranychivorus* and *T. ludeni* at 1 : 30, 1 : 24, 1 : 18, 1 : 12 and 1 : 6 ratio on okra plants. Total elimination of prey mite was observed in first half of 6th week in plants where predator release was made at 1 : 30 ratio while at 1 : 6 ratio total elimination was possible within 10 days. Nangia & ChannaBasavanna (1989 : *Indian J. Acar.*, **10** : 75-81) studied feeding potentiality of *T. tetranychivorus* on different prey species and reported that the predator could suppress the pest mite population. Feeding potentiality of different stages of prey was reported.

Kumari & Sadana (1996: *Exp. Appl. Acarol.*, **11** : 191-195) studied influence of temperature and relative humidity on development of *E. alstoniae*. Hariyappa and Kulkarni (1989: *J. biol. Contr.*, **3** : 31-32) studied interaction between *E. ovalis* and *P. latus* on chilli.

E. ovalis was reported to be feeding on *B. tabaci* infesting chilli. Its life cycle at different combination of temperature and RH was studied using both prey insects as well as castor pollen. It was reported that *E. ovalis* could be an effective predator of *B. tabaci* when pollen availability was scarce in the field (Borah & Rai, 1989, *Progr in Acar.*, **2** : 375-379).

Sadana & Sharma (1989: *J. Acarol.*, **11** : 51-54) studied development of *E. finlandicus*, an effective predator of *Eutetranychus orientalis* on citrus in Punjab and mentioned the duration of different developmental stages. Subsequently, Sadana & Sharma (1989: *J. Acarol.*, **10** : 65-74) described the morphological features of different stages of *Euseius finlandicus*.

Sharma & Sadana (1989) studied predator- prey interaction between *E. finlandicus* and *E. orientalis*.

Mass Multiplication

Manjunatha *et al.* (1999: *J. Acarol.*, **14** : 16-21) mass multiplied *E. ovalis* using castor pollen + honey and attempted their evaluation by making field release against *Polyphagotarsonemus latus* and thrips on chilli. A release of 20 mites per plant proved superior to control chilli thrips and mites as compared to recommended chemicals and untreated check. Karuppuchamy *et al.* (1988 : *Curr. Sci.*, **57** : 397-380) developed a new technology for mass rearing of predatory phytoseiid mites in the laboratory.

1.13 MITE TRANSMISSION OF PLANT VIRUSES

A. Plant Virus diseases transmitted by eriophyid mites

Some members of eriophyid mites are known to transmit different kinds of plant viral diseases. Among the other group of mites *Tetranyhcus telarius* (now *urticae*) and *T. ludeni* are known to transmit Potato Viruses Y and Dolichos Enation Mosaic Viruses, respectively. There are several reports indicating transmission of plant viral diseases by eriophyid mites. Those are Wheat streak and Wheat spot mosaic virus

(Slykhuis, 1955; *Phytopathology*, **43** : 484-485; *Phytopathology*, **45** : 116-128). Current reversion virus by *Cecidophyopsis ribis* (Smith, 1962, *Ann Rept. Long Astha Res. Stx*, 1961 : 170-172), Rye grass mosaic virus by *Abacarus hystrix* (Mulligan, 1958, *Ann. Rept. Rothamstead Expt. Sta.*, 1957 : 110-111), Fig mosaic virus by *Aceria ficus* (Wilson *et al.*, 1950, *Plant disease Reptr*, 39: 889-892). The eriophyids show a high degree of specificity between vector eriophyids and viruses they transmit and normally no two viruses are transmitted by one species except *Aceria tulipae* which transmits both Wheat Streak Mosaic Virus and Wheat Spot Mosaic Virus. The Viruses normally persist in mites at least for few days and transovarian transmission is known in mites. The eriophyids normally cause mosaic symptoms on leaves which indicate the appearance of irregular chlorotic areas on leaves. This group includes Wheat Streak Mosaic, Wheat Spot Mosaic, Rye Grass Mosaic, Fig Mosaic, Peach Mosaic and Cherry Mottled Leaf. Eriophyids are capable of transmitting to both monocots and dicots.

Characteristics of eriophyid mites and their role as vector of plant Viruses

Eriophyids are small arthropods and because of their small size are often overlooked. They occupy a small space and multiply very rapidly to build up a huge population within a short time. Some of these mites, apart from being vectors of plant viral diseases, are also plant gall makers. In addition, they also cause rusetting, blistering, crinkling, curling, twisting, rolling, erineum formations, witche's broom effect, big buds, sterility, etc. These are the symptoms they produce due to feeding and damaging plant tissues. However, there are still many who do not cause any damage. These mites mostly complete life cycle in a single host and sometimes they do not feed for several months remaining on the same host. Their dispersal is effected mostly by wind. The most interesting feature is that they are very much host specific barring a few which occur on more than one host.

These eriophid mites are mostly inhabitants of perennial plants but some are there who also infest annuals. Their mouthparts are suitable for piercing and sucking. Since their chelicera are short, their penetration of leaf tissues is never very deep (mostly upto epidermal cells). Since in many cases plant abnormalities occur due to injection of toxins along with saliva, the symptoms of toximaea are sometimes confused with symptoms of viral infections. Hence, according to Slykhuis (1963 : *Adv. Acarology*, **1** : 479pp.), the three conditions need to be satisfied to prove the vector nature of eriophyids. These are: (a) the presence of mite must be correlated with appearenece of disease nature (b) the development of disease symptoms on healthy plants must not depend upon continued presence of mites (c) the mite must not be able to induce the disease symptoms on healthy plants until after they have fed on diseased plants or have acquired viruses in some other way. Since some of the mite transmitted viruses are sap transmissible, the plants can be tested for the presence of viruses with minimum precautions against transfer of mites in the sap to another plant. A brief discussion regarding mite transmitted viruses is made below :

Wheat Streak Mosaic Virus (WSMV) : This virus is transmitted on wheat by *Aceria tulipae* and has been reported from many parts of the world including India. Apart from wheat, the other known hosts are *Poa compressa, Oryzopsis hymenoides, Elymus canadensis, Setaria viridis, Digitaria ischaemum, Hordeum jubatum.* Its life cycle is completed through egg, two nymphal stages, adult. The eggs can survive at a low temperature of -30.7°C for a few minutes and at 100% RH, the egg hatachability was maximum.

The virus is having distribution in North and South America, Canada, Australia Egypt, Europe, in many parts of the Asia (including India, Pakistan). The virus is elongated particle (15mμ x 60mμ) in electron micrographs of juice extracts from WSMV-infected wheat leaves but none on juice extracts of healthy wheat leaves (Gold *et al.*, 1953, *Phytopathology*, B: 485-459). The mite can retain the virus for at least 6 days. Orlobts (1966, *Phytopathology*, Z. 55: 218-238) demonstrated persistence of WSMV through the moult by transferring immobile, moulting nymphs from infected to healthy plants and effected transmission. Paliwal & Slykhuis (1967: *Virology*, **32** : 344-353) successfully inoculated wheat plants with macerates of infective *A. tulipae* but not with non-infectious *A. tulipae* or the two non vector species that were reared on infected wheat. The virus when present was found to be noncirculative in any tissue of the vector and it was concentrated in the lumen of the gut. The backflow of the virus to the mouthparts or elimination of virus from the anus or both, might be involved in its transmission. In case of defecation, the feeding punctures of the actions of the anal setae or anal sucker may cause punctured wounds through which the virus can be introduced into epidermal cells. The virus after acquisition remain in mite tissues, multiplies there and then it is transmitted. *Aceria tulipae* can transmit WSMV from wheat to corn and vice-versa. The corn may be an over-summering reservoir for *A. tulipae* and WSMV.

Symptoms include faint green mottling of the expanded leaves followed by light coloured streaks along the veins and stunting of plants. At later stage, chlorosis becomes more pronounced and heads are not formed in severely infected plants.

Wheat Spot Mosaic Virus (WSMV) : This virus is also transmitted by *A. tulipae* and its distribution is restricted in USA, Canada. It produces severe chlorotic mottling on leaves. Slykhuis (1955 : *Phytopathology*, **45** : 116-128) transferred *A. tulipae* from certain infected wheat plants showing mottling symptom to healthy wheat plants in greenhouse and reported that 50% of the wheat plants showed symptoms similar to the field plants from where *A. tulipae* were collected. This virus also is sap transmitted to healthy wheat plants from only about half of the plants that showed symptoms after transferring *A. tulipae* to them. Slykhuis (1956 : *Phytopathology*, **46** : 682-687) by destroying the population of *A. tulipae* on the plants that showed WSMV symptoms, observed the reappearance of symptoms in the absence of mites. This virus is also not transovarially transmitted. The symptoms of WSMV appeared only on plants receiving *A. tulipae* from diseased plants. Adult and both the nymphal stages are capable of transmitting the virus and the viruses are retained through moults.

The symptoms include chlorotic spots, severe chlorosis, stunting and necrosis instead of streak symptoms. All stages except the eggs can carry the virus. The hosts of Wheat Spot Mosaic include hosts like barley, corn, rye, several wild grasses etc. (Jeppson *et al.*, 1975).

Onion Mosaic virus : *Aceria tulipae* also acts as vector of Onion Mosaic Virus (Razvyazleina *et al.*, 1963).

Rye grass Mosaic Virus (RMV) : This virus is transmitted by *Abacarus hystrix* and is common in Europe. The acquisition -feeding period for this virus may be as low as 2 hours. All the stages of this mite are capable of transmitting this virus. The persistence period of this virus may be 6 hours (Oldfield, 1970: *Ann. Rev. Ent.*, **15** : 343-380). The ryegrass mosaic virus is in the form of flexuous rods. Sap inoculation of this virus was also possible on several British grasses. *A. hystrix* transmitted RMV has been recorded on Blenda oats but not to Proctor Barley or Capelle Wheat though both are suitable hosts for infective *A. hystrix*.

The symptoms include green to yellow mottling and streaking of leaves. Some isolates form severe brownish necrosis of leaves and reduced growth and vigour of some strains of rye grass. This disease is sap transmissible. All stages but eggs carry the virus (Jeppson *et al.*, 1975).

Currant Reversion Virus (CRV) : The reversion of black currant due to infestations of eriophyid mites reverses to the wild uncultivated type *Ribes nigrum* and that is a malady which is common in British Islands and other regions of European countries (Denmark, Germany, Netherlands, Russia, Sweden, Norway, Finland, British Columbia). The *Cecidophyopsis ribis*, the vector mite, spends most of its life within buds. This mite escapes from buds, the mite stands erect resting on caudal seta and in still air it leaps from the buds. Mites can not exist outside the buds for a longer period and are found only occasionally on exposed leaves and blossoms. During migration many mites die due to desiccation. A direct relation existed with big buds and reversion (going wild) symptoms. The seed transmission and sap transmission of reversion could not be established. According to Masse, *C ribis* can be regarded as a vector of currant reversion (Oldfield, 1970). The reverted bushes are many times more susceptible to infestations by *C. ribis* than were healthy bushes.

The Symptoms include reduced number of submain veins and coarsely toothed margin of the leaves. Development of crowded woody growth from lateral buds, abnormal flower colour, dropping of flowers and fruits are some of the other symptoms. This virus is not sap transmissible but it is graft transmitted. The time required is 18 months to appear the symptoms. The current varieties having lesser number of hairs are most susceptible to mite infestation and also to virus infection. This mite can also make gall like "big buds" (Jeppson *et al.*, 1975).

Fig Mosaic Virus (FMV) : *Aceria ficus* is the vector for this disease on Fig tree and its occurrence has been reported from India as well as from all countries where fig is grown. Since many fig leaves even though were heavily infested remained green and did not show the mosaic symptoms, the disease is due to direct effect of mite feeding, which some persons believe, but can be rulled out. In an experiment it was seen that virus free mites caused leaf destruction, chlorosis and russeting but these symptoms were distinguishable from symptoms of mosaic which appeared on the group that received infective mites. The virus is not transmitted through seed or sap. Apart from transmitting the fig mosaic virus, the feeding of *Aceria ficus* causes killing of epidermal cells, russeting and scarring of eye scales and seeds of the fruits besides stunting of twigs and premature leaf drop (Oldfield, 1970).

The mosaic symptoms appear like uniform spots of different sizes on leaves and fruits. The irregular spots of light green patches appear throughout the leaf blade. The leaves may be formed into an infinite variety of shapes and sizes. Similar mosaic symptoms as appear on leaves, also appear on fruits. This virus is not transmitted through seed or by sap inoculation and the disease is not transmitted through eggs (Jeppson *et al.*, 1975).

Peach Mosaic Virus (PMV) : This disease is prevalent in many parts of North America and Central America. *Eriophyes insidiosus* is the vector of this mosaic disease on peach. This mite occurs in adventitious buds found near the base of large scaffold branches causing considerable cell hypertrophy in these buds. This mite also occurs as unprotected on petioles and green stem tissues near leaf axils as well as in buds. In commercial peach varieties they are found inside retarted buds. The virus is not transmitted through eggs of vector. By holding infective mites on glass slides and then transferring them to healthy plants and effecting transmission, Wilson and Jones (1955-1965, fruit insects *USDA Res. Br. ARS, Entomol. Res. Div.*) showed that the virus persisted in the vector for at east 48 hrs.

The symptoms of this disease include shortening of the internodes, profuse growth of leaf axil buds and mosaic pattern of leaves. Such leaves are small, narrow, crinkled and irregular in outline. The host range of this virus is peach and plum varieties (Jeppson *et al.*, 1975).

Cherry Mottle Leaf Virus (CMLV) : *Eriophyes inaqualis* is the vector of Cherry Mottle Leaf Virus (*Prunus emarginata*). Wilson and Oldfield (1969, USDA, ARS, Ent. Res. Div.) transferred *E. inaequalis* from mottle leaf of infected *P. emarginata* to thirteen bitter Cherry trees. Apparent symptoms of mottle leaf developed on eight out of 13 experimental plants but not on any of the check plants that received no mites. It is distributed in cherry growing regions of USA, Canada. *P. emarginata* is the principal host of this mite (Oldfield, 1970: *Ann. Rev. Ent.*, **15** : 343-380).

It is a virus disease of sweet cherry. *Phytoptus inaequalis* is the vector. Virus transmission is effected when transfer of vector was made from infected bitter cherry to peach seedlings (Jeppson *et al.*, 1975).

Rose Rosette Virus (RRV) : This virus disease of rose is transmitted by *Phyllocoptes fructiphilus* (Keifer). Several species of rose were found infected with Rose Rosette Virus. Another very closely related species *Phyllocoptes slinkardensi* collected from wild species of rose in California showed witche's broom effect and graft transmission test proved this disease to be virus induced and *Phyllocoptes,* which was found on native rose could be the vector (Oldfield, 1970).

Latent Virus on Plum : *Aculus fockeui* transmits the latent virus of plum trees. The virus particles are about 750 nμ from *Chenopodium* leaves to which mites were transferred and that subsequently showed lesions and from Chenopodium leaves, that had been juice inoculatd. These particles were the viruses which the mite transmitted (Proeseler and Kegler, 1966, *Deut. Acad. Wiss. Berlin, Monatsber,* **8** : 472-476).

Aculus fockeui is the vector for this disease. The virus is transmitted as efficiently by immatures as by adults. Mechanical inoculation tests showed positive response towards transmission of disease (Jeppson *et al.,* 1975).

Pegeon Pea Sterility Mosaic Virus (PPSMV) : *Aceria cajani* is the vector of this virus disease on pigeonpea. Seth (1963, *Phytopathol,* **15** : 225-227). was the first to report this disease from India. Through an elaborate experiment it was established that mites when transferred from healthy Pegeon Pea did not become diseasesd but when mites transferred from diseased Pegeon Pea showed sterility mosaic symptoms. Infected plants show sterility (Flowers drop off, no pod formation) while mosaic symptoms appear on leaves. Such infected plants become bushy, pale green with leaf size reduced showing mottling. Secondary and tertiary branches from leaf axils appear and no pod formation takes place. The viral nature of pathogen hypothesized because of transmissibility through grafting, associated eriophyid mites and mechanical means (Rathi, 1983). Flexuous rod shaped virus particles (VLP) (size : 200-700μ) were isolated from infected sterility mosaic diseased leaves and from its vector mite, *A. cajani.* By DAS-ELISA and RT-PCR techniques, the PPSM was detected in infected Pegeon Pea leaves. More about this has been discussed under pulse crop.

Sugarcane Streak Virus (SSV) : Sithanatham *et al.* (1972) opined that *Aceria sacchari* is probably one of the vectors of Sugarcane Streak Mosaic Virus in India.

Agropyron Mosaic Virus : This virus differs from WSLV on the basis of particle size, sedimentation rate and stability towards selective denaturation procedures (Staples and Brakke, 1963: *Phytopathology,* **53** : 969-972). This occurs in *Agropyron repens.*

Grapevine Panaschure Virus : *Eriophye vitis* is believed to be one of the vectors for causing panaschure of vines in Germany. Ochs claimed that this virus is to be sap transmitted but no experimental evidence was given in support of the statement (Oldfield, 1970) and hence it is a doubtful case of transmission by Eriophyid mite.

Cadang Cadang Virus (CCV) : This is a degenerative disease of coconut and occurs in Philippines. A virus is suspected to be the causative agent and eriophyid is probably the possible vector for this disease.

Concentric Ring Blotch of Citurs Virus (CRBCV) : *Calacarus citrifolii* transmits this virus which causes this disease. The mites were transferred from diseased and healthy plants to healthy, rough lemon seedlings. Those which received mites from healthy plats did not develop symptoms of concentric ring blotch, but those which received mites from diseased plants developed symptoms (Rossouw and Smith, 1963: *S. Afr. Citurs J.*, **354** : 7-9). Subsequent report of Van der Merwe and Coates (1965: *S Afr. J. Agr. Sci.*, : 817-824). noted this mite as the cause of concentric ring blotch.

Plant Virus Disease transmitted by Tetrnychid species

Potato Virus Y (PVY) : *Tetranychus urticae* is incriminated to transmit this virus. The highest rate of transmission was achieved when mites were given a 5 mins. acquisition feeding period followed by a 5 mins. transmission feeding period. The other plant viruses like Tobacco Mosaic Virus, Potato Virus X, Onion Yellow Dwarf Virus and Tomato Bushy Stunt Virus could be detected in mites which fed upon the plants infected with these viruses. The *T. urticae* is believed to be capable to inoculate plants with TMV that was sprayed on to leaves.

Symptoms appear 19 days after inoculation. Symptoms include mottling in the topmost leaves and then the mottled appearance spread outward from veins. Necrosis appears down the petiole to the stem where brown longitudinal lesions appear. The affected plants become stunted, the leaves become brittle, internodes are shortened and leaves become mottled. *T. urticae* is the vector.

Dolichos Enation Mosaic Virus (DEMV) : Rajagopalan (1971: *Curr. Sci.*, **43** : 488-489) was the first to report the transmission of Dolichos Enation Mosaic Virus by *Tetranychus ludeni.*

Many of the transmissions of plant viral diseases, though reported but were not supported with adequate experimental evidence. Therefore, these aspects need more thorough investigations.

Tobacco ring spot disease : *T. urticae* is the vector. The mites after collected from infected plants when macerated on healthy plants, the disease symptoms appeared.

1.14 GALL FORMING AND LEAF DOMATIA BY MITES

The mites while feeding on plants produce various types of damage symptoms which included gall formation also. Reamur in 1737 (*Academie Royale des Sciences, Paris*, 421-423; 511-515), first noticed that some worm-like stages of insect organisms were responsible for galling. Duges (1834) believed that the adult mite present within galls were considered as insect larvae as because they thought that the insect after laying eggs within galls escaped through the minute aperture in gall and the worm like organisms were their larval stages. Siefold (1850) called the organisms as *Eriophyes* mites having two pairs of legs and were, in fact, adults (Scheuten, 1857: *Arch. Naturge,* **23** : 104-112).

The gall forming mites mostly belong to Eriophyoidea and Tenuipalpidae. The mite induced galls are very species specific. The feeding of mite induces some plant deformities of different kinds (Production of dense hairy outgrowth, blisters, russeting of leaves, witche's broom effects, big bud effects, as well as gall formation). The galls may be of different shapes (Pouch, Bladder, finger-like, bead-like, etc.) on leaves and buds. Thus, the eriophyids causing gall derives nutritional benefits from the plants while plants are deprived of their requisite nutritional requirements. The information of bio-ecology of gall forming mites is rather scanty and so is the information about their histopatholgy.

According to Mani (1973: *Plant Galls of India.* Mcmillan Co., 354pp), galls are pathologically developed cells, tissues, or organs of plants that arise mostly by hypertrophy or hyperplasy under the influence of parasitic organisms such as bacteria, fungi, nematodes, mites and insects. Among mites, Eriophyids and Tenuipalpids are gall makers. Eriophyid induced galls are of open type with soft and persistent ostiole and copious nutritive hairs inside. Gall forming Eriophyid mites are highly host specific and sometimes more than one species of Eriophyid species may be present in one gall along with inquilines comprising predators and parasites (Mani, 1964).

Eriophyid Galls

Deformities caused by eriophyids : The eriophyids cause various types of deformities but of all those the galls caused on leaves are the most significant. The galls may be elongate, hemispherical, rounded, bead-like and may be scattered irregularly on leaf lamina or in angles between veins. The galls are formed on leaf petioles, flower buds, flowers, leaf buds, leaf axils, etc. Because of feeding and damaging leaf tissues, morphological changes occur in leaf tissues. The parenchyma cells get transformed into meristem as a result of feeding by mites. The cells proliferate and this results into gall formation. The damaged tissues contain a large quantity of free amino acids indicating disturbed protein synthesis. As the galls mature, the red pigment material increase in some cases and gradually extend to other tissues. The feeding activity by mites induced different reactions in different plants. The contents of growth promoting substance like auxin as well as phenolics remain at higher level. (Balasubramanian and Purushothamanan (1972: *Indian J. Expt. Biol.,* **10** : 394-95) and Purohit *et al.,* (1979: *Curr. Sci.,* **48** : 714-716) in the gall than in normal leaf tissues. The saliva which is injected by eriophyids while feeding induces and promotes all these tissue changes. The nutritive tissue is characterized by hypertrophy and lobing of the nucleus, hypertrophy of nucleolus, fragmentations of vacuoles, abundance of organelles in the cytoplasm, higher density of ribosomes and endoplasmic reticulum and hypertrophy of the plastids (Westphal, 1977: *Marcellia*, **39** : 193-375), ChannaBasavanna and Nangia 1984 (in Bilology of Gall Insects. Ed. T.N. AnanthaKrishnan, 330). The differentiation of the nutritive tissue appears to show a gradual gradation from a mild effect as in erinea to complex galls (Westphal, 1977).

The mite feeding also induces a series of physiological changes involving higher rate of nucleic acid metabolism and higher quantity of growth promoting substances (Tandon *et al.*, 1976: *Ind. J. Expt. Biol.*, **14** : 211-213; ChannaBasavanna and Nangia, 1984).

Some of the types of galls made by eriophyids are as below :

Erineum : This is excessive growth of hairs forming a localized patches or covers an extensive area in the foliage or petiolar surface. Sometimes dense growth of hairs on ventral surface of leaves form hemispherical dome which project out from the outer surface. The cells pierced by mouthparts turn necrotic and grow into hairs which later become lignified.

In case of grape vine, the erineum caused by *Eriophyes vitis* appears in juvenile healthy grape leaves covered with narrow, bent, thin walled, unicellular trichomes. The trichomes are 2-6 celled in mature leaves. Ereneous trichomes are rounded at the apex. The trichomes finally dry out. The epidermal cells and stomata also undergo modification, significant changes occur in the mesophyll chlorenchyma in the erinea, finally resulting in local invagination of leaf blade towards upper leaf surface (ChannaBasavanna and Nangia, 1984).

Witche's Broom : In this, the shoot is modified, becomes somewhat branched with compact shortened internodes. The shortening of internodes produce a bud-like cluster of overlapping cottony leaves which are paler and thicker than normal branches. The presence of swollen epidermal cells which stain more intensely than the normal cell is the distinguishing feature of galled leaves from the normal ones. Swollen cells have dense cytoplasm within large nuclei and nucleoli. The witche's broom galls caused by *Aceria victoriae* on *Haloragis erecta* vary considerably in appearance, composed of bunches of discoloured leaves. The entire gall may be partly green and partly red. Some of the portions of galls may have a tumour-like fleshiness and other parts leaf-like, where maximum cell destruction takes place due to mite feeding. The disorganizations of meristem in the gall is the greatest. The apical dominance in gall is greatly reduced and this produces branching effect of the gall leaves (Jeppson *et al.*, 1975 : ChannaBasavanna and Nangia, 1984).

Needle Galls : *Eriophyes tiliae* var. *rudes* produces the elongated rod shaped galls on upper surface of leaves of *Tilia cordata*. Galls are 4-6 mm long and reddish brown. Qualitative and quantitative differences in carotenoid content of gall and lamina have been observed. The feeding induces more synthesis of carotene and inhibition of others. The content of *ß* carotene comprised 27.3% of all carotenoids in normal lamina and in gall lamina it was only 1.7%. Likewise, dihidroxy carotene comprised 19.2% of all carotenoids in normal lamina but this content was nil in the galls (ChannaBasavanna and Nangia, 1984).

Pouch Galls **:** This appears as depressed area and takes a definite shape characteristic of mite species and hosts. This is an open type of gall having an opening escape hole at the bottom of gall. The interior surface of gall is lying with succulent or turgid host tissues which vary from hair-like papilli to hypertrophid cells (ChannaBasavanna and Nangia, 1984).

Normal leaf of *Pavetta hispidula* possesses one layer of palisade cells and 6-8 layers of sponge cells with large air spaces. The lower epidermal layers are elongated horizontally than upper epidermal cells. In gall lamina, palisade cells are recognizable and sponge mesophyll cells appear hypertrophid without air chambers. Callus-like growth of sponge cells is evident and often the lower epidermis is ruptured. Due to continuous feeding, the peripheral collenchyma cells are hypertrophid, epidermal cells develop into erineal hairs.

This type of gall is formed in *Tilia platylla* by *Eriophyes tiliae* on abaxial side of undifferentiated leaf. The nutritive epidermis involved has smaller cells, but larger nuclei, and in the galls these cells have dense cytoplasm with well developed endoplasmic reticulum and ribosomes. Starch disappears at later stage. *Aceria pongamiae* causes elongated pouch galls on *Pongamia glabra* .

Circaces chakrabarti Keifer and *Colomerus alangii* Keifer make pouch galls on either side of leaf surface of *Allangium salvifolium.* The galls are haphazardly arranged on leaf lamina and filled with short shiny hairs. Gall initiation starts from lower surface of leaves giving rise to subglobose and sessile outgrowth on upper surface of leaf. Galls are also formed on upper surface of leaf in case of heavy infestation. Young plants show more attack by this gall mite and the plant growth gets affected (Ghosh *et al.,* 1989, *Progr. in Acarology,* **2** : 135-140).

Fitz Galls **:** This is formed on *Tilia intermedia* by a *Eriophyes leiesoma.* The very young leaves are covered with hairs having large nuclei and hypertrophied nucleoli than normal hairs. The hairs become later lignified.

Aceria cordiae ChannaBasavanna : This mite makes circular pouch galls on upper surface of leaf of *Cordia myxa.* Gall cavity is filled with dense white erineum initially, becoming brownish later. Galls appear during May-June. Galls often coalesce giving lumpy appearance to the leaf (Ghosh *et al.,* 1989).

Acalitus hibisci Mondal and Chakrabarti : This mite produces globose, hollow, sessile galls on *Hibiscus vitifolius.* They are greenish brown externally with short fine hairs internally with 1.5 to 3.0 mm. wide. Galls develop on both surfaces of leaves. Numerous mites may be found in each gall. Leaves suffer from distortion and disorientation due to gall formation. Abundance of galls are seen during January to February (Ghosh *et al.*, 1989).

Aceria pongamiae : This mite produces solitary, spindle shaped galls with truncate apices. Galls are irregular, greenish having internal cavity filled with numerous downwardly projected hairs. It prefers older plants and occurs throughout the year.

Eriophyes terminaliae ChB. : This mite produces epiphyllous leaf marginal roll galls on *Terminalia arjuna*. Leaf blade is rolled centripetally. Outer surface of gall becomes irregularly twisted. Gall cavity is fitted with fleshy gelatinous mass. Under severe condition the entire leaf blade is rolled and laminar surface is reduced considerably (Ghosh *et al.*, 1989).

Indosetacus rhinacanthi Ghosh and Chakrabarti : This mite produces pouch galls on upper leaf surface of *Rhinacanthus nasuta* almost throughout the year on young plants. The galls are sessile, hemispherical with large wide ostiole lying with whitish erineum. Affected leaf lamina gets twisted (Ghosh *et al.*, 1989).

Aceria sp. **(a)** : This undetermined species of *Aceria* produces globose, sessile, irregular bead galls on either side of leaf of *Randia dumetorum*. Galls are usually crowded in large numbers and cavities remain filled with white erineum. During August, some of the galls are found in apical shoot (Ghosh *et al.*, 1989).

Aceria sp. **(b)** : Globose, subsolid, sessile pouch galls are formed on *Adina sessilifolia*.Young galls are green and turn violet when become matured. Gall cavity remains filled with elongate, acuminate hairs. Gall size varies. Galls are more on twigs in NE India.

Aceria sp. **(c)** : This mite makes epiphyllous and sometimes hypophyllous, globose, yellowish, green pouch galls on lamina of *Croton caudatus*. Galls are solitary or scattered irregularly, often are numerous. A few galls are also formed on petioles. The cavities become filled with yellow colored erineum. Galling is peak during September to October in NE India.

Aceria sp. **(d)** : This mite produces moderate size subcuticular, hollow, sessile galls on leaf blade of *Premna latifolia*. Each gall is 2 -3 chambered. In case of severe attack galls appear on lower surface of leaf also.

Eriophyes negundi Hodgkiss : This mite produces large rounded pouch type galls on underside of leaf *Acer negundo*. The galls are solitary and wide spread on leaf blade but are not on the veins (Keifer *et al.*, 1982).

Vasates quadripedes : This mite produces pouch galls (also called bladder gall), on upper leaf surface of *Acer rubrum*. The galls are round or elongate and are usually crowded and numerous at the basal part of leaf blade (Keifer *et al.*, 1982).

Vasetes aceriscrumena (Riley) **:** This mite produces abundant pouch galls on upper surface of *Acer saccharum.* The galls are solitary, elongate with pointed or truncated apices (Keifer *et al.,* 1982).

Phytoptus laevis Nal. **:** This mite produces bead galls on both surfaces of leaf of *Alnus oregona.* The galls are formed singly or crowded along mid rib (Keifer *et al.,* 1982).

Eriophyes brachytarsus K. : This mite produces pouch gall on upper surface of leaf of *Juglans californica.* Galls are irregularly globular, shiny with roughened surface (Keifer *et al.,* 1982).

Eriophyes aloinis K. : This mite produces irregular outgrowth, clustered densly on the surface of leaf blade/axils of *Aloe nobilis* (Keifer *et al.,* 1982).

Phytoptus helicantyx (K.) : This mite produces marginal roll galls on *Pteridium aquilinum.* It looks like delicate, pale, lime green, lace border on the underside of pennule (Keifer *et al.,* 1982).

Phytoptus adenostomae K. : This produces typical pouch galls on leaf blade of *Adenostoma fasciculatomae* (Keifer *et al.,* 1982).

Phytoptus emarginatae **(K.)** : It produces typical pouch galls scattered at random over the leaf surface of *Prunus americana, P. domestica.* Each gall is elongate, clavate or finger-like (Keifer *et al.,* 1982).

Eriophyes cephalanthi Cook **:** The galls formed by these mites are haphazardly scattered on upper surface of leaf blade of *Cephalanthus occidentalis,* the outer surface of galls are covered with short, white hairs, and interior is filled with erineal-like hairs (Keifer *et al.,* 1982).

Phytoptus tiliae Pag. **:** It produces nail-like galls on lindane leaves *Tilia* sp. They are numerous and are scattered over the leaf surface. Each gall is elongated with pointed tip (Keifer *et al.,* 1982).

Aceria mangiferae Sayed : It produces mango bud gall. Young trees are most seriously affected (Keifer *et al.,* 1982).

Phytocoptella avellanae (Nal.) : This mite forms big bud gall (called big bud) on *Corylus avellana* L. This is formed by aggregation of swollen, thickened scale leaves, often containing hundreds of mites (Keifer *et al.,* 1982).

Eriophyes celtis Kendall : This mite causes brooms on the trees (*Celtis occidentalis*). Infestation of buds prevent normal growth. As a result, numerous buds are clustered together on the side of the stem. Eventually, buds develop into tightly bunched twigs. The twigs bear large buds with open scales and tend to show dieback symptoms after about a year (Keifer *et al.,* 1982).

Eriophyes neoessigi K. : It forms galls on poplus which look like bunch of grapes (Keifer *et al.,* 1982).

Trisetacus alborum K. : It produces rosette galls on *Pinus* sp. It is the clustering of numerous aborted buds and stunted needles (Keifer *et al.,* 1982).

Eriophyes fraxinivorus Nalepa : This inflorescence gall is produced on *Fraxinus* sp. Fully developed galls are conspicuously brownish, lumpy, remain attached on twigs from one season to next (Keifer *et al.*, 1982).

Eriophyes cynodoniensis (Sayed) : It causes leaf sheath and stem gall on *Cynodon dactylon*, Due to mite infestation leaf sheath becomes swollen, closely packed, thickened and bunched at stem node, leaf blades become stunted (Keifer *et al.*, 1982).

Tenuipalpid Galls

Tenuipalpid mites make galls as below :

Woody Gall on Ber (*Zizyphus jujuba*) : This is done by *Eriophyes cernuus* . Details have been discussed under Ber in the chapter of fruit tree mite.

Red Round Galls : This type of gall is made also on Ber (*Zizyphus mauritiana*) by *Larva*carus *transitans* and detailed discussion of which has been made under Ber in fruit chapter. These galls are lac-like, hemispherical, disc shaped, formed on cortical region of stem. At first the galls appear like minute specks, less than 10 μ long and then grow to maximum size of 6-7 mm. long, 4-5 mm. wide. Each gall starts with a single larva but sometime several larvae settle, close together producing several galls which coalesce into a single mass stretching along the twig, having a number of larvae within several partitions. Fertilization and development take place within the gall. The mite larvae escape through a small hole bored by the larva of *Anarsia* , a member of Lepidoptera which also is found within gall. *Phytoseius intermedius* also occupies the gall (Ghai and Baker, 1989, *Progr. in Acarology*, **2** : 81-89). The larvae remain within the galls throughout the year and come out during monsoon months when the galls rupture and mites migrate to build new colony (Sharma and Kushwaha 1989, *Progr. in Acarology*, **2** : 91-99). The gall intensity increased during May and thereafter, decreased gradually.

Sesamum Gall : Gupta (1974) reported raised gall-like swellings on leaves of *Sesamum* and on teasing the galls several members of *Brevipalpus phoenicis* could be detected. The role of the mite in making this gall has not been proved conclusively that these are caused by *B. phoenicis*. Apart from making leaf galls, the infected leaves become twisted and longitudinally folded due to mite feeding.

Ecology of gall mites

Chakrabarti (1999) shed some light on ecology of gall mite. According to him, the least severe injury ranking goes to pests which form galls on leaves, when all the life stages like egg, immatures, adults are enclosed within a living plant tissue.

The plants produce callus/parenchyma tissues as defence against these pests and the pest feeds on defensive tissues rather than on functioning plant parts. In gall formation, the pests remain embedded in plant tissues for a long time and the plant in turn, changes the pests' behavioural linkage to the plant. The changes towards alteration of biochemical levels of nutrients, defensive chemicals and plant hormones occur in the affected plant tissues.

Histology

Mite feeding induces cellular changes in affected plants. The upper epidermis remains unaffected except for bulging. The lower epidermis ruptures. Gradual loss of differentiation of mesophyll into palisade and spongy parenchyma was reported in *Acacia leucophaloea* caused by *Eriophyes* sp. and in *Hibiscus vitifolius* caused by *Acalitus hibisci*. The mesophyll cell layer gradually increases 2-3 times. Modified mesophyll shows some multinucleated nutritive cells (Chakrabarti, 1999).

Mite population and Gall intiation

The gall size, shape, etc. will depend upon size of inoculum, plant age, number of eriophyids, etc. (Chakrabarti, 1999).

Molecular basis of formation of Eriophyid Galls

According to Chakrabarti (1999) the galling by eriophyids depend upon bio-chemical changes as below :

a. Disturbance of C : N ratio due to herbivore feeding.

b. Nutrient stress may result to allocate photosynthates to other carbon-based compounds having role in plant defence against herbivores.

c. Change in plant hormones due to injection of some chemicals with saliva to the plant tissues. This acts as plant hormone or aromatic pathways in the plant body are stimulated leading to hormone production and that ultimately leads to production of galls due to callus formation.

The parenchyma cells react to the injuries caused by phytophagous as well as pathogens in more or less a similar way and the feeding by mite most likely causes similar response. Nutrient removal due to mite feeding may be due to direct cause of gall formation. In addition, the exo-elicitor like plant hormone injected by the mite in the plant tissues has also been proved to be reason for gall formation in few cases.

Leaf Tomenta and leaf Domatia

Walter (1996: *Ann, Rev Ent.*, **41** : 101-114) provided an excellent review on plant Tomenta and domatia and information given hereunder is mostly based on that. The plant associated mites often hide themselves in large raised veins, dense covering of hairs, tunnel - like rolled margins or small cave – like structures in the vein axils. The structures restricted to vein axils are called leaf domatia. They have no known function other than providing shelter to mites. The association of mite with leaf domatia is analogous to that between ants and formicaria on plants (Lundstrom, 1887: *Nova Acta Res. Soc. Sci. ups. ser.*, 3 : **13** : 1-87). The trees, shrubs and veins are inhabited by an extraordinary abundance and diversity of mites (Coy *et al.* 1993: *Tasmania NRCP. Tech. Report*, No. **9**, Dept. Arts Sport, Environ Territories, Canberra; Walter, 1995: *Rec. West Aust. Mus. Suppl.*, **52** : 49-53).

Foliar mites also inhabit a landscape of forms-leaf surface structures epiphyllus and debris that they must invade to locate their food and mates. These foliar facades influence many aspects of leaf microclimate and chemistry and influence behavior of mites.

Tomenta : The leaf which is smooth and glossy, hardly provides any suitable place to mite for hiding from the sun, rain, and enemies. On the contrary, the leaves which are coated with dense hairs, called tomenta, provide ideal place for hiding. The Tomenta that the leaves of many plants come in various forms and densities that provide surface habitats for permitting the invasion of the foliar mites. It has been seen that mite population will be quantitatively and qualitatively high in hairy leaves as compared to glabrous leaves or those coated with appressed scales. These foliar mites are dominated with plant parasites, scavenging microbiovores and predators and are far more abundant on hairy leaves.

In case of grape vines, the varieties with more dense leaves on undersurface had consistently more number of two predatory phytoseiid mites (*Typhlodromus pyri* and *Amblyseius aberans*) as compared to leaves of glabrous varieties. These predatory mites are both relatively small in size with narrow body, long legs, and can penetrate tomenta as compared to a large predatory mite of *Amblyseius* species occurs on glabrous leaves. The anthocorid bugs which are much larger can not penetrate the dense hair and hence can not suppress the prey mite i.e. *Tetranychus* population. This predator has elongated marginal setae on dorsal shield which help them to move through the webbing.

Glandular hair : Some leaves have hairs having glandular tips which secrete a sticky substance that entangles the mites or poisons the mites. Such plants can be considered as resistant variety. Most of the spider mites produce silk which provides some protection against entanglement. However, the larger phytoseiid predator, *Phytoseiulus persimilis* became trapped in glandular hairs on tomenta and thus their predatory efficiency is reduced considerably.

Extra foliar nectarines : Glands that produce sugary secretion outside of flowers are referred to as extra foliar nectarines. Many plant inhabiting arthropods take advantage of moisture, carbohydrate and aminoacids produced by nectarines. This, in turn, influences increased predator's reproduction, better survival and reduced emigration.

Acarodomatia (Mite house) : These are the structures found in vein axils on undersurface of leaves of many trees which provide shelter to mites. In comparison to "Formicaria" or ant house, which are large, the "Acarodomatia" are small, only 1-2 mm. diameter. Leaf domatia are plant morphogenetic structures and are formed whether or not mites are present unlike eriophyid galls or erinose patches, where mites are always present. A clear association exists between mites and leaf domatia.

Structure occupants of leaf domatia : The leaf domatia occurs in vein axils and provide shelter to predatory mites like Tydeidae, Stigmaeidae, Phytoseiidae and rarely the plant parasitic mites. Leaf domatia are normally in raised domes, relatively large pouches and pits that penetrate deep into leaf lamina and are common on leaves in warm, temperate and tropical forests. These carry a tuft of hairs and a minute opening. These are inhabited by predatory mites, scavenger mites and those feed on fungi and other microbes predominant in leaf domatia. The plants are benefitted from the leaf domatia because of elevated number of predatory mites which provide them protection from plant parasitic mites. It has been seen that leaves with domatia more attract the predators like Tydeidae, Stigmaeidae, Phytoseiidae which are common inhabitants of leaf domatia. Plants with leaf domatia normally have many more predators per leaf as compared to sympatric plants lacking this structure. (Grostal & O'Dowd, 1994; *Oecologia*, **97** : 308-315; Rosario 1995, *S. Asia Journal Tropical Ecol.*, **11** : 99-108). Spider mites are normally not found in domatia. Sometimes gall forming eriophyids and false spider mites share the same leaf domatia with phytoseiid predators but in that case these parasitic mites are fed by phytoseiid predators. Therefore, the plant parasitic mites are transient and rare inhabitants of leaf domatia while predatory mites are consistently and abundantly occupants of domatia. Probably a mutualistic association exists with leaf domatia and mites. The plants with domatia invite predators which get their shelter in domatia and in turn protect the plants from parasitic mites. If the domatia are plugged or shaved off, the predator number is drastically reduced on leaves. Phytoseiid mites preferentially use leaf domatia for oviposition and lay more number of eggs than in plants where leaf domatia have been removed. Besides, the predatory and fungivorous mites use domatia for moulting place.

So, from the foregoing account it can be concluded that leaf domatia provide defense against herbivores. Plants benefit from leaf domatia by presence of predatory mites within it and the predators get benefit by securing a safe shelter for food, oviposition and moulting. Leaf domatia indicates a long term and mutually beneficial interaction between plants and arthropods (Walter, 1996, *Ann. Rev. Ent.*, **41** : 101-114).

1.15 PARASITES AND PATHOGENS OF MITES

Like insects, mites are also attacked by a large number of microorganisms belonging to virus, bacteria, protozoa, rickettsia and nematodes. Since not much investigation on this aspect has been done in India in particular and world in general, to what extend these microorganisms will be effective is not known with certainty. Yet it is strongly believed that the pathogens have high potentiality and exploration and exploitation of these will be profitable in management of economically important pests. The different groupes of parasites are discussed below:

Nematode parasites of Mites

Nematodes are the parasites known to infest mites. The family of nematode-infesting mite is Allantonematidae under the order Tylenchida. Warren (1941, *Ann.*

Natal. Mus, **10** : 79-95) was the first who reported several *Acarinocola* species, *A. cuneifer* from gamasid mite *Cosmolaelaps cuneifer*, *A. claviger* from *Cosmolaelaps claviger* and *Hypoaspis* sp. *A. terribilus* from *Euryparasitus terribilis*. Wachek described *Howardula acarinorum* from the body cavity of *Parasitus fucorum* and *Poecilochirus necrophori* (Wachek, 1955, *Parasitol Schr. Reihe*, **3** : 119). The life cycle of these mite parasitizing nematodes follows a typical allantonematid cycle, in which the infective free living stage is a fertilized female which penetrates the host cuticle and goes to body cavity. This stage matures to parasitic female that produced the eggs and juveniles in her body. This is followed by another moult when juveniles exit from the mite and develop to maturity in the environment.

The allantonematid nematodes do not kill their host outright but the host gradually becomes weak, sterilized and life cycle becomes shortened. Thus, this nematode may act as a regulatory factor for control of gamasid mites. Nematodes, *Pelodera acarambates* attaches itself on the idiosoma of mite (*Macrocheles* sp.) and are carried to a new environment where it completes its development. Having too many nematodes on mite body may take them weak and become proned to attack by predators.

Some mites can also serve as intermediate hosts of nematode parasites of vertebrates. Filarial nematode *Litomosoides carinii* is an example for that. The adults of this nematode live in pericardial and peritoneal cavities of the cotton rat, *Sigmodon hispidus*. The tropical rat mite *Ornithonyssus bacoti* acts as intermediate host, which ingests microfilariae while feeding on the rodents. The nematode penetrating the body of mite developes there to form the 3rd stage infective juvenile and that stage enters the body of the rat through the wound which the mite has made to the rat through its bite. It is not known if the nematode while in mite body developes any pathogenecity. However, microfilariae occurs in other intermediate host nematodes.

Fungal parasites of mites

This is a more prevalent pathogen and can be easily recognized due to its mycelium and pores. The earliest record of fungal pathogen of mite is Entomophthorales (Zygomycota) by Vorce in 1881 (*Proc. Am. Soc. Microsc.*, **4** : 49-50). Subsequently, other fungal pathogens which were reported were *Entomophthora* attacking *Halotydeus destructor* (Petch, 1940. *Proc. Linn. Soc. NSW*, **65** : 259-260). Approximately 750 species of fungi under 56 genera are pathogens of arthropods (Hawksworth *et. al.*, 1995). Most species belong to Entomophthorales, Ascomycota and Mitosporic fungi. These are most virulent to insects and Acari. The conidia of *Entomophthora* adhere on the mite body, penetrate the cuticle and produce invasive hyphal bodies which fill the host body cavity. Consequently, the mite dies and spores are produced in the body of the mummified cadaver. *Entomophthora* has been reported from *Panonychus* (Fisher, 1941: *Fla. Ent.*, **34** : 83-88), *Tetranychus* (Carner & Canerday, 1968: *J. Econ. Ent.*, **61** : 956-959; Steinhaus & Marsh, 1962: *Hilgardia*, **33** : 349-390; Weiser, 1968: *Folia Parasitol.*, **15** : 115-122). Often, while rearing the predatory mites, for which the prey mites are used, those become susceptible to the fungal pathogen damaging the entire rearing procedure.

Hirsutella is another genus of fungi which attacks mites. *H. thompsonii* is one of the most studied fungal pathogens (Samson *et. al.*, 1980. *Mycologia*, **72** : 359-377) which attacks citrus red mite. Baker & Neunzig (1968) reported *H. thompsonii* as most important natural enemy of *Phyllocoptruta oleivora* in Florida where it causes epizootics belonging to rapid declining in mite population. This species produces fruit bodies. The phialides, the conidia supporting structure are elongated; borne singly and enlarged at the base. The conidia are covered with sticky mucous that adheres spores on the surface of mite. The spores germinate, penetrate the hosts cuticle, produce hyphae, which ramify throughout host body. The mite body becomes dark. Sometimes the internal mycelium forms multinucleate spherical chlamydospores in the host body. The commercially produced fungal acaricides in the name, Mycar, has been used since 1976 for tetranychid and eriophyid mites on coconut and greenhouses. *Neozygites floridana* is another fungus causes decline of *Eutetranychus banksi* population in Florida (Weiser & Muma, 1966: *Fla. Ent.*, **49** : 155-159).

The other fungal pathogens which are in use in the field/laboratory in mite control are *Beauveria bassiana, Hirsutella thompsonii, Verticillium lecanii, Paecilomyces fumosoroseius, Metarhizium anisopliae*, some members of *Fusarium,Penicillium* and *Pleurodesspora, Entomophthora*, etc. Rangrez & Rather (2007: *J. Acarol.* **17** : 32-34) while evaluating five species of fungi, viz. *H. thompsonii, V. lecanii, B. bassiana, M. anisopliae* and *P. fumosoroseus* against *T. urticae* on apple, each in two concentrations $2.5X10^7$ and $1.0X10^8$, reported significant differences between the treatments. Initially, the mortality was low but increased with time. The maximum mortality was registered in *H. thompsonii* after 72 h (41.10%) and it was 59.99% after 144 hrs. Similarly *B. bassiana, M. anisopliae, V. lecanii* caused 42.22%, 33.33% and 23.33% mortality after 144 hrs. at spore concentration of $1.0X10^8$ spores ml^{-1}, respectively. *P. fumosoroseus* was the least effective (1.65-4.44% mortality) at both concentrations. *H.thompsonii* at $2.5X10^7$ spore ml^{-1} registered a mortality of 23.33% after 144 h. However at $1.0X10^8$ spores ml^{-1}, *H. thompsonii* was superior (59.99%) to other fungi. Kumar & Singh (2000. *Indian Coconut J.*, **31** : 11-17) also reported *V. lecanii* to be superior over others both *in-vivo* and *in-vitro*. Poinar & Poinar (1998. *Ann. Rev. Ent.*, **43** : 449-469) achieved considerable success in controlling many mite species with *H.thompsonii* and that led its commercialization.

Kumar & Singh (2007: *J. Acarol.*, **17** : 35-37) conducted trial using pathogenic fungi like *P. fumosoroseus* WP, *P. fumosoroseus* WP+Azadirachtin, *P. fumosoroseus* WP+Neem oil, *P. fumosoroseus* + NSKE, *P. fumosoroseus* EC, *P. fumosoroseus* EC +Azadirachtin , *P. fumosoroseus* EC + Neem oil, *P. fumosoroseus* EC + NSKE against *T. urticae* and reported that *P. fumosoroseus* WP + Azadirachtin registered maximum mortality 55.83%) of adults followed by *P. fumosoroseus* WP+ Neem oil (48.33%). Muraleedharan & Selvasundaram (2005, UPASI. *Tea Res. Foundtion*, **15** : 1-3) also got similar result.

Sreerama Kumar & Singh (2007: *J. Acarol.*, **17** : 29-31) evaluated *H. thompsonii* against *T. urticae.* They reported that hydrophilic conidium attached itself on the body of the host. The more the mite crawling on the fungal culture, more was the number of conidia affixed on the mite body and that, in turn, influenced the degree of disease development. Conidia germinated with increase in humidity inside the closed moist chamber and those pierced the mite cuticle. The fungal hyphae gradually developed in central area of haemocoel and gradually filled in the haemocoel. Consequently, mite stopped feeding, became restless, started wriggling and sluggish movement and eventually became immobile. Ultimately, the mite was killed. Once the mite body was filled with fungal biomass, the hyphae emerged out from cadavers through mouth, anal and genital apertures, leg joints and through body walls. Inside the cadavers, the fungus disintegrated and formed multinucleate spherical chlamydospores as a means of survival of pathogen. The other workers who assessed *H. thompsonii* are Chandler *et al.*, (2005: *Biocontrol, Sci. & Tech.*, **15** : 37-54) against *T. urticae* on tomato; Gardener *et al.*, (1982: *Fla. Ent.*, **65** : 458-465); Gerson *et al.*, (1979 *Annals of Appl. Biol.*, **91** : 29-40), Kumar (2007: *J. Biol. Control.*, **21** (suppl.) : 187-192) on *T. neocaledonicus* and *T. urticae.*

Rangrez & Rather (2010: *Abst. Int. Symp-cum-Workshop in Acarology*, 8-10 Apr., 2010, p. 113) used various pathogens against *P. ulmi* on apple. The fungal pathogens which were used were *Metarhizium anisopliae* and *Paecilomyces fumosoroseus* with two concentrations 1.0X10^8 and 2.5X10 ^{7} spores ml^{-1}. The percent mortality was different at different concentrations. *Verticilium lecanii, P. fumosoroseus, B. bassiana* and *M. anisopliae* at 1.0X10^8 spores ml^{-1} were found at par with each other by recording a mortality of 9.99%, 7.77%, 6.66% and 6.66%, respectively. *H.thompsonii* was least effective at both the concentrations. Seventy two hours after treatment, the mean % mortality was highest 24.99% in *P. fumosoroseus* at a spore concentration of 1.0X10^8 spores ml^{-1}. It was significantly superior to others at similar concentration. *V. lecanii, M. anisopliae* and *B. bassiana* were at par inflicting mortality of 12.22, 8.88 and 8.88%, respectively at 1.0X10^8 spores ml^{-1}. *H. thompsonii* was least effective one. The trend was similar 144 hrs after treatment by recording a mortality of 55.09% in case of *P. fumosoroseus* at 1.0X10^8 spores ml^{-1}. It proved to be superior to all others. The authors concluded that entomopathogenic fungi was able to keep the mite population at check and may be of some help in management of ERM on apple in Kashmir.

Mazumdar *et al.*, (2010 : 112-113) tested *Hirsutella thompsonii* formulation against coconut perianth mite in West Bengal and reported that both non-parametric and parametric statistics suitable for this investigation revealed that application of *Hirsutella* with either meat or yeast extracts in the first year study and *Hirsutella* mycelium along with conidia and adjuvant in the second year study were superior treatments.

Metarhizium aniosopliae

It is an important entomopathogenic fungi which has long been used against insect pests for biocontrol. The fungus can be easily identified by green cylindrical conidia forming dense compact layer of spores.

Pathogenicity of *M. anisopliae* against Acari

The pathogenicity of this fungus on eggs,active immatures and adults of *T. neocaledonicus* was reported by Hanchinal & Majunatha (2000: *Karnataka J. Agric. Sci.*, **13** : 454-456) when used at conc. of 1.5X10^8, 1.5X10^6 spores/ml. Application of higher doses resulted in higher percentage of mortality of *T. neocaledonicus.*

Effect of fungal biocontrol agent and predatory mite

When *B. bassiana* was applied along with predatory mite *Amblyseius cucumeris,* for control of cucumber mite, it was observed that the predatory mites were compatible with the fungi and no detrimental effect on predator was seen (Jacobson *et al.,* 2001. *Biocontrol Sci. Tech.,* **11** : 391-400).

Pathogenicity of fungal biocontrol agents against eggs of Tetranychidae

Entomopathogenic fungi such as *B. bassiana* and *Metarhizium aniosopliae* are widely used as effective biocontrolling agents but no study is yet to be made on the effect of these fungi on tetranychid eggs. Hanchinal & Majunatha (2000) reported pathogenicity of *Metarhizium aniosopliae* on eggs of *T. neocaledonicus*. The mortality achieved was 21.37, 38.50 and 87.32 at 1,2 and 3 days after application, respectively. High ovicidal action of *B. bassiana* was also reported in case of eggs of *T. urticae* within 1-3 days of its application containing 1400-22,800 viable conidia. Feng (2004) demonstrated that two isolates of *B. bassiana* and one of *P. fumosoroseus* were found to have ovicidal activity against *T. cinnabarinus* under laboratory condition. Shi & Feng (2004: *Bio. Contr.,* **30** : 163-173) also reported the lethal effect of 10 isolates of *B. bassiana, M. aniosopliae* and *P. fumosoroseus.* The eggs shrunk and became orange brown.

Pathogenicity of *H. thompsonii*

Tetranychidae: Jeppson *et al.,* (1975) observed 94% mycosis of *T. cinnabarinus* (=*T. urticae)* within 4 days of inoculation at a constant 100% RH in laboratory experiment. Zoebisch *et al.,* (1992: *Manejo Integrado de Plagas,* **23** : 9-12) reported that *H. thompsonii* was the cause of natural epizootic in *Dolichotetranychus floridanus,* a pest of pineapple.

When Cassava green mite was treated with suspension of *H. thompsonii* @ 1.2X 10^{11} and 6.0X10^{10} per ha, the 76.6% of the cadavers developed disease in contrast to only 0.6% in control plots. *Hirsutella kirchneri* is also another fungus which can be used for control of plant mites.

The *H. thompsonii* is equally effective against eriophyids and tarsonemids. The LC_{50} of *H. thompsonii* was estimated at 2.4 X10^3 conidia per ml, 6 days after application (Penna *et al.,* 1996).

Beauveria bassiana

This entomopathogenic fungus is widely distributed and provides potential control against 70 insect pest species (Aleshina, 1980. *Rev. Appl. Entomol.,* **68** : 33-

84) and is widely used for control of different crops. The muscardine disease caused to insect is due to *B. bassiana*. However, the study on pathogenicity of mites has received little attention.

Pathogenicity of *B. bassiana* against *T. urticae*

Dresner (1949: *Contr. Boyce Thomson Inst.*, **15** : 319-335) got very good control when applied against *T. urticae* infesting bean. Another isolate of *B. bassiana* (No. 447) when tested against *T. urticae* in laboratory disc technique @ $5X10^6$ - $1X10^9$ conidia/ml, caused 50% mortality (Tamai *et al.*, 1996, *Abstr. 17th Brazil Congr. Ento. Rio de Janeiro* : 1066 pp). Alves *et al.*, (2002) tested yeast like cells and conidia of *B. bassiana* isolates 447. Yeast like cells and conidia had similar virulence against *T. urticae.*

Rabindra (2000: *RAMCOP*, 24-25 May 2000 : 26-27) reported *Hirsutella thompsonii* as a promising pathogen for management of coconut eriophyid mite *Aceria guerreronis.*

Moore & Howard (1996: *Elsevier Pub. B.V.* : 569-570) reported that *Hirsutella thompsonii* was isolated from samples of coconut mite from tropical America and West Africa. A mortality of 75% was achieved in Mexico using *Hirsutella thompsonii* (Espinosa & Carrillo, 198[illegible], *Tecnica en Mexico* 12 : 319-323) against *Aceria guerreronis* but no success was achieved in West Africa. In another experiment, a mortality of 88% was obtained with an isolate from *Aceria guerreronis* and 32% with an isolate from *Phyllocoptruta oleivora* (Sampedro & Rosan, 1989, *Revista Mexicana de Micologia,* **5** : 225-232).

McCoy *et al.*, (1971: *J. Invert. Pathol.*, **17** : 240-276) and Balazy & Wismiewski (1982 : *Bull. Polish Acad. Sci.*, **35** : 199-224) reported that *H. thompsonii* was normally associated with eriophyid and tetranychid mites. Howard and Moore (2006) reported *H. thompsonii* as good biocontrol agent of coconut eriophyid mite.

Aspergillus sp. and *Fusarium* sp. also were observed in cadavar of cassava green spider mite *Mononychellus* spp. together with *Hirsutella* sp. and *Neozygites* sp. (Bartowski *et al.*, 1986. *Insect Sci. Appl.* 9: 457-459). Pena *et al.*, (1996: *Entomophaga* 41: 27-36) reported *Polyphagotarsonemus latus* was susceptible to *Beauveria bassiana* and *Paecilomyces fumosoroseus*, although they were less virulent than *H. thompsonii.*

Protozoan parasites of Mites

Michael (1984: *R. Soc. London*, **1** : 326) was first to describe a gregarian protozoa from *Damaeus oblongus.* Among the protozoans reported, *Microsporidia* was most widely spread and also most pathogenic. *Nosema helminthorum* was reported from oribatid genera *Ceratoppia* and *Xenillus* (Moniez, 1887: *C.R. Acad. Sci.*, **104** : 1312-1314). Bjornsen *et al.*, (1996: *J. Invert. Pathol.*, **20** : 279-283) listed the protozoans collected from mites. The protozoa infection is initiated with ingestion of spores. It goes to midgut, emits polar filament which transfers the protoplasm of the parasite into the cells of the host. Development occurs in fat body, nerve cells of mite hosts. Thereafter, the spores are released in body cavity of host and with the host death it is released in environment.

Microsporidium phytoseiuli infects the predatory mite *Phytoseiulus persimilis.* Mature spores also develop in mite eggs indicating transovarian transmission. The rapid spread of the disease is achieved through autoinfection in gut nuclei and caeca. But interestingly, no infection was found in spider mite prey on which this predatory mite was multiplied.

The other protozoans which infect mites are *Gregarina, Nosema, Gurleya, Thelohania* and *Pleistophora* and those can be separated as per key proposed by Poinar & Poinar (1998: *Ann. Rev. Ent.,* **43** : 449-469).

1. Developing stages occur in intestinal cells; dispersal stages occur in gut lumen (Eugregarinida) .... *Gregarina*
- Developing stages in cells in the body cavity; dispersal stages free in the body cavity (Microsporidia) 2
2. Pansproblasts (sporocyst) not evident, spores appear to be borne singly .... *Nosema*
- Pansporoblast present, containing from 4 to many spores 3
3. Pansporoblast containing 4 spores .... *Gurleya*
- Pansporoblast containing 8 or more spores 4
4. Pansporoblast containing 8 spores .... *Thelohania*
- Pansporoblast containing more than 8 spores, usually 16 but sometimes more .... *Pleistophora*

No pathological condition exists in mites infected with gregarines. The damage is limited to destruction of few gut cells. The protozoan such as *Karyolysus lactertae* and *Hepatozoan muries* develop in parasitic mites like *Ophionyssus saurarum* and *Laelaps echidnus,* respectively and may cause pathological condition when applied in high dosage (Kudo) (1954: *Protozoology* Sprangfield, **1L** : Thomas, 966 pp.)

Rickettsiae associated with mites

Rickettsia are ubiquitous group of microorganisms exist as mutualistic, pathogenic or parasitic associations with wide range of organisms. *Rickettsia tsutsugamushi,* is transmitted by trombiculid mite causing Scrub typhus in many parts of Southeast and Fareast Asia. *Liponyssoides sanguineus* is also a vector of *Rickettsia akari* affecting both humans and rodents. Ricketssiae have been isolated from *Metaseiulus occidentalis* (Hess & Hog 1982: *J. Invert. Pathol.,* **40** : 98-106) but was not associated with any pathological condition. This rickettsial organisms are found in Malpighian tubules and rectal plugs in infected mites. Some do cellular damage and can be termed as pathogen.

Rickettsiella phytoseiuli in *Phytoseiulus persimilis* could be detected only from adult mites and not from larvae and nymphs. Since no pathological symptoms appeared because of this infection, its association with predatory mite was mutualistic. It is not known definitely how the predatory mite got infected with this rickettsial organism, may be through their prey because a sample of diseased *T. urticae* from Israel has shown the presence of Rickettsia when studied under electron microscope (Poinar & Poinar, 1998).

Bacteria associated with mite disease

So far no mite specific bacteria has been isolated. *Pseudomonas aeruginosa* infection was detected from a specimen of *T. urticae* when reared at 30°C under continuous light (Thomas & Poinar, 1973: *Hilgardia*, **42** : 261-360). Unidentified bacteria were detected from *Dendrolaelaps* sp. from Poland. Spider mites when inoculated with *Bacillus thuringiensis* did not produce infection on spider mites, however, the *Bacillus thuringiensis* exotoxin had detrimental effect on *T. urticae* and *Panonychus citri* (Hall *et al.*, 1971: *J. Invert. Pathol.*, **18** : 359-362).

Viruses

Muma (1955: *J. Econ. Ent.*, **48** : 432-438) was first to report a mite virus. Some flaccid citrus mite in Florida stucked to leaf surface in a deposit of black resinous material which exuded from anus. The virus particles developed in nuclei of epithelial cells and those were non- occluded virus. It possessed DNA - containing baciliform virons with smooth envelopes, typical of Baculoviridae (Reed & Desjardins, 1978: *J. Invert Pathol.*, **31** : 188-193). Numerous birefringent crystals in the midgut caeca of diseased mites could be detected (Smith & Cressman, 1962: *J. Insect Pathol.*, **4** : 229-236).

Non- inclusion virus was detected in tissues of *Panonychus ulmi* in California (Steinhaus, 1959, *J. Insect Pathol.*, **1** : 435-437). This was very similar to those collected from *P. citri* (Morel, 1991: *Boca Raton Fl. CRC Press*). The infected mites often die with their legs extended downward, and midgut contained birefringent crystals (Poinar & Poinar, 1998).

P. citri virus occurs in natural mite populations in California and Arizona and sometimes suppress the pest population below economic injury level. Its first formulation as microbial insecticide was made from an aqueous suspension triturated diseased mites collected through vacuum sucker method in field on virus free population of mites. The transmission of virus was effected under natural condition when virus were exuded from anus, mouth, reproductive openings of infected mites on leaves and those were ingested by healthy mites during normal feeding (Poinar & Poinar, 1998).

The spider mite, *T. urticae* population growing on bean plants and population of predatory mite, *M. occidentalis* were applied this virus and the disease appeared in *T. urticae* causing death. The mite passed through red colour phase and exhibited paralysis, stilt-leggedness, with shiny gleam cuticle and mouth parts adhering to leaf surface (Poinar & Poinar, 1998). Rod shaped virus particles could be detected in nuclei of mid gut cells. The nuclei of those cells became hypertrophied. The population of *M. occidentalis* also has shown disease symptoms. The ultrastructure studies revealed three separate types of virus-like particles in both spider mites and predatory mites.

This aspect i.e. the role of pathogens in mites and especially their profitable utilization in mite control is still in its infancy though there is enough potentiality of the pathogens to suppress the pest mite population. Hence, this area needs more in-depth investigation by acarologists and entomologists.

2. KEYS TO THE ORDERS AND FAMILIES OF MITES OCCURRING ON AGRI-HORTICULTURAL CROPS

Phylum ARTHROPODA

Class ARACHNIDA

Subclass ACARI

Key to the orders of ACARI recorded on plants (after Evans & Till, 1979)

1. With free coxae to ambulatory appendages, pedipalpal ambulacrum represented by a tined claw-like structure (apotele) near the inner basal angle of palptarsus, stigmata situated lateral to coxae III, IV and typical with elongate peritreme .... MESOSTIGMATA

- Lacking free coxae to ambulatory appendages, pedipalpal ambulacrum completely lost; stigmata never situated lateral to legs II – IV 2

2. Pedipalp small and comprising of 2 free podomeres and closely adpressed to the sides of hypognathum, chelicerae chelate, ambulacra of legs comprising a median (empodial) claw with an associated pulvillus or sucker-like pulvillus situated on an elongate pretarsus; stigmata and trachea never present; idiosoma without trichobothria, body never vermiform .... ASTIGMATA*

* Hysterosoma not divided by sutures, genital opening a transverse slit, without plate or with lateral and epigynial plates, female genital opening provided with lateral plates and closely associated suckers, claws. sometimes minute, propodosoma and hysterosoma separated by a suture, skin smooth, some dorsal body setae long and whip-like, with cervical setae, lens-like eye absent .... ACARIDAE

- Pedipalp usually with 3-5 podomeres and conspicuous; if small, with fewer podomeres and inconspicuous, then the idiosoma either vermiform or with overlapping sclerites dorsally in the female; Chelicerae chelate or variously modified into piercing stylets or hook-like organs; a respiratory system usually present; idiosoma with trichobothria 3

3. Gnathosoma with conspicuous rutella, chelicera typically chelate, dentate; one pair of podosomatic trichobothria almost invariably present and comprising piliform, barbed or clavate pseudostigmatid organ (sensilla) arising from conical depressions, the pseudostigmata(bothridia); pedipalp simple, tibia never with distal spurs; tracheal system when present open into the exterior in the acetabular cavities of legs I and II or through pseudostigmata; idiosoma heavily sclerotized in the adult stage and with ridges or wing-like expansions of the idiosoma which is never uniform .... CRYPTOSTIGMATA

- Gnathosoma only rarely with rutella; chelicera rarely chelate, dentate, propodosomatic trichobothria when present, usually without conspicuous pseusdostigmata; tarsus forming thumb-claw complex, trachea when present opening through paired stigmata situated between the chelicerae or on to the dorsal surface of propodosoma and often with associated peritreme; usually weakly sclerotized, never with ridge or wing-like expansions of the idiosoma which may be vermiform or covered dorsally by a number of discrete, usually overlapping sclerites .... PROSTIGMATA

Key to the families of Order PROSTIGMATA occurring on plants (Based on Meyer *et al.*, 1973)

1. Body worm-like or annulate with only .... ERIOPHYIDAE

   2 pairs of legs, plant feeders

- Body rounded, not worm-like or annulate, ... 2

  with more than 2 pairs of legs

2. Gnathosoma with minute palpi lying closely appressed laterally, chelae tiny and stylet-like with 4 pairs of legs or less, stigmata of female opening behind gnathosoma or propodosoma, male without stigmata or tracheae, empodium usually a membranous flap-like organ attached to claws. Leg IV of female ending in terminal and sub-terminal whip-like setae, plant feeders .... TARSONEMIDAE

- Gnathosoma usually conspicuous, with large chelicerae, palpi usually well developed, rarely without 4 pairs of legs, stigmata opens at base of chelicerae, empodium free, pad-like or claw-like arising from tarsus 3

3. Without a palpal thumb-claw complex 4

- With a palpal thumb-claw complex 8

4. Rod-like solenidion on tarsus I usually lying flush with tarsus in specialized membranous depression, anteriorly the propodosoma with a tubercle bearing one pair of setae, soft bodied, without projection over gnathosoma, free living, plant feeders .... EUPODIDAE

- Rod-like solenidion on tarsus I erect, arising from a small circular membranous base 5

5. Cheliceral bases fused, or if not fused, not capable of lateral scissors like motion over gnathosoma 7

- Chelicerae free, attached at base and free to move scissors-like laterally across gnathosoma 6

6. With 2 pairs of genital suckers, relatively long palp turned inward, distal segment usually claw-like, free living, predator .... CUNAXIDAE

- With 3 pairs of genital suckers, the relatively long palpi elbow-like, with distal setae long, free living, predator .... BDELLIDAE

7. Chelicerae long, recurved, whip-like, female genital opening transverse, tarsal claws with tenent hairs, palpi simple, plant feeders .... TENUIPALPIDAE

- Chelicerae short needle-like, genital opening not transverse 8

- Legs without a network, movable chelae larger and easily visible, free living or associated with plants .... TYDEIDAE

8. Body densely clothed with setae, larvae usually heteromorphic 9

- Body setae relatively few, arranged in transverse rows, larvae homomorphic 10

9. Movable chelae long, straight, extrusible, gnathosoma large, incapable of withdrawing into body, propodosoma not elongate anteriorly, larvae parasitic on arthropods, adults free living .... ERYTHRAEIDAE

- Movable chelae short, strong, hinged at base. Adults shaped like figure 8, tectum with only one or two setae, larvae usually with a single dorsal plate, seta on palpal coxa of larva posterior to palpal femur, larvae parasitic on vertebrates, nymphs and adults free living .... TROMBICULIDAE

10. Chelicerae free, hinged at base so that they are capable of scissors-like movements in a horizontal direction, palpal thumb long, prominent movable chela distal, hook-like, free living, predators .... ANYSTIDAE

- Cheliceral bases fused or partly fused, with needle-like or hook-like movable chelae 11

11. Cheliceral bases closely fused with gnathosoma and without indication of suture, peritremes usually M-shaped, may be present on gnathosoma, palpus with relatively strong claws and thumb short but conspicuous, may or may not have comb-like or sickle-like setae, tarsus II, III, IV and usually I with claws and empodia, free living, predators .... CHEYLETIDAE

- Cheliceral bases fused with each other but not with gnathosoma, having suture conspicuous, peritremes usually present on anterior portion of propodosoma 12

12. Movable chela forming a long whip-like stylet curving within body, cheliceral bases fused to form stylophore 13

- Movable chela straight, stiff, relatively short, no stylophore 14

13. Tarsi I and II with specialized duplex setae, female genitalia wrinkled, stylophore relatively broad, plant feeders .... TETRANYCHIDAE

- Tarsi I and II without duplex setae, possessing sensory pegs distally, female genitalia not wrinkled, stylophore relatively slender, dorsum of hypostome with 36 fan-shaped setae, the caudal end of body with series of flagelliform setae, plant feeders .... TUCKERELLIDAE

14. Body ovoid or nearly circular in shape, flattened, with spiniform dorsal setae, legs disproportionately long, stilt-like, tactile setae on genu of one or more legs often ultra long .... CAMEROBIIDAE, NEOPHYLLOBIIDAE

- Body globular, pyriform or fusiform, not noticeably flattened, longest legs, not longer that length of idiosoma, usually shorter 15

15. Dorsal plating absent or feebly developed, cheliceral bases fused or form a stylophore, which dorsally may be the sinuous chambered peritremes or else the peritremes reaching the chelicerae, free living .... CALIGONELLIDAE

- Dorsal plating variable, peritremes not reacting the chelicerae, cheliceral bases independent or forming a stylophore 16

16. Chelicerae form a stylophore, coxae II and III contiguous, free living .... RAPHIGNATHIDAE

- Chelicerae generally independently movable, but may be adnate or stylophore-like in a few genera, Coxae II and III not contiguous, legs I and II directed anteriorly, legs III and IV directed posteriorly .... STIGMAEIDAE

Order MESOSTIGMATA

Key to the families of MESOSTIGMATA occur on plants

1. Tectum with several processes, corniculae horn-like, widely separated and diverging, more than 23 pairs of dorsal setae, more than one pair of setae in R series .... ASCIDAE

- Never with more than one pair of setae in R series, corniculae slender, proximal, blade-like, Tectum smooth, 23 or less pairs of dorsal setae ....PHYTOSEIIDAE

Order CRYPTOSTIGMATA

Key to the families of CRYPTOSTIGMATA occur on plants

1. Pteromorphae movable, dorsosejugal suture continuous 2

- Pteromorphae immovable, dorsosejugal suture interrupted medially .... MOCHLOZETIDAE

2. Pteromorphae auriculate or semi circular, hinged, prodorsum with true lamellae .... GALUMNIDAE

- Pteromorphae never auriculate hinged, prodorsum with true lamellae .... XYLOBATIDAE

3. MITES INFESTING AGRI-HORTICULTURAL CROPS IN INDIA

3.1 CEREALS AND MILLETS

Rice is the staple food for over 65% of the world population (Mathur, 1999: *Oryza*, **36** : 195-2007) and is cultivated in tropical, subtropical and temperate climates of the world between 43°N and 39°S latitude and upto elevation of 2500 MSL in 146 million ha and the world annual production is 535 million tonnes, of which 97% is grown in Asia (India, Bangladesh, Pakistan, Myanmar, Thailand, China, Japan, Taiwan, Philippines, etc. (Srinivasa *et al.*, 2004).

Among the pests of rice, the most important ones are leaf hoppers, case worm, leaf folders, borers, mites and some pathogenic fungi. The attack of all these substantially damage the crops, reduces the yield and consequently the growers sustain economic loss. Though mite pests were not of much importance earlier but recently those are attaining increasing importance due to various factors mostly because of injudicious pest management practices. The important mite pests of rice are discussed below :

1. RICE (*Oryza sativa*)

Family : TETRANYCHIDAE

Oligonychus oryzae (Hirst)

Diagnosis : These are greenish mites, live on the undersurface of leaves in colonies covered with thin webs. (Nayak *et al.*, 2007: *J. Acarol.*, **16** : 57–59; *J. Acarol.*, **16** : 60–61; Srinivasa & Prabhakar (2007: *J. Acarol.*, **16** : 62–64).

Nature of damage : The feeding of this mite and sucking of sap produces yellowish specks initially and at later stage when the infestation becomes very acute, yellowing and drying of leaves occur. This symptom gives burning appearance to the infested leaves. The growth becomes stunted. The rice grown in low rainfall area and under canal irrigation system suffers greater loss. The infestation may cause loss to the extent of 25% (Nagarajan, 1957, Banerjee, 1989). The infestation starts from June and the peak population attains in south India during last week of September upto second week of October when the population may be 12.9–21.28 mites/sq. cm leaf area. This mite causes more problem in Karnataka, Andhra Pradesh, Tamil Nadu, West Bengal (Rao & Prakash, 1995). In other places, it is rather sporadic (*Oryzae J. Assoc. Rice Res. Workers*, **5** : 32–37.) Thereafter, natural declines take place. Mukherjee *et al.* (1989) recorded minimum mite population when mean temperature and RH were 27.2°C and 87.5%, respectively.

Life history : Its life cycle is completed in 10.58 days in male and 12.64 days in female. The fecundity was reported to be 30–70 ± 9.26 eggs, the male and female sex ratio was 1 : 2.7. (Misra & Israil, 1968).

Varietal preference and control : Mukherjee, Sarkar, Somchoudhury & Roy, 1989 (*Progress in Acarology*, **2** : 53–57) investigated the incidence of this mite on 9 varieties of rice in West Bengal (IR - 30, IR 32, IR 579, Dular, Jaya, Masuri, Jalkamini, CNM - 31, TN - 1) and found out the morphological basis of resistance. They also evaluated efficacies of 4 pesticides (sulphur, quinalphos, Bassa and Dicofol) at different concentrations. They reported maximum density of mite on IR - 30, followed by Jalkamini. No relation could be established between physical characters of leaves and mite population density except leaf width which had significant relation with density. Among the pesticides tried, Dicofol (0.05%, 0.01%) were found to be most effective followed by Quinalphos 0.04% .

Oligonychus manishi Gupta

This has been described from rice from Andaman Islands doing no economic damage (Gupta, 1979, *Rec. zool. Surv. India*, **77** : 115-116).

Oligonychus indicus (Hirst)

This is a greyish green mite with black blotches scattered all over dorsum and occasionally attacks rice causing appearance of whitish stipplings on under surface of leaves. It is a minor and sporadic pest of rice. The white spots produced by this mite later turn yellow and subsequently dry up.

Oligonychus ilicis McGregor

This mite has been reported from rice from Japan (Ehara, 1963). It is also known from USA, South America on other crops (Banerjee, 1989).

Schizotetranychus andropogoni (Hirst)

Diagnosis : This mite is pear shaped, pale with dusky spots on dorsal surface, short legs, the anterior two are directed forward and posterior two are directed backward. Its movement is rather sluggish.

Naure of damage : This mite builds colonies covered with white round webs arranged in longitudinal rows on undersurface of both sides of mid rib. Its feeding produces round/oval white patches at the points of feeding. Its attack on rice is seen more in eastern India than in other parts of the country.

Varietal preference : Its infestation was found to be maximum on NC 918 variety of paddy and minimum was in Sarika variety, while IR - 8 was completely free from mite (Gupta, 1985).

Control : Dicofol (0.05%) will be quite effective for control of this mite.

Family **TARSONEMIDAE**

Steneotarsonemus spinki Smiley

Leaf sheath mite or panicle rice mite

Diagnosis : This is a dull white mite, lives in colonies in all stages within intercellular air spaces of the upper part of the leaf sheath and occasionally on basal part of midrib of leaf blades. It is sometimes found in kennel and hull of the grain in Taiwan.

Distribution : India (in all major rice growing areas like W. Bengal, Orissa, Andhra Pradesh, Tamil Nadu, Karnataka), Madagaskar, Taiwan, Cuba, Brazil and Philippines.

Nature of damage : It feeds inside the tissues of midrib on the leaf blade causing brownish necrotic lesions. It also feeds between stem and inner surface of flag leaf sheath causing discontinuous brownish streaks. Later, those cause continuous poor excertion. Feeding inside the developing grains damages the ovary which causes ill - filled or chaffy grains. Due to the feeding, the brownish to balck discolouration of glumes are also seen. The yield loss extends from 30–90% (Xu *et al.*, 2001; Ramos & Rodriguez, 2000; Navia *et al.*, 2005; Karmakar, 2008). It is reported to cause panicle sterility and impart ill effect on rice grain quality in Madagascar, Taiwan, Philippines and Cuba. (Sadhukhan *et al.*, 2010: *Abst. Nat. Symp.* - Workshop, Kalyani : 63–64). This mite damages the parenchymatous tissues of rice plant, reducing the amount of nutrients to the developing grains resulting in reduction in grain weight and size. The mid-late to late maturing crops had higher incidence of damage as compared to early maturing crops. The rice sheath rot fungus *Sarocladium oryzae* also produces similar symptoms and mites help in disseminating the disease by providing entry points to the fungal conidia while injuring the leaf tissues during feeding (Panja *et al.*, 2010).

Varietal preference : The mite population was recorded in medium duration varieties like Ratna, Jaya, IR-36 and Kareen than in shorter duration varieties like Heera and Annada. (Rao, 1997: *Appl. zool. Res. CRRI, Cuttack*, p. 98).The rice varieties like Kaurav, Pankaj, Jaya, CRM-25, Gaurar were highly infested in coastal Orissa. Mites were found in colonies of 10-450 in between leaf sheath and stem, feeding on tissues. During wet season, the varieties affected were MTU 1001, MTU 2067, MTU 2077, MTU 70293, BPT5204, PLA-1000 in East & West Godavari districts of Andhra Pradesh (Rao & Das 1977: *Int. Rice Res. Newsl.*, **2** : *8)*. Patel *et al.* (2010 p. 59) reported that incidence of *S. spinki* as well as length of discoloured area was higher on the varieties of mid-late to late-maturing crop as compared to early maturing crop. The genotypes of *Masuri, Ranjit, Gobindobhoj, Kapurgandha* were found resistant and *Banskathi, Harurjhinga, Kumracot, Langalmuthi, Mala and Raghusal* were highly susceptible. Higher yield loss was from susceptible varieties (Sadhukhan *et al.*, 2010, p. 63-64). Rice variety IET 4786, IET 4094, *Nidhi*, IR-64., *Bikash* were highly susceptible. *Masuri*, MTU-7029 were resistant (Srivastava *et al.*, 2010: 65-66). Higher percentage of mite was recorded in closer spacing (15 cm ×15 cm) with significant higher % of grain infested in two wider spacings (15 cm × 20 cm and 20 cm × 20 cm) at 5% level of significance, though higher grain and straw yield were obtained from closer spacing, with 60 kg N and 90 kg N/ha. Application of nitrogen induced higher population than 30 kg N per ha.

Relation of mite incidence with nitrogenous fertilizers : Patel *et al.*, 2010 (*Abst. Int. Symp. workshop, Kalyani*, p. 57) studied effect of nitrogenous fertilizers to rice crop on incidence of rice sheath mite *S. spinki*. This mite causes considerable quantitative and qualitative losses in rice production. Application of nitrogenous fertilizer accelerates mite multiplication (Balasubramanian *et al.*, 1983, *IARI Newsl.*, **8** : 13–14 : Doval & Sharma , 1972 *Ann.Arid Zone*, **13** : 47–50). This experiment indicated significant difference among different doses of nitrogenous fertilizers, 140 kg/ha recorded highest mean length of discoloured area of leaf sheath (11.74 cm), 120kg/ha (10.16 cm) and 100 kg/ha (8.24 cm) while application of 0 kg/ha recorded lowest mean length of discoloured area and statistically at par with 40 kg N/ha.This effect was also seen in egg laying as highest egg laying was with application of 140 kg N/ha .The highest egg production was 16.16/leaf sheath and the lowest was 7.53 eggs/leaf sheath when 40 kg N/ha was applied. The untreated plot had 6.78 eggs/leaf sheath which was at par with 40 kg N/ha. Highest mean number of mites 37.19/leaf sheath with 140 kg N/ha and lowest was 17.58 mites/ leaf sheath with 40 kg N/ha. At 0 kg N/ha revealed 15 mites per leaf sheath. Differences were also recorded with regard to yield and application of nitrogenous fertilizers. The grain yield was highest of 5040.50 kg/ha with application of 120 kg N/ha, followed by 4480 kg/ha at 140 kg N/ha, 2995.63 kg/ha at 40 kg N/ha while untreated control gave 2910.13 kg/ha.

Association of fungus with mite damage : This mite carries conidia of fungus *Acrocylindrium oryzae* (=*Sarocladium oryzae*)on its body and that causes sheath rot disease. When the plants are infected by both fungus and mite, the damage is more acute than any of those singly. The fungus causes grain discolouration and browning of leaf sheath. Several species of fungi like *Alternaria, Aspergillus, Helminthosporium* sp. and *Penicillium* sp., *Curvularia* sp. could be isolated from chaffy grains and filled grains due to infestation of mites (Srinivasa *et al.*, 2004).

Dispersal and survival : The dispersal is effected by direct movement of adults from one plant to another and also by wind. Besides, the males often carry the pharate females from one place to another. During off season, this mite survives in rice stubbles and ratoon crops and then the surviving mites are carried over to the new rice crop. The grass *Cynodon dactylon* also acts as surviving host wherefrom this mite in all stages could be recovered on this host (Srinivasa *et al.*, 2004).

Seasonal occurrence : In Cuttack, this mite occurs throughout the year. Incidence is high during November and low during February. Population was highest in booting stage and declined with maturity (Ghosh *et al.*, 1997: *Entomon.*, **22** : 105-109). The population attained peak during milky stage which was the reason for disruption of the development of grains (Ghosh *et al.*, 1999; *Ann. pl. Prot. Sci.*, In Press). Chen *et al.*, (1997: *Recent Adv. Acarology*, **1** : 111–117) reported that this mite was observed from heading to milky grain stage and mite population was negatively correlated with rainfall and positively correlated with sunshine hours. Studies at Bangalore on varieties like HR-12, IR-36, IR-64. Morro and Mukthi, revealed that percentage of hills infested by mites during kharif period showed gradual increase from 80 days after planting reaching peak between 100–120 days after planting (42-52%). During summer, mite infestation appeared from 9 days after planting on leaf blade or sheath and maximum infestation of hills was observed to the extent of 42%. Mites could be abundantly seen on leaf sheath (22.1 mites) and panicles (1.0 mites/5 grains) at heading stage of crop between 100–120 days after planting. At the time of harvesting the kharif crop, the percentage of chaffy grains without discolouration, chaffy grains with discolouration and filled by discoloured, chaffy grains from mite infested plants ranged from 1.0– 3.1%, 11.5–24.7% and 2.1–13.7% respectively. The corresponding percentages during summer were 2.6–4%, 2.6–16.0% and 4.6–8.9%. Ghosh *et al.*, (1996: *J. Appl. Zool. Res.*, **7** : 160) reported *S.spinki* and *Tarsonemus cuttacki* Iswari, on almost all rice varieties grown under upland irrigated medium land and rainfed low land condition during Rabi & Kharif seasons. Jiang *et al.*, (1994: *Guangdong Agr. Sci.*, **5** : 37–50) dealt with this mite in China. Lo & Ho (1979 *Agr. Res. China*, **28** : 181–192) and Lo & Ho (1980: Pl. *Prot. Bull. Taichung*, **22** : 1–10) reported it from China and provided some ecological observations.

Life history : Its life cycle is completed in 17, 4 and 2.75 days from egg - adult stage at 25°C , 28 °C and 30°C, respectively. Longevity of female –15 ±1.0 days, Male – 7.6 ± 0.4 days at 25–28° C but both sexes lived for 5 days at 30° C. (Chen *et al.*, 1979). Females are parthenogenic. The virgin female produces only males while the fertilized ones produces individuals of both sexes.

Natural enemies : The important natural enemies are *Neoseiulus fallacis* (Garman), *N. taiwanicus* (Ehara), *Lasioseius parberlesei* Bhattacharya. Besides, spores of an unidentified microbe infected leaf lamina killing eggs, larvae and adults of *S. spinki* in Taiwan. (Srinivasa *et al.*, 2004).

Control : Prabhakar *et al.*, 2007 (*J. Acarol.*, **17** : 95–97) – suggested spraying of dicofol at late flowering and heading stage to minimize the sheath mite damage. Acaricidal treatment of paddy stubble will prevent mite outbreak in the following season. Ratoon crops should be destroyed. Foliar application of parathion, dicofol (0.05%), dimethoate (0.04%) can reduce 85% mite population. This may be done 75 and 90 days after planting. The treatment of infested plants with fungicides (hexaconazole and carbendazim) as 2-5 applications at 40, 50, 70, 80, 100 days also reduced the proportion of chaffy grains showing discolouration of glumes.

Steneotarsonemus furcatus (De Leon)

Along with *S. spinki*, sometimes another related mite, *Steneotarsonemus furcatus* also infests rice. Due to its feeding, characteristic brownish specks appear on the outersurface and brownish spots appear at the corresponding inner surface resulting in chaffy or partially filled grains and grain sterility. Infested rice plants had shown increased sterility rate and reduction in panicle neck length.

Tarsonemus cuttacki Iswari

It has been seen feeding on fungus, *Fusarium monilliforme* on rice. It completes life cycle in 5-7 days at 28–30°C. Longevity of male and female mite was 9.5 and 15.5 days, respectively and the male: female sex ratio was 1 : 4 (Ghosh *et al.*, 1993, *J. Appl. Zool. Res.*, **4** : 133–135; Srinivasa *et al.*, 2004). Life tables analysis on fungal diet under laboratory condition revealed intrinsic rate of increase was 13.05 times with mean generation time of 10.85 days. The finite rate of increase was 1.26 (Ghosh *et al.*, 1995, *Oryzae*, **32** : 98–100).

Family **ERIOPHYIDAE**

Cheiracus sulcatus Keifer

Mohanasundaram 1983 (Abstract 2nd *All India Acar.-Symp., Pune,* p. 30) reported this mite as vector of Rice Tungro virus disease in South India.

Abacarus oryzae Keifer

It is commonly called rice rust mite and is known to transmit Rice Tungro virus causing Tungro disease resulting in dwarfness of plants. It occurs mostly in Philippines.

Predatory Mites

The following predatory mites were reported on rice but their role in suppressing pest mite population is not known with certainty though some of these mites have been observed to feed under the field condition.

Family **PHYTOSEIIDAE**

Neoseiulus fallacis (Garman)	Assam	Feed on *O. oryzae*
Euseius alstoniae (Gupta)	Punjab, Delhi	,,
N. imbricatus (Corpuz & Rimando)	-	?
N. taiwanicus (Ehara)	outside India	Feed on *S. spinki*
N. longispinosus (Evans)	West Bengal	*S. spinki*
E. delhiensis (Narayanan & Kaur)	West Bengal	,,
E. ovalis (Evans)	-	
P. multidentatus Swirski & Shechter	West Bengal	Rice sheath mite

Famliy **ASCIDAE**

Lasioseius terrestris Menon & Ghai	Delhi	
Lasioseius parberlesi Bhattacharya	,,	

Family **TYDEIDAE**

Pronematus oryzae Baker	Delhi	leaf sheath

Family **CHEYLETIDAE**

Chelacaropsis moorei Baker	rice	W.B. Gupta, 1985

Fungal Associated

Tyrophagus palmarum Quel.

Rao & Prakash (1983: *Intl. Rice Res. News*, 1.10 : 13–14), reported *Tyrophagus palmarum* damaging rice seedlings.They studied their biology and extent of damage.

2. WHEAT : (*Triticum aestivum*)

Wheat (*Triticum aestivum* Linnaeus) is an important cereal crop and contributes over 20% of total food grain production of the country. The wheat is infested by a number of insect pests like *Macrosiphum miscanthi, Schizaphis graminum, Mythimna separate, Oxya nitidula* of which mites are increasingly becoming important pests and those are dealt with in detail in the following paragraph.

Family **TETRANYCHIDAE**

Petrobia latens (Muller) **(Brown Wheat mite)**

Diagnosis : This is a greenish brown mite with pale yellow legs. Males unknown. It is a non - webbing mite.

Host : It severely infests wheat in India and apart from that, it infests several other crops like barley, oats, sorghum, coriander, garlic, grasses, etc. Sometimes, it also infests cotton, sorghum, onion, gladiolus in other parts of the world like Europe, USA, Africa, China, Japan, Austrailia (Gupta , 1993). Its Indian reports are on wheat Bindra & Kittur 1961 from M.P, Menon & Ghai (1968) from Rajasthan, Delhi, Punjab, Haryana, on oats (Singh & Khan, 1979), on maize (Sandhu *et al.*, 1976), on coriander (Jain & Yadav, 1986), on cumin, (Gupta 1990), on onion (Menon & Ghai, 1968), on pear (Gupta, 1970), on rapeseed and mustard (Sharma & Pareek, 2000), on citrus and weeds, *Convolvulus arvensis* (Khan *et al.*, 1969), on weeds, *Heliotropium ellipticum., Melilotus indica, Panicum antidotale, Wedelia calandulacea, Artiemisia seuparis, Phalaris minor, Corchorus sativus* (Anon., 1997; Sharma & Srinivasa, 2004).

Nature of damage : All stages of this mite feed on the plant by desapping from both surfaces of leaves, leaf sheath and spikes. Infested leaves start drying from tip downwards even when there is sufficient moisture in the soil. The infested plants become chlorotic due to loss of cell sap hampering normal grain formation. Heavily infested plants show sickly, yellowing or bronzing appearance. (Bindra & Kittur 1961: *Indian J. Ent.*, **23** : 71), Gupta (1985), Sharma & Bhatnagar 1992: *Sci. & Cult.* Gupta, 1993). The attack is more in unirrigated crop though both types of crops are attacked. This mite is not a problem in irrigated wheat crop. The damaged crop shows symptoms like those seen under drought condition.

Seasonal occurrence and life cycle : Thousands of mites are seen on the leaves and a little jarking of clumps will dislodge the mites. The period of activity is during December to April, attaining peak during February–March. Low temperature and drought condition favour its multiplication (Gupta *et al.*, : 1973). The incidence was high on east–west side than north–south side. Maximum mite activity was observed during mid–day period (Sharma & Srinivasa, 2004). A significant positive correlation was noticed between population of *P. latens* and minimum temperature and RH.

Biology : A single female lays 6-10 summer eggs and 1-3 winter eggs per day and during life time as many as 23-90, summer eggs and 18-27, winter eggs are laid. The egg -adult stage is completed in 7-8 days with duration of different stages varying between 2-3 days each. The winter eggs are deposited on dry leaves of wheat and barley. It lays two types of eggs–non–diapausing winter eggs and diapausing summer eggs. The brick red winter eggs are laid singly or in batches and white diapausing summer eggs are laid in cluster on soil clumps. A single female lays 8-13 winter eggs or 2-5 summer eggs/day with 29-110 winter eggs and 11-43 summer eggs are laid during entire life time (Sharma & Srinivasa, 2004). Larval period 1-2 days, green to brown protonymph lasts for 0-3 days, followed by deutonymph which lasts for 1-4 days. In between each stage there is a quiescent stage. Adult starts feeding after emergence. Diapausing eggs remain dormant throughout the summer and are coated with white substance. Those hatch with suitable soil temperature. Longevity of adult female is 20 days.

Control : Sulphur dusting @ 30-40 kg/ha or monocrotophos @ 0.1- 0.15 kg ai/ ha will effectively control this pest. Soil application of micronutrients like boron and zinc are good as minimum mite population was reported in Zn. treated plots of wheat. (Sharma & Sharma, 1998, In : Halliday *et al.*, : 349–351). Alteration of sowing date is also suggested. Application of dimethoate, monocrotophos, oxydemeton methyl @0.10, 0.15 and 0.10 kg ai/ha, respectively control this mite.

Varietal preferences : This mite shows varietal preference as reported by Khan *et al.*, 1969; Sharma & Bhatnagar, 1992; Anon., 1997). Maximum mite incidence was reported on C-306 variety of wheat while the variety Sonalika was found resistant.

Natural enemies : *Lasioseius terrestris*, (reported by Menon & Ghai, 1968), *Euseius alstoniae* (reported by Sharma, 2001) are effective predators of *P. latens*. *Neoseiulus indicus* also feeds on wheat mite (Gupta, 1985).

3. BARLEY : *Hordeum vulgare* Linnaeus

It is an important serial crop in the world and its production in India is 432 million tonnes ranking next to maize and rice.

Petrobia latens Muller

Diagnosis : Same as given for wheat.

Host & distribution : Same as given for wheat. It is a serious pest of barley in arid and semiarid regions of Rajasthan.

Nature of Damage : Same as in wheat. Its population on barley was relatively low as compared to that on wheat. It attacks both irrigated and unirrigated crop fields.

Varietal preference : The maximum mite population was seen in Azad variety of barley and RD 227 was the most tolerant (Ann., 1997: *Final Rept. ICAR Project, RAU, Bikaner;* Sharma & Srinivasa, 2004).

Biology : as in wheat.

Seasonal occurrence : As mentioned in wheat. Its infestation remains upto 2nd week of April. Mite population increased and decreased yield with alteration in sowing dates.

Control : As mentioned in wheat. Ethion (0.05%) was most effective in suppressing mite population upto 2 weeks whereas wettable sulphur (0.025%) was least effective.

Bryobia praetiosa Koch

This mite is also known to occur on barley (Gupta, 1985) but nothing is known if it causes any noticeable damage.

4. SORGHUM (*Sorghum vulgare* Pers.)

It is important food and fodder crop.Its kharif yield is 1,100-1,200 kg/ha and that of Rabi crop is 60-700 kg/ha.

Family **TETRANYCHIDAE**

Oligonychus indicus (Hirst)

Diagnosis : As mentioned in rice. It occurs on undersurface of leaves in colonies densely covered with webs.

Nature of damage : This mite infests sorghum regularly in South Gujarat in second fortnight of August. Due to feeding, initially reddish spots appear which coalesce to form reddish patch on under surface of leaves giving those burnt appearance. Such leaves become necrotic.

Biology : A female lays about 60 eggs during oviposition period of 2 weeks. Incubation period is 3-4 days, larval period is 2-3 days, protonymphal and deutonymphal periods are for 3-4 days each and after that the adult emerges. There is a resting period between every moulting which lasts for a very brief period (Banerjee, 1989).

Seasonal occurrence : This mite attacks during second fortnight of August and attains peak in second fortnight of October, when crop is in milky stage (Patel *et al.*, 1999. *J. Acarol.*, **14** : 96–99). Rainfall and RH did not show any significant influences on population .This mite harbours in *Dicanthium annulatum* prior to end of Southeast monsoon and then attacks sorghum. The population during postmonsoon period attains very high and causes damage. (Banerjee, 1989).

Varietal Preference : Maximum leaf infestation was seen on variety GJ–36 which was comparable with SR-389, GJ-37 (Patel *et al.*, 1999). Sreedhar and Reddy, 1995 (Abst. Bangalore Sym, p. 91) reported high degree of antixenosis for colonization and that was variable at different growth stages such as RS–29, IS–2146, Sel-3 and Swathi at 25 days old, CSV–8R, CSV-14R and M 35-1 at flag leaf stage; and IS 2146, CSV 8R and CSV 14R at half bloom stages for adults and RS-29 and M 35-1 for larval, protonymphal and deutonymphal stages. Similarly, high level of antixenosis for oviposition was also noticed on RS-29, SPV-913 and Swathi. Kulkarni *et al.* (1978: *Acar. Newsl.*, **6** : 7) studied relative susceptibility of 19 varieties of sorghum against this mite (Gupta, 1985).

Control : Maximum control with higher cost benefit ratio was seen with Methyl-o-demeton (0.025%) giving 1 : 19.14, followed by wettable sulphur giving 1 : 17.45 and dicofol (0.04%) giving 1 : 16.63 q/ha(Patel *et al.*, 1989). Manjunatha *et al.*, (1995) evaluated 10% water extracts of different plants against *O.indicus* infesting Sorghum and reported that majority of those gave good mortality (70% above) of eggs and active stages. The promising ones were seed extracts of *Gossypium herbaceum, Piper nigrum, Rauvolfia serpentina* and *Thuja orientalis.* Tetradifon 0.03% and dicofol 0.03% were also quite effective. (Patel *et al.*, 1989: *Progress in Acrology*, **2** : 423-427).

Oligonychus tylus Baker & Pritchard

Sirsikar & Nagabhasanam (1983: *Indian J. Acar.*, **11** : 95-99) reported this mite attacking sorghum. Its life cycle was completed in 9.90±0.45 days, incubation – 4.55 ± 0.49 days. Adult longevity was 15.55 ± 1.23 days (female)and 10.60 ± 1.40 days (male).

Natural enemies : Manjunatha & Puttaswami 1989 (*Curr. Sci.*, **58** : 272) reported the spider species on sorghum as predators of *O. indicus* : *Uloborus* sp., *Argyrodes* sp., *Theridula* sp., *Theridion* sp., *Cheiracantheum* sp.

Oligonychus simus Baker & Pritchard

Banerjee (1989) listed this species occurring on sorghum in Malawi.

Schizotetranychus andropogini (Hirst)

This is a serious pest of sorghum in south India. During monsoon it inhabits *Dicanthium annulatum.*

Biology : Life cycle takes 9-12 days for completion. Oviposition period is 16 days.

Control : Removal of infested plants at the very early stage, followed by application of sulphur will be good for its control (Banerjee, 1989).

Family **ERIOPHYIDAE**

Aceria sorghi ChannaBasavanna

This mite has been reported from sorghum (Gupta, 1985) but no economic importance of this mite is known.

Family **PHYTOSEIIDAE**

Neoseiulus fallacis (Garman)

This has been reported on sorghum (Gupta, 1985) but no economic importance is known.

5. JOWAR *(Sorghum halepense)*

Oligonychus indicus (Hirst)

This is a light greyish green mite and has been recorded on jowar but nothing about its importance is known on jowar (Gupta, 1985).

Tetranychus neocaledonicus Andre

This has also been reported on jowar (Gupta, 1985) but nothing is known about its economic importance on jowar.

6. MAIZE *(Zea mays* Linn.)

It ranks 5th in total area and 3rd in total production.The Indian states growing maize are Punjab, UP, Bihar, Rajasthan, MP, AP, HP, WB and J. & K. contributing 95% of India's production.

Family **TETRANYCHIDAE**

Petrobia latens (Muller)

Sandhu *et al.*, 1973 (*Sci. & Cult.*, **39** : 226–227) reported it as a dominant species on maize.

Diagnosis : As given in case of wheat.

Nature of damage : As given in wheat.

Oligonychus indicus (Hirst)

This is a most prevalent species on maize.

Nature of damage : The infestation of this mite on maize produces reddish patches on undersurface of leaves. Its infestation is high 12 mites/6.25 sq cm area. Infested leaves gradually wither (Roy *et al.*, 2006: *Sci. & Cult.*, **72** : 213–215).

Varietal preference : Maize was found to be the most preferred host and 30°C the most preferred temperature for development of this mite Gupta *et al.*, (1974) as reported in Gupta (1985). At this combination of temperature and food, the life cycle was completed in shortest time with high fecundity of both fertilized and unfertilized females. Sorghum was the second best host.

Oligonychus pratensis (Banks)

Banerjee (1989) listed this species attacking maize.

Oligonychus plegas Baker & Pritchard

Banerjee (1989) listed this species occurring on maize in Mauritius.

Tetranychus neocaledonicus Andre

Roy *et al.*, (2006) recorded it on maize leaves without causing any noticeable damage. Its occurrence on maize is accidental.

Tetranychus urticae Koch

This mite probably came to maize plant through drifting. Colonies developed on undersurface of leaves but had shown no damage symptoms.

Eutetranychus orientalis (Klein)

Gupta (1985) reported this species on maize without causing any damage symptom.

Tetranychus ludeni Zacher

Roy *et al.*, (2006) reported it infesting maize during April – May producing no noticeable damage symptoms. Its occurrence on maize is unusual, may be through drifting from the neighbouring vegetable field.

Family **TENUIPALPIDAE**

Brevipalpus californicus (Banks)

Its occurrence is in record on maize (Gupta, 1985).

Family **TARSONEMIDAE**

Tarsonemus sp.

Sandhu *et al.* (1976) recorded it on maize in Punjab.

Family **PHYTOSEIIDAE**

Scapulaseius sorghumae Gupta

This predatory mite has been recorded on maize but its economic importance is unknown (Gupta, 1985).

Euseius delhiensis (Narayanan & Kaur)

Its report has been made on maize but its economic importance is unknown (Gupta, 1985).

Euseius finlandicus (Oud.)

This phytoseiid mite has been recorded on maize but its importance is not known (Gupta, 1985). Roy *et al.*, (2006) recorded it in the colonies of *T. ludeni*. Its population was low during entire period of observation.

Neoseiulus indicus (Narayanan & Kaur)

The record of this mite is known from maize, (Sandhu *et al.*, 1973; Gupta, 1985).

Euseius alstoniae (Gupta)

Roy *et al.*, (2006) recorded it on maize during August feeding upon eggs of *O.indicus*. This was a most commonly occurring species on maize, Gupta, 1977 (*Indian J. Acar.*, **1** : 28–37) stressed its predatory importance against phytophagous mites.

Euseius ovalis (Evans)

Roy *et al.* (2006) recorded it from undersurface of maize leaf during May but disappeared with onset of rain. Predatory nature was not very evident though otherwise it is a very good predator.

Euseius prasadi Chant & McMurtry

Roy *et al.*, (2006) recorded it on undersurface of maize leaf but its population was very poor.

Neoseiulus longispinosus (Evans)

It was collected from the colonies of *O. indicus* on maize leaves feeding voraciously on all its life stages including adults. The well- fed predator looked reddish (Roy *et al.*, 2006). This was one of the most commonly occurring species on maize.

7. RAGI (*Eleusine coracana)*

Oligonychus indicus (Hirst)

This mite occasionally infests Ragi doing very little damage.

3.2 PULSES

Pulses are important source of dietary protein and have unique property of maintaining and restoring soil fertility through biological nitrogen fixation as well as conserving and improving physical properties of soil by virtue of their deep root system and leaf fall.India grows pulse crops in 23 million ha producing 14.4 milllion tonnes of pulse grains (Anon., 2009). Common pulse grains of India are Bengal gram, pigeonpea, Green gram, Black gram, Lentil, Field pea, etc. The mite species which infest, various pulse crops in India are as bellow :

1. PIGEONPEA (*Cajanas cajan*)

Aceria cajani ChannaBasavanna

This is popularly called Pigeonpea sterility mosaic (PPSM) mite. This mite acts as a vector of PPSM disease which occurs more to the young plants. The damage is so serious that the pods are not produced, though the vegetative growth of the plant is normal and looks greenish and healthy. The infestation of the mite and transmitting the virus make the flowers sterile, shed off and no pod formation takes place. If the plants are infected with virus at the later stage, the least damage is caused and can give yield 50–75%.

Pigeonpea Sterility Mosaic Disease

The information given under the following paragraphs was based mostly on Srinivasa *et al.* (2004).

Pigeonpea is cultivated in tropics/subtropics and semi arid regions of the world. This crop is severely attacked by a sterility mosaic disease in India like Uttar Pradesh, Bihar, Punjab, Gujarat, Maharashtra, Tamil Nadu, Andhra Pradesh, Karnataka and Chattrishgarh (Srinivasa *et al.*, 2004) and besides India, it also occurs in Bangladesh, Nepal, Sri Lanka, Myanmar (Srinivasa *et al.*, 2004). This disease is incriminated to a mite, *Aceria cajani.*

Economic loss : Infection at early stages within 45 DAS causes complete sterility causing total yield loss. The yield reduction is related to percentage of infection of plants whereas when it affects some of the branches, it causes partial sterility and that is not correlated with percentage of infection. Drastic reduction in pod length, pod width, number of grains per pod and 1000 grain weight, shoot and root, nodule weight, nodule number, etc are caused due to this disease. The ratoon crops and perennial crops are more seriously attacked and losses in those cases are huge. The estimated yield loss may be more than two lakh tonnes in India (Kannaiyen *et al.*, 1984; Srinivasa *et al.*, 2004).

Symptoms : The sterility mosaic virus which is transmitted by *Aceria cajani* causes the sterility mosaic disease. Infected plants show sterility (the flowers drop off, no pod formation while mosaic symptoms appear on leaves). Such infected plants are bushy, pale green with leaf size reduced showing mottling. The secondary and tertiary branches from the leaf axils appear and no pod formation takes place. The reproductive structures show complete cessation. Severe reduction in internodal length, shortening of branches and filliformed leaves are the other symptoms (Srinivasa *et al.*, 2004). The symptoms can be categorized under three types :

Complete sterility : Leaflets show severe mosaic, no flower and pod formation take place and this is caused when infection takes place within 45 days after sowing.

Partial sterility : The leaflets show mild mosaic symptoms. The infected branches produce no flowers and pods. This occurs when infestation takes place beyond 45 days after sowing.

Ring spot : In this case the infected leaflets show green islands surrounded by chlorotic halo. However, with the maturity, those symptoms may disappear. This type of symptoms are common in some of the sterility tolerant cultivars e.g. ICP - 2376 (Reddy *et al.*, 1998). However, due to this, the flowering may not be affected.

Causal organisms : According to Capoor (1950, 1952), a virus is involved for causing this disease. The viral nature of pathogen is hypothised because of transmissibility through grafting, associated eriophyid mites and mechanical means (Rathi, 1983). Several authors (Reddy *et al.*, 1989, 1994, Nene 1995. Singh *et al.*, 1999) ruled out the theory that the sterility mosaic disease has no relation with mite toxaemia/fungi/bacteria/mycoplasma/nematode, etc.

Flexuous rod shaped virus particles (VLP) (size 200–700 nμ) was isolated from infected sterility mosaic disease leaves and from its vector mite *A.cajani*.Electron microscope examination of ultra thin sections from the infected leaves as well as quick dip method also did not reveal any virus–like particles or mycoplasma-like bodies (Reddy *et al.*, 1990). The failures of tetracyclines and Penccillium to suppress symptoms ruled out possibilities of MLOs/RLOs (Rathi, 1983; Ghanekar *et al.*, 1992). Ultrathin sections from the infected leaves revealed neither VLPs nor inclusion bodies MLOs.

With the new purification method during 1999–2000, the causal agent has been indentified as a new virus (Pigeonpea Sterility Mosaic Virus or PPSM) (Kumar *et al.*, 1999 a,b,c, Kumar *et al.*, 2001a,b, 2002). By DAS - ELISA and RT - PCR technique, the PPSM was detected in infected pigeonpea leaves.From *A. cajani*, the virus was detected by DAS - ELISA with a minimum of 50 mites and by Dot - ImmunoBinding Assay (DIBA) with a minimum of 5 mites but not by RT - PCR (Kulkarni, 2003; Srinivasa *et al.*, 2004).

The nucleotide sequence of some cDNA clones made to PPSMV RNA and the analysis of virus specific 32kDa protein by matrix - assisted laser desorption ionizination - time of flight (MALDI - ToF) found no significant sequence matches to any known viral sequences in data based searches. Kumar *et al.* (2001) derived a Oligonucleotide primers and a reverse transcription RT-PCR based method for sensitive detection of PPSM in plants. The purified PPSMV preparations were not infective to plants but it was transmitted experimentally to *Nicotiana benthamiana* and *N.clevelandii* by mechanical inclusion of fresh leaf sap extracts of SMD. Symptoms in leaves of (ICP 8863, ICP 2376) and *Nicotiana benthamiana* infected with PPSMV, detected quasi-spherical membrane bound bodies (MBBs) of c.100–150 nμ and amorphous electron dense material (EDM). The structures were distributed singly or may be distributed in groups in the cytoplasms of cells except those in conductive tissues.Fibrous inclusions composed of randomly fibrils with electron lucent areas were present in the cytoplasm of infected palisade cells (Kumar *et al.*, 2002, Srinivasa *et al.*, 2004).

Distribution pattern : This mite preferred basal part of leaflet at both top and middle canopies. Thus basal ¼ portion of leaflet recorded significantly more number of mites followed by other successive portions of leaflet in the same order. The basal half of leaflet which harboured nearly 60–65% of mite population, was suggested for sampling as it gave more reliable estimate of mite vector population (Srinivasa *et al.*, 2007: *J. Acarol.*, **16** : 135–138). Dhar & Rathore (1994: *Indian J. Pulses Res.*, **7** : 137-143) also noticed that vector mite populations were more concentrated towards the petiole and younger leaves in sterility mosaic infected pigeonpea plant.

Transmission : The transmission of the disease is most probably by graft transmission method and it is neither seed borne as reported by Nene & Rathi (1972) and Ghanekar *et al.* (1992) nor by sap transmission using leaf juices from the infected plants (Singh *et al.* 1999). Some suspected the role of nematodes (*Rotylenchulus reniformis* and *Tylenchorhynchus* spp.) in transmitting this disease (Narayanaswamy & Ramakrishna, 1965a) and others suspected it soil borne or pollen borne. Top crop with 0.1 M phosphate buffer (pH 9.0) and with petiolar grafting, 87% infection was observed. Mites from infested plants successfully transmitted PPSMV to pigeonpea (Kulkarni, 2003). Stapling of mosaic infected leaflets carrying *Aceria cajani* on to 2-weeks old healthy pigeonpea seedlings resulted in successful transmission of sterility mosaic and mosaic symptoms were noticed from 1–2 weeks after stapling. The extent of disease transmission with a single stapling on susceptible varieties like Maruti and TTB7 ranged from 18–46% and 32–66%, respectively (Narayanaswamy, 2004; Srinivasa *et al.*, 2004); Reddy *et al.*, (1989) studied transmission and spread of sterility mosaic disease in pigeonpea.

Vector : The transmission of PPSM by *Aceria cajani* from diseased to healthy plants was reported by Seth (1962) and later was confirmed by Nene (1972), Nene & Reddy (1976) and it was also reported that a single mite is capable of transmitting this disease.

The life cycle of this mite is as below :

Eggs : 30-40 μm, parallel sided, milky white, rounded at the ends, loosely attached to filamentous trichomes, hatch within 4–5 days.

Nymphs : I stage nymph - duration unknown, II stage nymph - 48 hrs to less than 5 days.

Adult : II stage nymph moults to adult. Adult is 200–250 µm long.

Total life cycle - About 2 weeks.

Adult male : smaller than female, deposits stalked spermatophores which remain firmly attached to leaf with an expanded base.

Adult female : Have parallel ribbed flap covering the genitalia.

Preoviposition Period : 24 hours.

Oviposition : Eggs are laid 1–3 per day.

Chaurasia (1993) observed variations in the symptoms of sterility Mosaic in Nepal and India which indicated the presence of biotypes of *A.cajani.*

Dispersal of vector : According to Nene *et al.* (1983) and Mehan & Reddy (1990) the dispersal of vector is mostly by air current. The disease spreads in the downwind direction upto 2 km from the source of inoculum while the spread in the upwind direction is very limited. However, the incidence and spread of disease depend upon vector population in the field (Reddy *et al.,* 1989a).

Pathogen–vector relationship : The pathogens transmitted by eriophyid mites are not known to be transmitted by any other organisms. Both nymphs and adults are capable of transmitting the pathogen. The efficacy of a single mite to transmit the PPSMV was 20–60% (Reddy *et al.,* 1989a), Kulkarni (2003). The pathogen once acquired by mite will be retained for the entire life period provided the mite continues to feed upon the susceptible host like pigeonpea cultivar BDN - 1. The minimum acquisition access period was 15 minutes and inoculation access period was 25 minutes having no latent period (Kulkarni, 2003). The starvation of mite was positively correlated with PPSM virus concentration on leaves. The minimum number of vector mites required for successful transmission of disease would be 1–5 and vector mite did not prefer to survive on infected plant beyond 4–6 weeks after expression of disease symptoms (Narayanaswamy, 2004; Srinivasa *et al.,* 2004).

Some of the pigeonpea cultivars found resistant to PPSMV at one place became susceptible at another place and that indicated the possibility of existence of different biotypes of both vector and pathogen (Nene *et al.,* 1990, Srinivasa *et al.,* 2004). A large variation in disease incidence and symptom expression was observed by genotypes between locations and between seasons.

A large season - to - season variation in the incidence of disease or vector in farmer's field is a common feature for which no proper explanation is available.

Reddy *et al.,* 1989. (*Progress in Acarology,* **2** : 121–127) studied role of eriophyids in transmission and spread of sterility mosaic of pigeonpea.

Population dynamics : The vector mite remains in field throughout the cropping period and population gradually increases from 45-60 days after sowing and the peak is attaimed during 120-150 days old crop. (i.e. between October-November). The increase in vector population was associated with simultaneous increase in the extent of disease. They reported population increase from 45-60 days reaching a peak in mid October to mid November (Prabhuswamy *et al.*, 1995).

Role of sowing dates in relation to incidence of disease : Incidence of disease was higher during March-October planting and low in December-February planting of a susceptible cultivar BDN - 1. Staggered sowing of pigeonpea cultivars TTB - 7, Coorg 11 and ICP 8863 from March-September at Bangalore, during 1990-93 had shown higher incidence of disease and vector on early shown crops during May-June as compared to crops sown in July (Srinivasa *et al.*, 1995). Under Navsari, Gujarat condition, crops sown during July harboured more vectors compared to sown in August. According to Narayanaswamy (2004), early sowing of most of the varieties had shown higher disease incidence compared to late showing.

Role of weather factors with SM disease/vector : The summer rainfall, lower temperature, relative humidity helped the survival and multiplication of mite vector in the off-season leading to SMD and outbreak in the following crop season. A significant positive correlation was reported with ambient temperature and sunshine hour (Anonymous, 1992-94). A positive correlation of mite vector with summer rainfall and RH was observed but with temperature, the relationship was negative (Reddy & Raju, 1993). According to Ghanekar *et al.*, (1992), the areas with good vegetation and higher humidity throughout the year, caused higher incidence of disease than other places. Prabhuswamy *et al.*, (1995) studied seasonal incidence of *A. cajani* on pigeonpea. They reported that the population gradually increased from 45-60 days after sowing, reaching a peak in mid - October and mid November in 120-150 days old crop. Increase of mite population coincided with increase in incidence of disease. Population of vector mite decreased in later stages of crop.

Role of pigeonpea varieties/lines with SMD pathogen/mite vector : Among Leaf Stapling Technique (Nene & Reddy, 1976b) and Twig Tying Technique (Nene, 1972), the former is superior as the symptoms were expressed rapidly. Spreader Row Inoculation Technique is another one where several rows of susceptible cultivars are sown throughout the field about 4 months in advance of the test crop at a frequency of 1 : 10 i.e 1 row of spreader to 10 rows of test material. In this method more uniform disease spread was achieved more quickly. Lakshmi Kantha & Prabhuswamy (1995) reported that among the varieties of pigeonpea screened, it was found that the varieties of pigeonpea which were resistant to mite were grouped into 5 categories. ICP 7234 and ICP 8862 had least mite and least disease incidence whereas ICP 8863 and ICP 7893 had high incidence and high mite population.

Infestation of *Aceria cajani* on pigeonpea produced sterility Mosaic symptoms and on the basis of degree of infestation the 400 varieties which were screened were categorized into severe mosaic (SM), mild mosaic (MM), ring spot (RS) and resistant (R). With all these categories of damage, the eriophyids were found associated.The predatory mite, *T. tetranychivorus* could keep the eriophyids population at low level. Incidence of *A. cajani* was positively correlated (0.612) to temperature and RH and no correlation was seen with density of mite and severity of disease. Eriophyids were high on middle and top trifoliates rather than on bottom leaves (Nangia & ChannaBasavanna, 1995: *J. Acarol.*, **13** : 75-79).

According to Ghanekar *et al.*, (1992), majority of the resistant sources of SMD were medium or mid-late maturity groups IEP - 8136 was resistant to pathogen but not to mite vector. ICP 7035, ICP 80025, ICPL 92220, ICP 87101, ICPL 88023, ICPL 86005 were found tolerant to disease/vector mite in Coimbatore (Srinivasa *et al.*, 2004). Screening of wild relatives of pigeonpea viz. .*Cajanus scarabaeoides, C. platycarpus, C. cajanifolia* and *C. albicans* is needed to be investigated for useful resistant gene against disease/pest. Patel *et al.*, (1995) reported that incidence of PPSM disease and vector mite population were higher than that in Surat and Bharuch districts. 80 % diseased plants were recorded in Khothamadi followed by 70% in Valsad. Mites occurred on plants throughout the crop period (kharif), maximum was in February. July sown crop was highly infested and its incidence was higher in December-February, irrespective of date of sowing. Mite was seen throughout the year in perennial and ratoon crops. Mites were most active in summer months (April - May). Population increase was directly related to temperature and sunshine hours.The dispersal was through wind. Cultivars ICP 7035, ICPL 87108, 88025, 90028 were completely free from disease.

Survival of *Aceria cajani* on Rotoon Crops : Narayanaswamy & Srinivasa (2007: *J. Acarol.*, **16** : 82-85) studied survival of this mite on Ratoon Crop and *Atylosia scarabaeoides* and reported that the survival on the latter crop was from January-October in various proportion ranging from 10-53.6 mite/trifoliate leaf and lowest was in February, though it survived on *Atylosia scarabaeoides* throughout the year and that may act as potential source for spread of vector in absence of other possible sources like stubbles, ratoons, etc.

Relationship of sterility Mosaic disease with other pests/diseases : The leafhopper *Empoasca kerri* Pruthi preferred leaves with SMV symptoms as those leaves showed lower C : N ratio compared to healthy leaves (Jayaraj & Seshadri, 1967: *Curr. Sci.*, **36** : 353-355). Likewise, *Schizotetranychus cajani* and *Eutetranychus broodryki* preferred leaves having SMV disease (Sitanantham *et al.*, 1986, Anon, 1994-96) Reddy *et al.*,(1990b) reported at ICRISAT that SMD infected plants were less susceptible to *Fusarium* Wilt and dry root rot. Sterility mosaic plants were more predisposed to the attack by powdery mildew fungus *Oidiopsis* sp. (Reddy *et al.*, 1984: *Jour. Trop.Pl. Disease*, **2** : 35-40).

Spatial distribution : Srinivasa *et al.*, (2007: *J. Acarol.*, **16** : 135-138) studied distribution pattern of *Aceria cajani* on pigeonpea and reported that this mite preferred basal portion of leaflet both at top and middle canopies which recorded significantly more number of mites followed by other successive portions of leaflets in the same order. The basal half of leaflet harboured nearly 60-65% of mite population on a leaflet and for that it is suggested that the area for sampling as it gives more reliable estimate.

Relationship of plant metabolism with SMD : The diseased leaves of pigeonpea had lower level of chlorophyll, xanthophyll, carotene and total carbohydrate contents due to derangement of photosynthesis activities and reduction in translocation of sugars (Narayanaswamy & Ramakrishna, 1965a). A general reduction of organic acid content in leaf, petiole, stem and buds and ascorbic acid content in tissues was observed. Melic acid and citric acid were absent in diseased leaves and petiole, respectively. Infected plants had shown increased rate of respiration throughout the day. Total carbohydrate content was significantly low in diseased plants. Infected leaves had higher amount of reducing sugars, with low starch and resin contents. Infected leaves had lower concentration of Ca, K, Na, Mn but had higher concentration of aminoacids. Apart from physiological and biochemical changes other morphological changes like reduction in thickness of leaves, epidermis, palisade cell, etc. were also noticed (Prameela *et al.*, 1990: *Biochem. Physiol. Pf. Lanzen,* 1086 : 55-61).

Effect of staggered sowing : Srinivasa *et al.* (1995) studied the effect of staggered sowing of pigeonpea var TTB – 7, Corg – 11, ICP – 8863 during March-September/ October-1990/1991/1992 at UAS, Bangalore. It was found that higher incidence of disease and vector were seen in early sown crops (May-June) compared to crops sown in July. Incidence was nil or low in crops sown in August.

Control of Sterility Mosaic Disease/mite vector :

1. Arjunan *et al.* (1989) – application of phorate 10g @ 1kg/ai/ha at sowing + foliar spray with monocrotophos on 30th day from sowing.
2. Rathi (1983) – Seed treatment with aldicarb 10G protected crop from sterility Mosaic.
3. Anon. (1994-96), Patel *et al.* (1990) – dicofol (0.05%) between 30 and 45 days after sowing.
4. Natarajan & Beevi (1992), Singh (1992) – Wettable sulphur @ 2.5g/L. of water, 60 and 90 days after sowing.
5. De *et al.* (1996) – seed dressing with carbosulfan @ 15g/ha or soil application of phorate @ 1.5 kg ai/ha, followed by folair spray with dicofol at 30 and 45 days after sowing.
6. Reddy *et al.* (1993) suggested following measures for control of vectors
   I. Growing resistant varieties (Bahar/ICPL – 151, Hyd – 3C).
   II. Breaking pigeonpea cycle by crop rotation, changing sowing date.

III. Destroying infected plants during crop season and voluntary diseased plants during off season.

IV. Spraying acaricide once during first two months of age.

7. Chinniah & Mohanasundaram (1995) reported mortality of *A. cajani* with different chemicals giving mortality as dicofol (91.62%), NSKE (90.95%) ethion (88.65%), monocrotophos (88.31%), wettable sulphur (87.77%), neem oil emulsion (87.73%), neem cake extract (86.41%), phosalone (86.41%), dithane M (64.19%). All the neem based formulations were very effective.

Predators : *Transeius teranychivorous* can keep the population of eriophyid mite at low level (Nagia & Muniappa, (1995: *J. Acarol.*, **13** : 75-79).

Eotetranychus broodryki Meyer

This mite is popularly called Pigeonpea green mite. The adults are greenish white, colonise on lowersurface of leaves near midrib. The infestation is more acute on the young leaves at the tips where due to feeding brownish discolouration appears. This attack is more during December - January and affects the pod yield. According to Desai *et al.*, (1999: *J Acarol.*, **14** : 109–111) population of *Eotetranychus broodryki* Meyer - started building from September and attained peak in January I fortnight in kharif shown pigeonpea. Population was higher on lower leaves. Sunshine had significant positive correlation with mite population. Dicofol 0.04% was significantly superior to monocrotophos (0.05%), methyl - o- demeton (0.025%), ethion (0.1%), dimethoate (0.03%) and deltamethrin (0.05%), which were at par with each other. Neemark (0.5%) was superior to NSKE (5%).

Schizotetranychus cajani Gupta

This mite also infests pigeonpea in different parts of India (Satpathi *et al.* 1992 *Ann.Ent.*, **10** : 51–58). Dhooria and Cheema 1995 (Bangalore symposium, p. 42) studied biology of *S. cajani* on red gram. Life cycle was completed in 7.87 days in August and 43.18 days in February. Incubation, larval, nymphal periods varied from 2–22, 1–9 and 1–13 days, respectively. Population was maximum in December-February, heavy rainfall in July–August drastically reduced population. *Agistemus* sp and *Amblyseius* sp. were predators. Karuppuchamy *et al.*, (1990: *Legume Res.*, **13** : 183–187) studied biology, varietal screening and control of *S .cajani* on red gram. The varieties T-21, 4758, Khargaon - 2, 148 were equally susceptible. P-1141 was least susceptible (Gupta *et al.* 1971), in west Bengal.

Satpathi *et al.*, (1992 *Annals of Ento.*, **10** : 51–53)listed insects and mites infesting pigeonpea and reported *Schizotetranychus cajani* from West Bengal.

Tetranchus urticae Koch

According to Kalisekar & Thakur (2007: *J. acarol.*, **17** : 7–8), this mite assumes as major pest of pigeonpea in Meghalaya. The pest appears in August and remains in field upto September. The affected leaves progressively loose turgidity at points of feeding. Finally such leaves dry up. As many as 12 mites per leaf may cause the onset of hypersensitivity symptoms after 3 days of feeding. The studies of Iatrou *et al.*, (1995: *Exp. Appl. Acarology*, **19** : 518–591) showed that mite density of 1–32 per 1.5 cm sq of leaf area on bean plant for a feeding period of 1–5 days produce the symptoms. The activity of oxidative enzymes, peroxidase and polyphenol oxidase increased in leaves of injured plants as a result of mite feeding which led to drying of leaves and leaf dropping.

Tetranychus ludeni Zacher

Karuppuchamy & Mohamasundaram (1987, *Entomon.*, **12** : 89–94) reported *T. ludeni* – on *Cajanus cajan* producing characteristic damage sympyoms.

2. GREEN GRAM (*Vigna radiata*)

Tetranychus urticae Koch

Srinivasa Rao *et al.* (1990: *Ind. J. Ent.*, **52**(1) : 158–159) reported *Tetranychus urticae* attacking green gram, *Vigna radiata.*

Tetranychus sp.

Katagihallimath (1995) reported infestation of *Tetranychus* sp. in Gulbarga area of Karnataka causing leaf drop which was earlier thought to be due to pod borer for which chlorinated hydrocarbon was used.

Tenuipalpus mustus Chaudhri

Gupta and Gupta (1982: *J. Ins. Sci.*, **1** : 65-68) recorded this mite on this host.

3. BLACK GRAM (*Vigna mungo*)

Tetranychus urticae Koch

Gupta & Dhooria (1973: *Sci. & Cult.*, **39** : 401–402) reported this mite on this host damaging the crop substantially.

Tetranychus macfarlanei Baker & Pritchard

Gupta & Dhooria (1973: *Sci. & Cult.*, **39** : 401–402) reported this on this host damaging the crop substantially.

Tenuipalpus punjabensis Maninder and Ghai

This mite has also been reported on this host.

Polyphagotarsonemus latus (Banks)

All the affected leaves became crinkled, curled and flowers were malformed with reduced flowering. Population was less on fresh leaf than on crinkled leaf. Galecron registered 90.8% mortality (Gupta & Dhooria 1973: *Sci. & Cult.*, **39** : 401–402).

4. MUSURI (*Les culinaris*)

Excepting *Polyphagotarsonemus latus(* Banks) infesting apical young leaves and *Euseius ovalis*(Evans),a predatory mite,no other mite could be recorded on this host.

5. BENGAL GRAM (*Cicer arietinum*)

The young apical leaves often are attacked by *Polyphagotarsonemus latus(* Banks) causing curling of leaves. A predatory mite, *Euseius alstoniae* (Gupta) was recorded on the colony of this mite.

6. RAJMAH/FRENCH BEAN & KHESARI (*Lathyras sativum*)

Tetranychus urticae and *P. latus* often infest these two plants.

3.3 FIBRE CROPS

The fibre crops which have been considered in this chapter are cotton, jute, sunhemp.

1. COTTON (*Gossypium herbaceum/G. hirsutum /G. barbadense /G. arboreum*)

India has 8.97 million ha under cotton crop,ranks first in the world in area and third in total production which is 272 lakh bales during 2004-2005. India cultivates all the four varites of cotton mentioned above. The mites infesting cotton are mentioned below :

Acalitus gossypii (Banks)

Nature of damage : This eriophyid mite is an important pest of cotton (Katagihallimath, 1995). The attack of this mite produces galls which increase with increase of attack and later the leaves become curled. Besides, it also causes changes in the level of chlorophyll a, b, carotene. The former decreased by 18.05% and 39.01%, respectively in galled tissues while carotene content increased by 59.8% in galled tissues. This mite also produces erinea on leaves and flowers. The densely infected squares do not open into the flowers or may cause additional shedding of squares. Since chlorophyll content is reduced due to infestation, the fixation of carbon and consequently nutrient stress happened. The matured galls became yellow. The infested bolls shriveled and fell off.

Damage may be to the extent of 50% (Misra, 1920: *Proc. 3rd Ent. Meeting, Pusa* : 547-561). Since the cotton leaves turn ashy, the disease has been called "Chhasia" (Jhaveri, 1921: *Proc. 4th Ent. Meet. Pusa* : 96-97). Jhaker & Desai (1929) reported wide spread infestation of this disease in Western India. This mite is available in the field throughout the year.

Control : Jhaveri (1921) got excellent control by steeping the seeds in mercuric perchloride solution before sowing. Applying sulphur may cause shedding of leaves (Thaker & Desai, 1929). Carbaryl or endrin when used showed non-effectiveness against this mite. However, with the addition of sulphur, the mite population reduced and that, in turn, induced three times higher yield than that obtained in control plots (Katagihallimath, 1995). Cleaning of cotton fields and maintaining sanitation are most essential.

Tetranychus macfarlanei Baker & Pritchard

Jose & Shafi (1985) (*Gujarat Agr. Univ. Res. J.*, **13** : 12–18) from south Gujarat reported this mite as a pest of cotton in Gujarat during October to February.

Nature of damage : Due to feeding of this mite, yellowish patches appear on leaves, which later turn greyish brown. In case of acute injury, the plants may die. The peak population is attained during December.

Bioecology : During off-season (July–September) mites harboured weeds like *Operculina turpethum* and *Clerodendrun inerme*. During March–July this mite harboured brinjal and okra. This mite survived on one or the other host throughout the year.

Control : Monocrotophos (0.04%), amitraj (0.06%), phenthoate (0.05%), dicofol (0.03%) were good for its control. Monocrotophos, quinalphos, dicofol, amitraz, cypermethrin, fenvalerate had shown good ovicidal action (Jose & Shah 1989: *Progress in Acarology*, **2** : 417–421). Removal and destruction of weeds from the cotton fields is suggested to check carry over of population.

Tetranychus ludeni Zacher

The occurrence of this mite on cotton has also been reported doing characteristic damage symptoms of tetranychid mite (Banerjee, 1989).

Oligonychus gossypii (Zacher)

This mite is also known to attack cotton (Banerjee, 1989).

Tetranychus urticae Koch

This is another important pest of cotton throughout the cotton growing areas of the world. It colonizes on undersurface of leaves and envelopes the plants heavily with dense web.

Nature of damage : This mite feeds on undersurface of leaves causing appearance of yellow spots on leaves near the basal part. Gradually, with increasing of feeding, the spots increase, which coalesce to form reddish brown patches. The infested leaves gradually dry up and defoliate.

Seasonal occurrence : The high temperature is more preferred by this mite during which the mite problem is more acute.

Biology : The incubation period is 3-4 days. The larvae are sluggish, period lasts for 3-5 days. The protonymphal and deutonymphal periods are of 2-3 days and 2-

3 days, respectively. The life cycle is completed in 10-15 days, depending upon the season. The number of generations may be as high as 30 per year.

Control : Dicofol (0.05%) will provide effective control. Fluvanilate 25 EC at 75 g.ai/ha gave temporary reduction of mite population but afterwards it increased. Hostathion (triazophos) 40 EC (at 0.1%), dicofol were also found to be very effective. A combination of monocrotophos (40 EC) and dicofol (20 EC) at 0.05% was found to be best for reducing mite population on cotton.

Tetranychus lombardinii Baker & Pritchard

This mite occasionally attacks cotton in India but never attains a serious pest status.

Nature of damage : The feeding produces yellow spots on leaves.

Biology : The life cycle takes about 10-12 days on cotton

Control : Dicofol (0.05%) will provide good control.

Brevipalpus karachiensis Chaudhri *et al.*

Sadana *et al.* (1983: *Sci. Cult.*, **49** : 184–186) recorded it on *Gossypium* sp.

Polyphagotarsonemus latus (Banks)

Occasionally this mite attacks cotton on undersurface of leaves. The young apical leaves are damaged causing curling, rolling and defoliation of leaves.

Abacarus gossypii Mohanasundaram

This mite attacks cotton leaves in Tamil Nadu producing white erineum on undersurface of leaves. This is of not much economic importance.

Aceria puttarudriahi ChannaBasavanna

This mite has been reported from Karnataka and Tamil Nadu.

Nature of Damage : This mite produces felt-like outgrowths of white hairs on tender shoots including squares, leaves, etc. The affected plants become stunted and boll formation is affected (ChannaBasavanna, 1966).

Predatory mites on cotton : Apart from the phytophagous mites, some predatory mites have also been reported on cotton some of those are of stray occurrence, while some are of importance in biological control. The reported species are :

Euseius alstoniae (Gupta)

Gupta (1977: *Indian J. Acar.*, **1** : 28–37) recorded this predatory phytoseiid mite on cotton from Gujarat and Punjab.

Amblyseius sp.

Venugopal Rao and Reddy (1989: *J. Biol. Control*, **3** : 11-12), recorded this predatory mite on Cotton white fly, *Bemisia tabaci.*

Typhlodromus fleschneri Chant

Gupta (1977: *Indian J. Acar.*, **2** : 1-11) reported this mite on cotton from West Bengal.

Euseius finlandicus, Neoseilus longispinosus, Amblyseius largoensis, A. channabasvannai, Paraphytoseius multidentatus, Amblyseiulella nucifera, Lasioseius sp. are the other predatory mites recorded on cotton but none are of much importance for biocontrol of mite pests on cotton.

2. JUTE (*Corchorus capsularis/C. olitorius*)

This is one of the most important fibre crops in India especially in West Bengal, Assam, Northern Bihar, Southern Orissa,Tripura, Meghalaya, Estern UP. It is grown in 0.80 million ha annually. About 95% 0f fibres are used in industries for manufacturing hessain, sacking, carpet making, etc. This crop is attacked by a number of mite pests as below:

Polyphagotarsonemus latus (Banks)

This is a serious pest of jute in all jute growing areas. All life stages will be found on undersurface of young apical leaves and tender shoots.

Nature of damage : The attack of this mite on young apical leaves, causes retarding of apical growth of developing plants (Roy *et al.*, 2010). The affected leaves become silvery white and ultimately dry up and drop down prematurely. Consequent upon it, the growth is retarted resulting in reduced fibres. The infested apical leaves curve downwards, become boat-shaped. In some cases, the infested leaves become darker than normal leaves. The internodes become shortened and fibre quality is affected. The infestation drastically affects plant height. The extent of loss may be as much as 36-42% in a variety (20 KR variety). The mites suck sap from the ventral surface of leaves as a result, the leaves do not become of normal size, turn copperish brown and drop down prematurely.

The vertical vegetative growth is arrested. Das & Mallick (1988: *Env. Ecol.*, **6** : 515–516) studied effect of time of sowing in incidence of yellow mite on jute. Das *et al.*, (1957: *Env. Ecol.*, **5** : 37–40) studied histomorphological changes in jute leaves due to attack of mite.They reported that upper and lower epidermis became compressed and galls were formed just below the lower epidermis. Palisade and mesophyll cells became compact causing reduction of intercellular spaces. That led to significant yield loss (42%) depending upon level of infestation which may vary from 20-90% (Chakraborti *et al.*, 2010, p 59-60). Das *et al.* (1987: *Sci. & Cult.*, **53** : 252–253) studied anatomical changes in jute leaves due to yellow mite feeding. Das & Singh (1974: *Jute Bull.*, **36** : 1-2) reported that mite free plants showed 60.5% gain over control whereas highly infested plants with control measures showed 38.3%

gain. This indicated relationship between population of yellow mite with growth and weight of fibre.

Biology : Das & Singh (1988: *Ann. Agric. Res.*, **9** : 20-25) studied life cycle of yellow mite on jute in West Bengal. The female lays eggs on lower surface of leaves and tender shoots. The males often carry the quiescent females in their chelicerae, so that as soon as the females become fully matured, the males mate with them. The life cycle is completed in 5 days, with several generations per year. The life stages are egg, followed by active nymphal stage - quiescent nymphal stage - adult. Incubation period is for 30 hours. Nymphal stage lasts for 24 hrs (in females), 18 hrs (in males), quiescent nymphal period is of 24 hrs. The Male : female sex ratio is 1 : 3.6.

Varietal preference : Significantly higher mite population was observed on variety 20 KR. Chakraborty *et al.*, (2010) screened some varieties against this mite. The cultivars JRC-321 was found to be less susceptible among capsularis cultivars. The variety JRO-632 was reported to be a susceptible variety with 10.90% leaf infestation with 18.99 mites/leaf. This mite incidence had positive correlation with plant height, number of leaves per plant, leaf area and moisture content of leaves but fibre thickness, chlorophyll content of leaves had no effect on incidence of yellow mite (Rahmana & Khanb, 2010). Among olitorius cultivars, the maximum yield loss was recorded in JRO-8432 (Shakti) followed by S-12 and minimum was on JRO 524 (Nabin).

Seasonal occurrence : Roy *et al.*, (2010) performed step wise regression technique to find out the effect of different weakly ecological parameters on mean abundance of mite population at varying stages. The infestation started developing from April and attained peak during later part of May or early June. The mite population was influenced by abiotic factors like temperature, wind velocity, rainfall and RH. The mite population first started appearing 20 days after date of sowing and peak was attained 33 days after date of sowing.

Control : Dicofol 3 ml/1L and difenthiuron (0.5 g/L) were found to be most effective even 7 days after spraying and that registered mortality of 84.78% and 79.15%, respectively. Regarding effective period of spraying, it was found that the period between 20-35th day was the best period for getting effective result. 40 days after spraying gave highest yield. Anon. (2009) reported that extracts of Neem (*Azadirachta indica*) and Karanja (*Pongamia pinnata*) were very effective against immature stages of this mite till 7th day after spraying and recorded 72% and 70.75% mortality, respectively. The extract of *Pachyrhizus* was at par with Neem (69.71%) and lowest mortality was recorded in turmeric (57.1%) followed by garlic (56.43%). Among newer acaricides diafenthiuron, propergite, profenofos, fenazaquin, chlorpyriphos, all were very good but the conventional pesticide dicofol registered 94.32% mortality and was superior to others.

Das and Raychoudhuri (1986, *Env. Ecol.*, **4** : 228-230) and Das & Singh (1985, *Jute Dev. J.* Oct.-Dec., p. 7) reported best control of yellow mite with endosulfan

(0.04%), followed by dicofol (0.04%). The comparison of ultra low volume, low volume, and high volume sprays was done against this mite and no difference was found among these three modes of spraying. No. residue was left on soil, run off water and jute fibres by endosulfan (Das, *et al.*, 1988: *Env. Ecol.*, **6** : 615–619).

Tetranychus urticae Koch

The record of this 2-spotted spider mite on jute was made by Gupta (1985).

Nature of damage : It mainly attacks the olitorius variety. Due to sucking from undersurface of leaves by both nymphs and adults, the dull white patches appear along the midrib of the leaf. These patches later coalesce to from yellow patch. The infested leaves wither and drop down. This consequently affects the growth (Das, 1980, *Sci. & Cult.*, **46** : 232).

Varietal screening : The most susceptible varieties were crumpling leaf, soft stem, soft stem-N, Br-4, Cap Main land China, JRC 6340, JRC 321 and Lanka Assam with 25.33, 23.50, 21.38, 20.86, 20.53, 20.40, 20.33 and 20.21%, incidence, respectively (Das, *et al.*, 1987, *Env. Ecol.*, **5** : 123–125).

3. SUNNHEMP (*Crotalaria juncea*)

Aceria crotalariae ChannaBasavanna

This mite seriously infests sunnhemp crop in West Bengal during May–July. Infestation causes twisting of apical leaves which become shortened, discoloured and ultimately turn yellowish. Infested portion of stem becomes brownish. Infested leaves and stems also produce erinea. Ultimately, the attacked portion of stem becomes deep brown due to thick growth of brown erinea. The internodes of infested stems become shortened and plants become stunted (Pradhan & Pandit, 1982: *Sci. & Cult.*, **48** : 391-392). ChannaBasavanna (1966) while describing this species also reported production of erinea on tender shoots.

PREDATORY MITES

Paraphytoseius multidentatus Swirski & Shechter

Pradhan & Pandit (1982) reported this mite associated with *Aceria crotalariae* on sunnhemp in West Bengal.

Amblyseiulella nucifera (Gupta)

This was reported on sunnhemp in West Bengal in association with *Aceria crotalariae* (Pradhan & Pandit, 1982)

4. MESTA (*Hibiscus sabdariffa/H. cannabis*)

Polyphagotarsonemus latus (Banks)

Like jute, this mite also attacks young apical leaves of mesta producing similar damage symptoms (Das *et al.*, 1987: *Env. & Ecol.*, **5** : 37–40).

5. SHIMUL (*Bombax malabaricum/B. ceilea)*

Eotetrancychus hirsti infests this crop but the damage is almost of no economic importance.

3.4 OILSEEDS

India is one of the largest vegetable oil economics in the world next only to USA and China. Oilseeds like groundnut, rapeseed, mustard, soybean, safflower, sesame, sunflower and two non-edible oils like castor and linseed are grown in India. Oilseeds occupy13% of total cropping area and account for nearly 10% value of all agricultal commodities. Mustard occupies 25-30% of total oilseed production.

1. GROUNDNUT (*Arachis hypogaea* L.)

Tetranychus urticae Koch

This mite attacks groundnut in many groundnut growing areas of India. This mite heavily envelopes the plants by web where dust particles adhere affecting normal physiological activities of plants. The heavily attacked plants look seriously unhealthy and may die.

Ravi & Puttaswamy (1995) conducted histological and histochemical studies on three varieties of groundnut genotypes Robut 33-1, TMV-2, ICGV-87160. Direct damage can be caused to hypodermis and spongy chlorenchyma and even in the palisade parenchyma. Robut 33-1, is a tolerant genotype having more leaflet thickness followed by moderately tolerant genotype TMV-2 and susceptible genotype ICGV 87160. Thickness in leaflet in tolerant genotype did not alter much after mite feeding. Reduction of thickness of leaflets was much in susceptible genotypes. Histochemical observations showed change in number and size in starch grains and protein and RNA contents in the mesophyll tissues of three genotypes due to feeding of *T. urticae.* Susceptible genotypes had higher reduction in starch grains than moderately tolerant and tolerant genotypes indicating that size and number of starch grains impart resistance against *T. urticae* not much difference in protein and RNA contents was seen among the three genotypes.

Varietal preference : Kateshia *et al.* (1999: *J. Acarol.*, **14** : 47–48) performed varietal screening of 10 varieties of groundnut.The variety. TG-26 had least number of mites (9-12 mites/15 leaves), followed by GGT-4, ICGS-37, GG-3, TG-26 and ICGS-37 which were at par. The varieties J-11, Kaderi-3, JL-24, ICGS-44 and GG-20 were moderately susceptible, var GG-2 was most susceptible.

Tetranychus macfarlanei Baker & Pritchard

This mite has also been reported on groundnut and its feeding makes the leaves yellowish and then brownish. Subsequently, such leaves dry up and pod formation is affected.

Tetranychus hypogeae Gupta

This mite was described from specimens collected on groundnut from West Bengal. All the infested leaves become heavely covered with webs and all those leaves turn yellow. The infested plants look sickly and growth is adversely affected (Gupta, 1976, 1985).

Neoseiulus longispinosus (Evans)

This was reported from Tamil Nadu Anon. (2003).

2. CASTOR (*Ricinus communis*)

Tetranychus urticae Koch

This mite commonly occurs on castor. It colonizes on undersurface of leaves, cover their colonies with dense webbing and feeding causes yellowing and browning of leaves followed by drying and defoliation. The population of this mite starts developing from October-December with onset of winter and reaches peak during January-March. Population declines and becomes negligible in May-September. Population is minimum during August due to heavy rainfall. Population was negatively correlated with temperature, positively correlated with RH while, rainfall affected mite population adversely (Gupta *et al.*, 1976: *Oilseed J.*, **6** : 16-18).

Tetranychus ludeni Zacher

It was reported from West Bengal (Anon., 2003)

Tetranychus macfarlanei Baker & Pritchard

Gupta & Gupta (1978: *Indian. J. Acar.*, **3** : 87-91) also reported this species on castor. It produces the characteristics damage symptoms known for the species.

Eutetranychus orientalis (Klein)

Gupta & Gupta (1978: *Indian J. Acar.*, **3** : 88) and Sadana & Gupta (1983: *Entomon.*, **8** : 1-6) recorded it on castor in M.P. It colonizes on upper surface of leaves which remain covered with webs where dust particles adhere and affect normal physiological activities. Ahuja (1994: *Ind. J. Ent.*, **56** : 1-5), studied seasonal incidence and chemical control of this pest on castor.

Gynaeseius ricini (Ghai & Menon)

This has been recorded on castor in Gujarat and UP (Gupta, 1977: *Indian J. Acar.*, **1** : 11-18).

Euseius coccineae (Gupta)

Its record on castor was made from Gujarat (Gupta, 1977: *Indian J. Acar.*, **1** : 28-37).

***Euseius ovalis* (Evans)**

Anon. (2003) from West Bengal.

3. SAFFLOWER (*Carthamus tinctorius*)

Mahto (1988: *Bull. Ent.*, **29** : 230–232) reported *Tetranychus macfarlanei* on safflower.

4. SUNFLOWER (*Helianthus annuus*)

Brevipalpus phoenicis (Geij.)

This mite sporadically occurs on castor (Gupta & Gupta, 1978: *Indian J. Acar.*, **3** : 88). It causes no noticeable damage.

Tetranychus urticae Koch

Its record on sunflower was made from Kashmir valley (Rather, 1995 *Abst. V Nat. Symp. Acarology, Bangalore* p. 36) producing typical damage symptoms for this species as well as reported by Ayganna *et al.* (1978: Indian *J. Ent.*, **40** : 353–356) from Andhra Pradesh.

5. SESAMUM (*Sesamum indicum*)

Polyphagotarsonemus latus (Banks)

This causes similar damage symptoms as it does on other hosts. The damage often becomes serious causing substantial loss.

Brevipalpus phoenicis (Geij.)

All stages of this mite were seen on undersurface of the leaves and on the uppersurface as well in case of heavy infestation. Because of continuous sucking of plant sap, light brownish spots appeared at the points of feeding which later became deep brown. The attacked leaves became twisted and folded longitudinally. Raised gall- like swellings appeared in some of the leaves. Young twigs were also affected. One *Amblyseius* species fed on all stages of *B. phoenicis* (Gupta, 1974: *Sci. & Cult.*, **43** : 361)

6. JATROPHA (*Jatropha curcus*)

Polyphagotarsonemus latus (Banks)

This mite attacks jatropha severelly in hot and humid climate of Bengal basin. It retards the growth, development, flowering, fruiting of the plant so severely that the plants seldom bear fruits. The mites attack on ventral surface of young apical leaves. The infested plant parts curl, become twisted causing flower and flower buds to drop down prematurely. This mite ravages the plant throughout the entire warm part of the year from March-November with peak during September-October. It also harbours the perennial plant all round the year from where they disseminate to many other crops like chilli, jute, sesame, cowpea, etc. (Karmakar & Gupta, 2008: *Syump. In Sustainable uses of natural resources from Medicinal and aromatic plants*, 24-25 Dec. 2008, p. 72-73).

7. MUSTARD (*Brassica rapus* L.)

This plant is normally not seriously attacked by any mite species. Occasionally, stray occurrence of *Tetranychus ludeni* and *Brevipalpus californicus* were noticed in West Bengal doing no major damage.

3.5 PLANTATION CROPS

A large group of crops including Tea, coffee, arecanut, coconut, betelvine, rubber etc. are grown in India covering an area of 38.20 lakhs ha. (about 20% of total crop area), contributing Rs. 7500 crores of export value. These crops also contribute in employment generation (Chadha, 2010).

On coconut, which is an important crop, depends upon about one crore of people in cultivation and other coconut related business activities. The main coconut growing states in India are Kerala, Karnataka, Tamil Nadu, Andhra Pradesh, Orissa, Maharashtra, Goa, Assam, West Bengal, Pondicherry, Lakshadwip and Andaman-Nicobar Islands. It is grown in over 19.1 lakh ha. producing 149.50 crore nuts. India ranks first among 90 coconut producing countries of the world. The coir, shell and shell-based products have high demand having ornamental values in international market.

Aracanut is an important commercial crop cultivated as source of betel nut. India produces 3.30 lakh tonnes of betel nut and Karnataka is the major arecanut growing state in India.

Tea is the second largest area covered in India (4.36 lakhs ha.). The major tea growing areas are Assam, West Bengal, Tamil Nadu, Kerala and Himachal Pradesh. Indian tea accounts for 17% (2,309.43 crores) of the total world export. It produces 592.32 million kg of tea, of which 200 million kg is exported.

India is the largest rubber producing country covering 8.9% of world production. Kerala, Karnataka and Tamil Nadu are the traditional rubber producing states.

Betelvine, commonly called *pan,* is cultivated in tropical and subtropical regions in India, mainly in Assam, Goa, Karnataka, Kerala, MP, Maharashtra, Mizoram, Nagaland Orissa, West Bengal, Tripura, Delhi and Tamil Nadu. Annual turnover is Rs. 800 crores and provides employments throughout the year for cultivation, harvesting, grading, packaging and marketing.

1. COCONUT (*Cocos nucifera*)

Apart from being an important Medicinal plant and considered as one of the 20 most important crop plants in the world, coconut plant has high aesthetic and religious values and provides livelihood to a great section of people by way of coconut based industries such as coir/coconut oil/soft drinks/cattle food/furniture/ handicrafts/paints/fuel/varnishes/mattress/mosquito repellent/filler materials. Kernel is taken as food by many in coconut growing areas.

Aceria guerreronis Keifer (Coconut perianth mite)

This is a worm-like mite, creamish coloured and difficult to see in unaided eyes. It feeds only on the soft parts of meristematic region but not on hard tissues.

History : The malady which is wide spread now in India is caused by a tiny mite called eriophyid mite and not due to Mobile Tower or due to high tension electric wire, as is believed by common man. In 1964, this mite was discovered by Keifer who collected it from a place in Mexico, called "Guerrero". Later, it was collected from many other places of South America, Brazil (Rio de Janeiro), Caribbean islands in West Indies, USA (Florida), East Africa, West Africa, Sri Lanka. In India, it was not known before 1995 and entered through Kerala (Ernakulum) and thereafter spread to Tamil Nadu, Pondicherry, Karnataka, Andhra Pradesh, Orissa, Goa, West Bengal, Bihar, Lakshadweep, and Gujarat.

Biology : Adult lays in her life time of 15–25 days about 200 eggs which are white, oval and those hatch in 2 days to I - stage nymph, after 2–3 days that moults to II - stage nymph and after 2–3 days moult to adult. Egg – adult period takes 8–10 days.

Damage : Thousands of mites are found under perianth in the form of white dust. When nut is 1 month old, perianth is tightly pressed to nut. So mites can not enter underneath perianth. When nut develops after fertilization from 1 ½–2 months old, although the nut increases in size but not the perianth – so a gap is made, through which the mites crawl under perianth. As many as 500–2000 mites of all stages can be found in 1 sq cm area.By needle like chelicerae they pierce the cell and suck the cell sap which oozes out. While feeding, they inject toxin through saliva causing nut deformities. First damage symptom is the appearance of white triangular V – shaped mark on green coconut surface near perianth. That gradually turns brown. The fruit surface becomes necrotic with uneven growth resulting in causing deformation. Later, appearance of fissures, reduction in nut size, stunting of nut growth, extensive premature nut dropping, secretion of resinous material which oozes out from fissures, etc. may be seen. Such nuts become unsuitable for use. Copra yield is reduced by 30%. The dehusking becomes more labour intensive. Often the coconut seedlings are also killed. The damage causing to 8–10 months old nut is rare. Coir output from affected nuts becomes poor or coir is reduced or at the most such coir can be used as fuel. In some cases, the button dropping may also be seen. Due to all these, the yield loss is 30–60%. Karmakar (2003: *Ann. Entomol.*, **21**(1-2) : 29–31), reported severity of infestation of *A. guerreronis* on coconut in Southern Bengal.

Seasonal occurrence : According to Saradamma (1972: *Agric. Res. J. Kerala*, **10** : 61–62) it is a major pest of coconut in Kerala. Its relationship with weather factors (temperature/rainfall/RH/sunshine hrs) showed negative correlation with population of different stages of mite. The weather parameters showed highly significant correlation with total mite population (R= + 0.8301), adult (+0.8274) and egg (+ 0.8233) while nymphs did not show any significant relationship (+0.3756).

Weather factors influenced mite population to an extent of 68–69%. The population dynamics of coconut eriophyid mites in Tamil Nadu indicated that mites are capable of surviving extreme low and high temperature regimes. Severe infestation was recorded during 2nd quarter (April–June 2000) (65.50%), and during 4th quarter (Nov. - Dec., 2001) (69.80%). Increase of eriophyid mite population tends to cause higher percentage of damage, irrespective of symptoms. Bhaskaran and Ramaraju (2007: *J. Acrol.*, **16** : 72–75). Nandihalli (2007: *J. Acarol.* **16** : 76–77) while studying the perianth Eriophyid mite in Dharwad, reported its seasonal occurrence. It was reported that during March, the infestation was seen in 96% trees and 78% nuts were infested. Infestation level subsided during June–December, 2006. Similar observations were recorded by Zuluaga and Sanchez (1971: *Oleagineu*, **26** : 767–776) and Yaligar (2004: M.sc. Thesis UAS, Dharwad). Haq (1999: *J.Acarol.*, **14** : 56–66) reported that population of this mite was positively correlated with temperature and negatively correlated with rainfall. Population density slightly increased from July - August, declined upto October and steadily increased from November reaching peak during March–April.

Varietal preference and Alternate host : Jamaica Tall/Malayan Golden dwarf/ Malayan yellow dwarf/Malayan Green Dwarf are highly susceptible cultivars. Cambodian cultivar was reported to be tolerant

Borassus flabellifer (Palmyrah palm) has been reported as Alternate host.

Cultural Control : Field sanitation. nutritional management (FYM/Compost - 50 kg/palm/year, Neem cake 5 kg/palm/year, NPK (500 : 320 : 1200g/palm/year, (1 kg urea, 2 kg sup. Phosphate, 2 kg muriate of pottash/palm/year, are the suggested cultural control measures (Mallik *et al.*, 2004).

Chemical control (Spraying on bunches) : Neem oil (2%) + garlic extract (2%) + 0.5% soap solution. or Azadirachtin 1% @ 4 ml/l.or

Azadirachtin 5% @ 1 ml/l. or Triazophos 40 EC - on bunches. Methyl-o-demeton (4 ml/l). Flufenzin (2 ml/l)-All appear to be very good for control of this mite.

Root feeding : After selecting a spot 2–3 ft away from base of tree, soil is digged out 1½ - 2 ft to expose feeding roots (pinkish colour). The soil is removed around roots. An oblique slit by a sharp knife is made to the root. In a polythene pouch (8 x 12 cm) equal quantity of pesticide + water is taken and the cut end of root is immersed in pouch. The opening of the pouch is covered by a rubber band. After this, the root is to be covered with fallen leaves (not soil/stone). Following day, pouch is to be examined and if pesticide has not been taken in, the operation is to be repeated (Mallik *et al.*, 2004).

Control : Muthiah *et al.* (2007: *J. Acarol.*, **17** : 63–64) while studying nutrient management of coconut eriophyid mite, it was revealed that application of macro and micronutrients reduced the mite damage. Application of Borax (3.75), Calcium (3.82), MgSo4 (3.84) and $CuSO_4$ (3.85) alone and along with recommended dose of NPK and FYM registered low damage grade index than the nutrients applied in combinations due to mite in the harvested nuts. Assessment of annual nut yield after 2 yrs of treatment revealed that it was significantly more (154 nuts/palm/year) in NPK + FYM + MgSo4 0.5 kg/palm/year and NPK + FYM + Ca (151 nuts/palm/year) compared to control (96 nuts/palm/year).While studying the control of coconut mite with insecticides, it was reported that Flufenzin when applied (2.0 ml and 1.6 ml/lit), was superior in efficacy to standard check with dicofol, whereas Clofentezine was at par with dicofol. Ramaraju *et al.*, (1999 *J. Acarol* 14: 82 - 83) reported very effective control of this mite with monocrotophos, triazophos or methyl-o-demeton but mite population started increasing after 23 days of spraying. Chinnamade Gowda *et al.*, (2007: *J. Acarol.*, **17** : 65–67) reported good control with clofentezine 2.4 ml/lit or Flufenzin 1.6ml/lit. The application of *Hirsutella* with either meat or yeast extract in the first year of study and *Hirsutella* mycelium along with conidia and adjuvant in the second year of study were superior treatments in control of coconut perianth mite. (Mazumdar *et al.*, 2010 : 112–113).

Natural enemies : Though a number of predatory phytoseiid, bdellid, cunaxid and acarid mites as well as some thrips are often seen within perianth, feeding on those mites but to what extent these are effective biocontrol agents is not known with certainty. In addition, some entomopathogenic fungi are also present like *Hirsutella thompsonii, Paecilomyces fumosoroseus, Fusarium* sp. and their efficiency as biocontrolling agents are being examined. *Typhlodromus pyri, Cheyletus cocos, Agistemus industani, Amblyseius* sp., *Bdella* sp. which were the predators were found feeding on *Aceria guerreronis,* in Kerala. *Typhlodromus pyri* devoured all stages of prey and its feeding pattern on different stages of prey was in the order of adult female > deutonymph > protonymph = male > larva. Eggs were the most preferred and adults were the least preferred stages of the prey consumed. (Sobha and Haq, 2007: *J. Acarol.*, **17** : 45–47). Some insect predators feed on this mite which are Coccinellidae, Cecidomyidae, Chrysopidae and Thripidae. Clubionid spiders are also dominant predators (Sathiamma, 1995).

Oligonychus iseilemae (Hirst)

Sathiamma (1986: *J. Pl. Crop.*, **14** : 71–73) reported this mite infesting coconut foliage causing characteristic damage. Sathiamma (1995. *Entomon.*, **20**(3-4) : 237–243) recorded this mite on coconut and reported the suppression of this mite on coconut foliage by *Euseius eucalypticus* and *Cunaxa setirostris.*

Tetranychus fijiensis Hirst

This is a pest of coconut specially in South India and Andaman & Nicobar Islands (Cherian, 1931: *J. Asiat. Soc. Bengal,* **27** : 141–147, Gupta, 1985). Feeding causes the appearance of whitish spots on the leaves. Later, the spots turn brown and coalesce to give brownish patches on the leaves.Sarkar & Somchoudhury, 1989) also reported this mite from West Bengal and mentioned that the population reached peak in June (3.98 mites/leaflet) and October (2.29 mites/leaflet). Population declined with onset of rainy season. Temperature had significant positive correlation.

Brevipalpus phoenicis (Geij.)

Jagadesh *et al.* (1983: *Acar Newsl.*, **13** : 4) reported this mite as a pest of coconut in Karnataka.

Raoiella indica Hirst

This mite attacks coconut in many parts of the world including South Africa, Sudan, Mauritius, Egypt besides India. This reddish mite colonizes on undersurface of coconut leaves in Kerala and it is considered as a major pest there (Saradamma 1972: *Agric. Research J. Kerala,* **10** : 61–62). Its relationship with weather factors (Temperature, rainfall, RH, sunshine hours) showed negative correlation with different stages of mite. The weather parameters showed highly significant correlation with total mite population (R= + 0.8301), adult (+0.8274) and egg (+0.8233) while nymphs did not show any significant relationship (+0.3756). Weather factors influenced mite population to the extent of 68–69%. Sarkar & Somchoudhury (1989) reported that the population commenced from January and reached peak in June (5.31 mites/leaflet) and September (5.50 mites/leaflet). Population declined during rainy season. Temperature had significant correlation with mite density. Cumulative effect of abiotic factors was non significant.

Dolichotetranychus cocos Flechtmann & Fernando

This mite has been reported on coconut from Kerala (Santhosh & Haq, 2010 : 56). They studied developmental biology at 25 ± 1° C, 88% RH. Female started oviposition 4–5 days after emerging as adult. Fecundity was 6-12 eggs. Hatching took 20-30 minutes. Egg -larval period was 15.42 days (female), 13.93 days (male). Male exhibited multiple mating behaviour. Authors discussed morphological features of various stages.

Dolichotetranychus ramaniae Mallik & Paul

Mallik & Paul (1995: *J. Acarol.*, **13** : 9–14) described *Dolichotetranychus ramaniae* as new species collected on coconut under the persistent calyx of coconut in Kerala.

Dolichotetranychus vandergooti (Oudemans)

This mite was reported on coconut perianth in Kerala (Sathiamma, 1985: *J. Pl. Crops.*, **13** : 73-75).

Notogalumna nortoni Ramani & Haq

Ramani & Haq (1990: *Acarologia*, **31**(4) : 401–404). reported some oribatid mites from coconut which included *Notogalumna nortoni*, as new species.

Neoseiulus paspalivorus (DeLeon)

This predatory mite was also recorded on coconut in association with coconut perianth mite.

Bdella sp.

This predatory mite was also recorded on coconut in association with coconut perianth mite.

2. TEA (*Thea sinensis*)

Oligonychus coffeae (Nietner)

It is one of the most serious pests of tea throughout the tea growing areas in the world. Apart from tea, it attacks several other crops which include some ornamental plants, rubber and weeds (Banerjee, 1989). Females are bright crimson dorsally and purplish or bronzy ventrally. Males are light-coloured. It occurs on upper surface of leaves normally but in case of heavy infestation may migrate to lower surface of leaves as well.

Distribution : India, Bangladesh, Sri-Lanka, East and South Africa, Australia, Indonesia, Middle East, Japan, Formosa, USA, and South America.

Damage : Due to continuous sucking from leaves and petioles, yellow spots appear which subsequently turn bronzy discolouration on upper surface which later turn bronzy. Finally, the entire leaf turns copperish brown which ultimately dry up and fall off. Old leaves are most seriously attacked than the young ones. The attack starts form midrib and veins and gradually spread in leaf lamina and margin. Tea plants are often covered with thick webs.

Variation in morphological features : Somchoudhury *et al.*, (2007: *J. Acarol.*, **17** : 19) reported variation in 3 morphological characters in Assam and China types. Variations were reported in setal length in respect of Dorsal propodosomal (DP), Dorsal hysterosomal-2 (DH 2) and Leg IV. No significant variation was found with regard to DP setal length in specimens collected in Assam Type, from Terai region and Dooars region but it showed significant variation in China type collected from Dooars and Terai regions. Significant differences were reported in respect of duration in life-cycle on China and Assam types. The duration of protonymphal, deutonymphal, oviposition periods and fecundity per day and female longevity also showed significant variation. As regards rate of hatching, oviposition period, longevity, egg laying capacity per day, were significantly higher in China type as compared to Assam type. The shorter duration of life cycle and higher fecundity in Assam type indicated it to be better and more suitable host.

Seasonal occurrence : The population of this mite is abundant throughout the year in Subhimalayan North Bengal tea plantation excepting during rainy season (July). The attack on tea starts from March and population increases with increase in temperature and becomes heavy during April-June. As the monsoon starts, the population dwindles and reappears thereafter during September-October to reach the second peak during second week. Early pruned plants are more attacked and therefore pruning in December reduces possibility of attack during following summer. The leaves under study condition show more infestation. Dhanapati and Varatharajan (2007: *J. Acarol.*, 26 : 43–44) reported the occurrence of this species in Manipur though its fluctuation varied in different months. Population was negatively correlated with minimum temperature and positively correlated with maximum temperature. Panigrahi & Mukhopadhyay, (1993: *J. Pl. Crops.*, **21**(Suppl.) : 195-201) studied population dynamics of *O. coffeae* infesting 4 young cultivars from Darjeeling.

Biology : The life cycle is completed in different times on different varieties of tea and at different temperatures and humidities. Almost 5-6 eggs are laid by female/day. Those hatch after 4-11 days depending upon temperature. The larval, period and deutonymphal stages take 7-11 days. Time taken from egg - adult - 12-24 days. Preovposition period – 1-3 days, oviposition period - 13-24 days, incubation period – 5-13 days (Banerjee, 1989). Saha *et al.*, (1999, *J. Acarol.* 15: 84 – 88) studied effect of temperature and RH. on longevity and fecundity of this mite. Life cycle took shorter time (5.88 ± 0.60 days) with higher fecundity of both fertilized (75.50 ± 2.66 eggs) and unfertilized (69.11 ± 4.26 eggs) females, with longer longevity of female and males were seen at 33.2^{0}C and 79.85% RH as compared to 26.60^{0}C with 71.6% RH and 30.5^{0}C with 76.50% RH. According to Saikia *et al.*, (1999: *J. Acarol.*, **14** : 22-26), the sex ratio was 1 : 1.10 during May-June and 1 : 2.20 (February-March) and 1 : 1.46 during April. The males were short lived. Panigrahi & Mukhopadhyay (1993: *J. Pl. Crops*, **21** : 195-201) studied population dynamics in Darjeeling.

Control : According to Banerjee (1989) prophylactic treatment with tetradifon immediately with the appearance of pest will be very effective. Dicofol, ethion are also effective. Tetradifon can kill the eggs also. Dhanapati and Varatharajan (2007) got good result with Neemazal (5%) followed by sulphur and Neemazal (3%).

Relative toxicity of acaricides when evaluated against *O. coffeae*, the order of toxicity was found to be abamectin > fenzaquin> fenpyroximate> fenpropathrin> propergite> profenophos> dicofol> ethion. Resistance was high against ethion and moderate against dicofol and profenophos (Roy *et al.*, 2010, p. 76). CHA 2062 @ 14.40 – 16.00 g.a.i. /ha gave excellent check to this mite pest. It was compatible with abamectin (Ghosh *et al.*, 2010, p. 89-91). Guruswami *et al.* (2010, p. 109) evaluated aqueous extracts of seeds of *Azadirachta indica*, leaves of *Acorus calamus*, *Xanthium strumarium*, *Polygonum hydropiper* and *Clerodendron infortunatum* and hydrocarbon oil under laboratory condition. All those registered above 80% mortality at 10% concentration. Ovicidal action was also seen in *Azadirachta indica*, *A. calamus*, *X. strumarium*. Viability of eggs and adult emergence were also reduced with these treatments.

Tetranyctus urticae Koch

Banerjee (1989) recorded this mite on tea.

Tetranychus lombardinii Baker & Pritchard

Banerjee (1989) listed this mite occurring on tea.

Petrobia harti (Ewing)

Banerjee (1989) listed this mite occurring on tea.

Eotetranychus sp.

Banerjee (1989) listed this mite occurring on tea.

Brevipalpus californicus (Banks)

This mite also damages tea. It occurs on undersurface of leaves near the midrib and petioles. This mite prefers matured leaves. Heavily infested leaves become yellow to yellowish brown and then defoliate.

Damage : Dark orange red or yellow necrotic patches appear near midrib on lower surface and petiole. Necrotic patches also appear on margins.

Biology : The elliptical, bright red eggs are laid on undersurface of leaves and remain glued there. After 5-8 days, the eggs hatch to larva, the period of which varies from 7-8 days. The larva passes through two nymphal stages i.e. the protonymphal (7-8 days) and deutonymphal (6-7 days) and then reaches adulthood. The total life cycle takes about 5 weeks (Banerjee, 1989).

Control : Application of dicofol or ethion will control this mite.

Brevipalpus obovatus Donnadieu

This mite also occurs on tea in India (Gupta, 1989; Pande & Nandi, 1983: *Sci. & Cult.*, **49** : 141-142).

Brevipalpus phoenicis (Gcij.)

This mite congregates on petioles and under surface of leaves along mid-rib. Eggs are brick red or scarlet, laid in clusters on undersurface of leaves, sometimes on stems. Maximum eggs/female - 54, incubation - 7 days (January–March), 9-10 days (October–November). Life cycle takes 30-36 days. Several generations are available per year.

Gope & Das (1992: *Two Bud*, **39** : 23-28) studied biology and effect of pruning and skiffing on the distribution of scarlet mite on tea in northeast India.

Polyphagotarsonemus latus (Banks)

The female is yellowish in colour, males carry female nymph.

Damage : They attack the flush and young leaves. The attack is sporadic in isolated patches. This mite prefers cool humid sheltered condition. Infested flush becomes stunted, deformed, brittle and pale yellow. In severe cases, the undersurface of attacked leaves becomes corky brown, resulting in indirect loss of crop.

Pink mite, *Acaphylla theae* (Watt)

This mite has been reported from Northeast and South India (Gupta, 1985). Mohanasundaram (1999) recorded it on tea in Tamil Nadu.

Damage : It occurs on both surfaces of leaves but more on lower surface as well as petioles. The damaged leaves initially become yellowish, pale coloured and with leathery texture. In case of severe damage, the veins and midribs become pinkish and hence the name Pink mite. Severly affected plants suffer from retardation of growth.

Biology : Though it occurs all round the year the peak population is attained during March-May and declines during rainy season. The eggs laid on leaf surface hatch after 2-3 days to elliptical whitish nymph and then turns orange. Two nymphal stages are seen taking 5-7 days depending upon the season. Total life-cycle takes 8-10 days.

Control : Application of ethion on undersurfase of leaves will control this pest (Bennerjee, 1989)

Purple mite, *Calcarus carinatus* (Green)

It is a serious pest of tea in tea growing areas in Asia (India, Indonasia, Vietnam, Srilanka and Bangladesh).

Damage : The older leaves under droughty condition are more affected. Both surfaces of leaves are attacked but more prevalent on upper surface and sometimes on petioles. The infested leaves show brownish discolouration which later turn bronzy. The presence of white cast skins on leaves are clear symptoms of mite damage.

Biology : It occurs on leaves almost throughout the year but least during rainy season. Female deposits eggs on leaves which hatch to I nymph and that after 3 days moults to II nymph and that after another 2 days moults to adult. Total life-cycle takes longer time in winter months (12-15 days) and shorter time in summer months (6-9 days) (Banerjee, 1989). Muraleedharan (1994: *Entomon,* **19** : 53-56) studied its seasonal abundance and vertical distribution. Mohanasundaram (1995) – reported this species from Tamil Nadu. Radhakrishnan *et al.,* 1992 (*J. Pl. Crop.,* **20** : 97-102) studied bioecology and recorded predators.

Control : Selvasundaram *et al.,* (1999: *J. Acarol.,* **15** : 89-92) evaluated Azadirachtin formulation at higher dose (0.1000% conc.) induced maximum ovicidal action giving 51.25% and nymphal mortality of 74.0%. Azadirachtin (0.075%) and 0.1% also prolonged development period from egg to adult. Neem formulation @ 400 ml./ ha. significantly reduced mite population in the field.

Mohanasundaram (1995) recorded it in Tamil Nadu on Tea. Murthy and Rao (1980: *Curr. Sci.*, **49** : 639–640) reported this mite as a new pest of tea. Muraleedharan and Ambalatharasu (1983: *Pestology*, **7** : 21-22) recorded it in south India.

Acaphylla indiae K.

Mohanasundaram (1995) recorded it on tea in Tamil Nadu. It is also common in Assam. It attacks on under surface of leaves especially in lower part of bushes. The infested leaves become rusty with presence of cast off skins (Das, 1965).

Acaphylla steinwedeni K.

Gupta (1989) listed the occurrence of this species on tea.

NOTHOPODINAE

A new species under this family was recorded on Tea in Tamil Nadu (Mohanasundaran, 1995).

Natural enemies : Banerjee (1989) and Gupta (1989) reported several natural enemies on tea which may be of some help in suppressing tea pest mites, if judiciously conserved and profitably utilized. These are:

CECIDOMYIDAE

The larval stages of this dipterans, *Feltiella* feeds upon eggs and immature stages of spider mites. It takes about 18 days to complete the life cycle. The 2nd and 3rd instar larvae consume 9-12 eggs per day.

PHYTOSEIIDAE

Phytoseiid mites associated or feeding on tea mites are :

Amblyscius herbicolus, A. rhabdus, Euseius ovalis, Paraphytoseius multidentatus, Scapulaseius arecae, Typhlodromus darjeelingensis, Typhlodromus neotransvaalensis (Gupta, 1989)

Ascidae : *Lasioseius* sp.

Stigmaeidae : *Agistemus fleschneri, Agistemus* sp., *Ledermuelleria* sp.

Bdellidae : *Cyta* sp.

Anystidae : *Anystis* sp.

Cunaxidae : *Neocunaxoides* sp.

Tydeidae : *Pronematus* sp., *Parapronematus* sp., *Tydeus* sp.

Erythraeidae : *Erythraeus* sp.

Eupodidae : *Eupodes* sp.

Oppiidae : *Oppia* sp.

Acaridae : *Acarus* sp.

3. COFFEE (*Coffea arabica*)

Oligonychus coffeae

The damage done on coffee by this mite is similar as is done by this mite on tea. But it is not a serious pest on coffee.

Brevipalpus phoenicis (Geij.)

Banerjee (1989) listed it, occurring on coffee.

Calacarus coffeae K.

Banerjee (1989) listed its occurrence on coffee.

Epitrimerus congoensis K.

Banerjee (1989) listed it on coffee.

Abacarus afer K.

Banerjee (1989) listed it on coffee.

Diptacus cephalanthi Das & Chakraborti

Das & Chakraborti, 1993 (*Entomon.*, **18** : 65–71) described this species from coffee.

Dolichotetranychus sp.

This was recorded on coffee in Tamil Nadu.

4. ARECANUT (*Areca catechu*)

Tetranychus fijiensis Hirst

Daniel (1978: *Acarologia*, **19** : 220-221) recorded this mite as pest of areca palm in Kerala.

Raoiella indica Hirst

This mite normally infests arecanut and coconut. It is a reddish round flat mite with long serrate setae, colonizes on undersurface of leaves. Eggs are tiny red.

Damage : This mite infests both nursery and grown up plants, but the former is preferred. The feeding causes appearance of reddish spots on leaves. The colonies remain covered with thin webs when the infested nursery plants are planted in main field, the infestation spreads there.

Seasonal occurrence : Population of injurious density remains in field during March–June. The population remains in field throughout the year.

Biology : Egg – 6 days, larva – 9 days, protonymph – 6 days, deutonynph – 10 days, total life cycle – 33 days.

Control : Chinnamade Gowda *et al.*, (2007 : *J. Acarol.*, **17** : 68–69) evaluated some acaricides against this mite infesting arecanut and observed that all chemicals (dicofol 0.025%, 0.05%), profenophos (0.05%, 0.10%), wettable sulphur (0.25%, 0.5%) were effective in controlling this mite and their efficacies were at par. Tetradifon (3%) also effectively controlled this pest (Patel *et al.*, 1993).

Oligonychus indicus (Hirst)

This mite attacks the young plant during summer. This is a greenish white mite, colonizes on undersurface of leaves which remain covered with thick webs.

Damage : The feeding of this mite leads to gradual drying of leaves. Even leaves of old tall trees are also attacked and in that case control measures become difficult.

Tetranychus fijiensis Hirst

This reddish mite occasionally attacks arecanut palm. The colonies of this mite are made on undersurface of leaves.

Damage : The feeding induces yellowish patches at the points of feeding.

5. BETELVINE (*Piper betle*)

Betelvine is a perennial, evergreen creeper and is grown in India. Its leaves are chewed unprocessed which gives stimulating effect. It also has Medicinal properties like juice is used as eye drop in painful eye infections and in night blindness, fruits are used with honey in case of cough and roots are used to prevent pregnancy. It is an important cash crops in Andhra Pradesh, Bihar, Karnataka, Maharashtra, Tamil Nadu, Tripura, Uttar Pradesh and West Bengal covering 50,000 ha in India. The leaves are exported to Pakistan, Bangladesh, Indonesia, Malayasia. This crop has a good market value transacting business of Rs. 7000 million every year (Balasubrahmanyam *et al.*, 1994; Karmakar *et al.*, 2010). Some of the phytophagous/ predatory mites reported on betelvine are as below :

Acaridae – *Calogyphus* sp.

Phytoseiidae – *Amblyseius* spp.

Anystidae – *Walzia indiana*

Bdellidae – *Bdella* sp.

Cunaxidae – *Cunaxa* sp.

Stigmaeidae *Agistemus* sp.

Tenuipalpide – *Brvipalpus phoenicis*

Tarsonemidae – *Tarsonemus* sp., *Daidalotarsonemus* sp., *Hemitarsonemus* sp.

Tydeidae – *Pronematus* sp.

Brevipalpus phoenicis (Geij.)

Excepting *B. phoenicis* which is available abundantly, the other mites are less dominant and majority belong to predatory group. Nakat *et al.*, (1995) reported. B. *phoenicis* as an important pest of betelvine causing production of characteristic patches and minute depressions on leaves. These make the leaves roughened. This results in reducing number and size of leaves. The affected plants become stunted and leaves become unacceptable in the market. This mite occurs throughout the year but population is higher during March-May and September-October.

Tetranychus neocaledonicus Andre

The infestation of this mite on betelvine was seen in Howrah district of West Bengal causing yellowing and then producing brownish patches on leaves.

Tetranychus urticae Koch

This mite often attackes betelvine in Tamil Nadu causing the appearance of reddish brown patches and in case of serious infestation, the entire leaf lamina becomes rusty. The varieties "Karpori" and Krupri Pachai Kodi" were more susceptible to the attack of this mite. Ethion (0.05%) registered highest mortality while dicofol (0.05%) treated plants gave maximum yield but wettable sulphur was most economical (Sivakumar & Murmuthu, 1987: *Entomon.*, **12** : 315-319).

PREDATORY MITES

Tencateia kanthiensis Gupta

This predatory Anystid mite was recorded on betelvine in Kanthi, West Bengal feeding on *T. neocaledonicus* (Gupta, 1992).

Walzia indiana Smith-Meyr & Ueckermann

It was recorded in Medinipur, West Bengal from the undersurface of leaves (Smith-Meyer & Ueckermann, 1987: *Ent. Mem. Dep. Agr. Water Suppl. Repub. S. Afr.*, **68** : 14-16)

Tencateia sp.

Raut and Bhattacharyya (1989) reported this species on betelvine. This is an active predator in betelvine orchard in West Bengal. Population density remains, highest in March and lowest during August. Rainfall is the controlling factor. Its prey includes a number of species of white flies (Raut and Bhattacharyya, 1989).

Amblyseius largoensis (Muma)

It was found feeding upon *T. neocaledonicus* during December (1991).

Proctolaelaps pygmaeus Muller

It was recorded on undersurface of leaves. No economic damage was seen (Raut & Bhattacharyya, 1987)

Acarus sp.

This was recorded in Tamluk in West Bengal during October-December and was distributed from 7th leaf down upto 15th leaf. It was found feeding upon fungi (*Fusarium monilliforme*) as will as eggs of *Alleurocanthus rugosa* and *Dialeurodes pallida*. The population of mite was seen from late March - early June and mid-October to late December and that coincided with fungal population. Temperature and RH had no influence on population of this mite but rainfall had significant relation. The development period of different stages was incubation - 213.3 ± 35.8 hrs, larva - 150.3 ± 24.12 hrs., protonymph - 97.8 ± 22.08 hrs and tritonymph - 85.2 ± 16.48 hrs. (Raut & Bhattacharyya, 1987: *Abst. IV Nat Symp. Acarology*, Calicut, P. 31-32; Raut & Bhattacharyya (1999: *Expt. Appl. Acarol.*, **23** : 319-325)

Unguizets clavatus Aoki

This was recorded in Ramnagar, Tamluk, West Bengal on undersurface of leaf and was found feeding upon eggs of *D. pallida, T. gibbosulus, M. indicus, Z. ricini* and *M. garruda*. It may prove to be an effective biocontrolling agent against the insect pests on betelvine .

6. RUBBER (*Ficus elastica* Roxb./*Hevea brasiliensis*)

Oligonychus ponmanaiensis Karuppuchamy & Mohanasundaram

This species was described by Karuppuchamy and Mohanasundaram (1987: *Entomon.*, **12**(2) : 89–94) collected on rubber plant.

Hemitarsonemus dorsalis

This was reported on rubber plant (Radhakrishnan *et al.* (1983: *Agr. Ent.*, **2** : 310–318).

7. CASSAVA (*Manihot esculenta*)

Tetranychus sp.

This undetermined spider mite infests cassava. Pillai and Palaniswamy (1983: *Entomon.*, **8** : 373-375) studied economics for the control of spider mites on cassava. Lal (1982: *Indian J. Acar.*, **7** : 5-10) reported that population of *T. urticae, T. neoculedonicus* and *E. orientalis* on cassava was very poor or absent during June-December, thereafter increased suddenly attaining peak during January-April. Increase in population was correlated with decrease in humidity and insignificantly correlated with increase in maximum temperature. Minimum temperature and rainfall exhibited non significant negative correlation.

Lal and Pillai (1980: *Indian J. Acar.*, **4** : 68-77) tested 27 pesticides against *E. orientalis* infesting cassava and reported dicofol, dimethoate, methyl demeton, monocrotophos, phosalone, ethion, thiometon were most promising having both initial knockdown effect as well as residual effect.

Olgonychus biharensis (Hirst)

This infests cassava plant. Due to its infestation the epidermal cells of leaf become irregular, distorted, and mesophyll layer becomes damaged. Palisade parenchyma showed reduction in number of cells and were punctured with large intercellular spaces in comparison to control leaves which had closely packed parenchyma cells. Spongy parenchyma cells also collapsed, punctured with increased intercellular spaces with reduction in chloroplasts and reduction in Chloroplast contents (Blairs & Groves, 1952: *J. Hort. Sci.*, **27** : 14-43); Avery & Briggs (1968: *Ann. Appl. Biol.*, **61** : 277-288). The punctured cells do not take part in metabolic activities of the plants. This study supports the findings of Tanigoshi & Davis (1978: *Internat. J. Acarol.*, **4** : 47-56).

Saradamma & Nair (1975: *Acar. Newsl.*, **1** : 5) studied relative susceptibility of different varieties of Tapioca to *T. urticae* and reported that Elavan, Kayyalchady, H 226, Monkozhunnan & Sundarivella harboured significantly lesser number of mites than the other varieties.

3.6 FRUIT TREES

India accounts for a total of 10% world production of fruits. India leads in the world in production of mango, banana, sapota and acid limes besides recording highest productivity of grapes. The production of fruits has increased from 55 lakh tonnes in 1952-53 to 440.42 lakh tonnes in 1999. Some of the largest producing states of India are Maharashtra, Karnataka, Andhra Pradesh, Bihar, Uttar Pradesh.

Mango is the most important fruit accounting for 37.60% area and 22.21% of total fruit production. Citrus fruits stands second with 13.09% of fruit production. Limes, lemons, sweet orange and mandarine are the major citrus fruits in India. Banana ranks 3rd in area with 4.64 lakhs ha covering 12.46% of total area and 150.73 lakh tonnes of productivity. Apple is the 4th major crop with 13.80 lakh tonnes production. Guava is the 5th important fruit with 18.0 lakh tonnes followed by papaya with 15.80 lakh tonnes of production. The other fruits like grapes, litchi, pineapple and sapota are also grown quite extensively. In addition, there are a large variety of indigenous fruits like, jack fruit, black berry, falsa, wood apple, etc. which are also grown in many parts of the country. Some exotic fruits like kiwi, olive, kinow, pitch, plum have been introduced in temperate climate and many of those are well-established (Chadha, 2010).

In this chapter, mites infesting about 40 types of fruit trees in India are discussed giving host records, nature of damage, bio-ecological aspects and management.

1). Citrus : (*Citrus aurantium, C. sinensis, C. medica, C. decumana*)

Citrus fruits refer to here include fruit trees like grapefruit, lime, lemon, malta, mosambi, orange, pomelo, all belong to Rutaceae family. It covers 4,54,000 hectares which is next to mango and banana. The total yield of citrus fruits is 3.86 million tonnes. The yield is less as compared to the yield of many countries like Brazil, USA, Mexico, Spain, China. Among several factors responsible for declining in yield, is the pest infestation which is certainly one of the most important ones (Bindra, 1970) which causes citrus decline in India and also other losses amounting to 30% (Butani, 1979: *Pesticides*, **13**(4) : 27–33). As many as 42 spp. of mites infest citrus, 25 of those are phytophagous. As per Leclerg (1965 - USDA.ARS Handbook No.291, 120 pp), the loss due to mite infestation is 2.5%. The mite pests infesting citrus are discussed here.

Eotetranychus frosti (McGregor)

Gupta, 1978 (*Indian J. Acar.*, **3** : 87–91) reported this species on citrus from MP. No serious damage is caused.

Eotetranychus mandensis Manson

This was described on the basis of specimen collected on citrus in Assam. No serious damage is caused.

Eotetranychus pamelae Manson

This was described on the basis of specimen collected on citrus in Assam. It is not known to cause any noticeable damage.

Eutetranychus africanus (Tucker)

This also infests citrus and peach in Africa and India.

Damage : The infested leaves fall off prematurely.

Eutetranychus orientalis (Klein)

This mite is commonly called oriental citrus mite or citrus brown mite or citrus red mite. It is a major pest of citrus and also attacks other plants like pear, peach, etc. The mites are greenish or light brownish with long legs, found normally on uppersurface of leaves, more near the mid rib and lateral ribs wherefrom they suck sap. The eggs are light brownish and laid on upper surface of leaves. Gupta, 1978 (*Indian J. Acar.*, **3** : 87–91) reported this species on citrus from MP.

Distribution : It has a wide distribution like, Afghanistan, Cyprus, Taiwan, Egypt, India, Iran, Israel, Jordan, Kenya, Lebanon, Mozambique, Pakistan, Sudan, Turkey, Venezuela.

Damage : This mite infests upper surface of leaves. The infestation starts from midrib of leaves and gradually spreads on either side of midrib. The infested leaves develop webbing where dusts accumulate. Such dust-covered mite colonies get better protection from pesticidal applications. Sometimes fruits are also attacked giving chlorotic symptoms. At the points of feeding the green leaves show discolouration and later those gradually turn brown. Dusts accumulate on webs. Such leaves dry up and fall off. Many mites may be seen on the upper surface of leaves. The infested leaves develop speckled appearance, later become yellowish or light brownish. Such leaves dry up. The population is more during summer months and less during monsoon.

Biology : Dhooria (1985: *Indian J. Acar.*, **9** : 82–88), studied development of citrus mite *E. orientalis* at 30° ± 0.50°C on 4 host plants. *Ricinus communis, Phaseolus vulgaris, Citrus aurantifolia* and mandarin, *Citrus reticulata*. In all the host plants, mean duration of larvae, proto and deuto nymphs was higher on dorsal surface of young leaves followed by that on dorsal surface of old leaves. Development of mite was faster on castor, French bean and lime than on mandarine leaves and longevity and fecundity were higher on castor, while lime and French bean were next most suitable hosts. Mandarine was least susceptible as there was very low fecundity and longevity. Dhooria (1982: *Indian J. Acar.*, **6** : 77-83) reported that bittergourd, bottlegourd, cabbage, datura, egg plant, litchi, Ornamental palms, falsa, tomato, exhibited non preference for oviposition.

Ecology : Das & Gupta, 1991 (*Modern Acarology*, **1** : 581–587) reported the occurrence of this species throughout the year on citrus and temperature had positive influence on population. Higher rate of multiplication was observed during warmer months (March–October). RH had no relation with mite population. During June–October rainfall was high and mite population was also high during that time. During two years of investigation, in 1986, temperature, RH and rainfall had shown positive correlation with population. In 1985, temperature RH had shown no relation with predator population but rainfall had shown positive relation. In 1986, the temperature exerted profound influence on population dynamics of predator. During April–August, high predator mite population was noticed. The predator population was independent of RH. In 1985, high population of *E. orietalis* was recorded in May–June when predator population was also high. With gradual decrease of pest population during August onwards, the predatory mite population also declined. According to the authors, predatory mite would be a limiting factor in determining maximum population density of pest mite. Dhooria & Butani (1983) studied seasonal incidence of *E. orientalis* on citrus and reported peak population during May–June, September and negligible during December–March. The population attained peak in March–June and September–October. The correlation of mite population with temperature, RH and rainfall, was positive with the first one and was negative with the other two factors.

Varietal preference : Sweet lime and sour lime were comparatively more susceptible as on these hosts higher fecundity, longevity, feeding and ovipostion responses were observed. Kagzi lime, mussambi were relatively resistant (Dhooria, 1983). Kagzi lime, *Citrus lemon, C. aurantifolia* and surat orange were relatively resistant to mite attack (Dhooria *et al.*, 2005) while sour lemon var. galgal, sweet lime (*C. limmetioides*), "Kharna Khatta", grape fruit, *Citrus acida* are most susceptible

(Dhooria, 1982: *Ind. J. Acar.*, **6** : 77–83). In peach, almond, champa, mite infestation was very high during October – November. Among different root stocks, *Citrus aurantifolia* was found resistant followed by *Citrus amblycarpa* (Makar *el al.*, 1983: *J. Maharashtra, Agri. Univ.*, **8** : 37-38).

Control : Aldicarb, carbofuran, disulfoton and phorate, each at 0.50, 0.75, 1.00, 1.50 and 2.00 g.ai/potted malta plant (2 yrs old) in soil provided good control except carbofuran. Aldicarb exihibited its effectiveness after 7 days of application and remained effective upto 70 days even at 0.5g ai/per plant. Disulphoton and phorate showed effect after 14 days and remained effective for more than 3.5 months. Aldicarb @ 0.5 g ai/plant appeared to be most promising (Dhooria, 1983, *Indian J. Acar.*, **8** : 13–21). Dicofol, ethion, oxydemeton methyl, monocrotophos and tetradifon (each at 0.075%) proved to be most effective, (Dhooria, 1983: *Indian J. Acar.*, **7** : 15–19). Chlorfenthol, Chlorfenthol + chlorfenson were very effective against adults, larvae and nymphs. All OP pesticides were more effective against all stages than chlorinated hydrocarbons but the latter had better ovicidal action than the former. Tetradifon was more toxic to eggs and larvae

Natural enemies : Predatory mites *Neoseiulus cucumeris, Euseius hibisci, Pronematus* sp., *Agistemus* sp. were found associated with this mite (Dhooria, 1981: *Acar. Newsl.*, **10** : 6), *E. alstoniae* also actively fed upon all stages of citrus mite. In addition, *Scolothrips indicus* was also seen actively feeding upon eggs. First instar larvae of *Stethorus pauperculus* fed on eggs and larvae of this mite while its latter stages fed on deutonymphs and adults.

Tetranychus hypogeae Gupta

Chatterjee & Gupta (1995) reported it from *Citrus decumna* from West Bengal.

Schizotetranychus hindustanicus (Hirst)

This has been reported on citrus. It is a greenish, flat mite, occurs on uppersurface of leaves along midrib. Chatterjee & Gupta (1995) recorded it from West Bengal.

Damage : The feeding of this mite produces characteristic symptoms of yellowish green stipplings on upper surface of leaves and such infested leaves can be easily detected. Later, such leaves dry up and fall off.

Panonychus citri (McGregor)

Reddish mite, with long setae on dorsum placed on strong tubercles. The eggs of this mite are also red, flattened, stalked.

Host range & distribution : Citrus, rose, almond, pear, castor, beans, ornamentals, papaya, etc. It is a serious pest of citrus in many parts of the world like South Africa, Japan, China, South America, USSR, India (Meghalaya, Asam, West Bengal, H.P., J. & K., Punjab, Andaman Islands). Chetterjee & Gupta (1995) reported it from West Bengal on citrus while Gupta (2005) reported it on papaya.

Biology : The life cycle takes 14.75 days at 23.6° C. and 65% RH. About 50 pearly white eggs are laid/female. Longevity varies from 7–11 days (female), 6–9 days (male). Most favourable temperature and humidity are 30°C and 49% RH. Active period of this mite is August–March and rarely occurs during hot summer.

Damage : The feeding produces stipplings, yellowish spots on leaves. Infested leaves look silvery white. Heavily infested plants suffer defoliation and fruit drop.

Seasonal incidence : The population increases during spring and fall but in summer (temperature 40–50°C) the population suffers heavy mortality. The prolonged high humidity is also detrimental for mite.

Chemical control : The chemicals found effective against *E. orientalis* will be effective against this mite.

Tenuipalponychus citri ChannaBasavanna & Lakkundi

ChannaBasavanna & Lakkundi (1977: *Indian J. Acar.*, **1** : 23-26) described this new species on citrus from Karnataka but no damage symptom has been reported.

Petrobia harti (Ewing)

This has been reported as sporadic pest of citrus and often the damage becomes serious (Banerjee, 1985).

Distribution : Africa, Austrailia, India.

Damage : Silvery white blotches appear on the leaves and later those become yellow. Heavy defoliation occurs.

Biology : A female lays 1–2 eggs/day for about 3 weeks. Eggs are elliptical, bright red, laid on undersurface of leaves singly. The eggs hatch after about a week to larva (7 days) and that passes through protonymph (6 days) and deutonymph (6 days) and then becomes adult. In between each life stage, there is a quiescent period or resting period which lasts for 2–3 days.

Control : Dicofol, ethion at their recommended doses may be effective for control of this pest.

Brevipalpus obovatus Donnadieu

It also attacks citrus along with several other plants.

Distribution : This is a widely distributed species including India, South Africa.

Damage : The mite attacks undersurface of leaves, petioles. The feeding produces yellowish specks on the green leaves and later those turn deep brown or bronzy.

Biology : The eggs are elliptical, bright orange initially, the colour darkens with the age of the egg. The life cycle is completed in shorter time at higher temperature (30-32°C) and longer time at lower temperature (26°C).

Control : Application of any acaricide will control this pest.

Red and black flat mite : *Brevipalpus phoenicis* (Geij.)

This is a red coloured mite with dark patches on body. Eggs are elliptical, reddish orange, laid singly in sheltered places.

Host and distribution : This mite has a wide host range (Dhooria *et al.*, 2005) and it has also been reported as pest of apple, guava, grapes, pear, peach, papaya, tea, coffee and many Ornamental plants.

Biology : Its life cycle is completed in 15–22 days at 23 ± 3° C and 85% RH. The most suitable temperature and RH were 25°C and 70% RH.

Seasonal occurrence : Results of the study of population fluctuation of *Brevipalpus phoenicis* during December, 1993–December, 1994 indicated peak population at high temperature (32.99° C), max day length (13 hrs), moderate wind velocity (5.68 km/h), sunshine (11.77 hrs), lower RH (32.50%) and no rainfall. Low to moderate temperature (12.22° - 22.26° C), moderate day length (10–11 hrs), low wind velocity (2.64–4.32 km/h), sunshine (5.02–9.66 hrs), moderate to high RH (56.43–81.86%) and low rainfall reduced its population level (Goel & Sadana, 1995).

Damage : Mites feed on both surfaces of leaves and fruits. Due to feeding on leaves, chlorotic patches appear. The damage is more serious when the plants are under stressed condition. Heavily infested plants suffer defoliation and in nursery stage, the plants may die. On fruits, this mite causes rind disorders (area 0.5–1.5 cm across harbouring 15–25 adult mites). Mites damaged epidermal region and infested fruits became brownish/blackish with irregular corky skin. Such rind - disordered fruits fetched less price. Chaudhuri & Mali (1978: *Sci. & Cult.*, **44**(4) : 166–167) reported leprosies of citrus from Ahmednagar.

The authors analysed biochemical components like total sugar, reducing and non - reducing sugars, starch, proteins, phenols, free amino acid, nitrogen, phosphorus, sodium, potassium in citrus hosts like Kaghzi, nimbu, kinnow, grape fruit as well as other fruits like guava, papaya, banana due to infestation of *Brevipalpus phoenicis*. Results revealed that host plants contained significantly higher amounts of starch, free amino acids, nitrogen, sodium, potassium and lower amount of proteins, phenols and sulphur as compared to non host plants. These components were responsible for making these hosts suitable. No significant difference in host and non host plants was seen in respect of total sugars, reducing/non reducing sugars, lipids and phosphorus contents (Goel & Sadana, 1995).

Varietal susceptibility : Kinnow fruits were reported to be more severely damaged exhibiting mite damage in more than 50% cases. Grape fruits, pomelo, orange recorded 10–15% damaged fruits. Sadana & Joshi (1979: *Sci. & Cult.*, **45**(10) : 413–414) reported sweet lime as most susceptible host while Satsumas, Marsh grapefruit and Dancy tangerines as least susceptible.

Chemical control : Conventional acaricides can be used for control of this mite.

Natural enemies : *Typhlodromus homalii* was found feeding upon *B. phoenicis* (Kumari & Sadana, 1990: *J. Insect. Sci.,* **3**(2) : 186–187).

Brevipalpus californicus Banks

This is small, oval, red mite with dark reticulation pattern along central line of body.

Distribution : Africa, Austrailia, India, USA

Host range and distribution : It is widely distributed in different parts of the world and from India, it is known from many states in eastern, northern and southern India occurring on over 70 host plants (Dhooria *et al.,* 2005); Chatterjee & Gupta (1995) reported it from West Bengal.

Biology : Female lays one egg/day for 25 days. Eggs are elliptical, bright red, eggs remain tightly glued on its surface. Incubation period is for 9 days at 18–24° C, 55% RH. Eggs hatch to larvae which are red and then moult to nymphal stages, the duration of both stages taken together is 21–25 days. Oviposition period ranged from 8.2–12 days. The development from egg - adult takes lesser time in summer - (May–July) (Sadana & Joshi 1986: *Abst VII International Congress of Acarology*).

Damage : This mite has been reported to cause leprosies of citrus from USA. The feeding causes appearance of nail - head rust on leaves/fruits. The infestation of fruits causes silvering of fruit surface and damage is also done on twigs called scaly bark. In case of grape fruits, it causes rind spotting (Pena *et al.* 2002: CAB International, UK).

Varietal preference : Sweet lime was found to be highly susceptible while grapefruit and Dancy tangerines were least susceptible (Sadana & Joshi, 1979: *Sci. & Cult.,* **45**(10) : 413–414.

Chemical control : Any conventional pesticides can be sprayed for its control.

Priscapalpus piarai

This has also been reported from citrus.

Citrus rust mite : *Phyllocoptruta oleivora* (Ashmead)

This is a minute mite, fusiform, creamy white to light brownish and are found in large numbers on the young leaves and fruit surface, often occurring throughout the year. The infested leaves become yellowish white. The infested fruits develop silvery white colour, the normal green colour is lost. Subsequently, the infested fruits become brown, dry up, shrivel and fall off. Heavily infested fruits may develop cracks. The infested plants give reduced yield. It is a tiny mite. The eggs are spherical, semi translucent and laid in groups' on fruits or on ventral surface of leaves.

Distribution : Throughout citrus growing areas of the world.

Host range distribution : It occurs only on citrus throughout the world.

Biology : A female lays 20–30 eggs. The eggs hatch after 3 days to nymphs and the nymphs after 3–11 days moult to adults. Total life cycle takes about 10–14 days, depending upon season. The life span is of 20 days.

Shivaraju and ChannaBasavanna (1995: *Bangalore Abst.*, p. 30) studied biology of *P. oleivora* on citrus. Incubation period at 15° C was much longer (9 days) than at 30°C (2 days). Proto and deutonymphal periods were both reduced from 6 days at (15°C) to 2 days (at 30°C). Survival was 90%, 50%, 20% and 10% at 15, 20, 25, 30° C, respectively. Temperature had significantly positive correlation on building of mite population, RH, rainfall had shown – negative correlation. Authors also studied dispersal of this mite by hanging microslides at different heights 60, 120, 180 cm and that revealed 23, 42, 35 mites, respectively trapped on slides smeared with grease.

Nature of damage : The fruits are attacked even when those are in small size. Initially, the symptoms of damage are the appearance of patches on fruits which are silvery white, and then those become reddish brown and finally purplish black. The fruit surface often becomes rusty, shrivel. On grape fruit and lemons, feeding results in a silvery dark skin appearance. The damaged leaves show bronzing symptoms. The damaged fruits become small, juice contents are reduced and possess more soluble solids, sugars and ascorbic acid content as compared to normal fruit (Dhooria *et al.*, 2005).

Seasonal occurrence : The infestation is more in warm and humid weather and the mites prefer to fruits than leaves in summer.

Varietal preference : Lemon is preferred over other citrus species.

Chemical control : Spraying of monocrotophos and dicofol are suggested to control this mite. Shivaraju and ChannaBasavanna (1995) reported amitraz, dicofol, monocrotophos which could suppress the population of citrus rust mite, *P. oleivora* upto 4 weeks at lower concentration while dicofol and amitraz at 0.05% provided effective control upto 2 weeks.

Citrus bud mite : *Eriophyes sheldoni* (Ewing)

This tiny mite (170–180 microns long), live within leaf buds. Among the different varieties, lemon var. of citrus is most seriously damaged. The affected buds dry up. The mites will be seen on opening the buds.

Biology : The female lays about 50 subspherical eggs which hatch in 3–4 days at 25°C and 98% RH. So, to complete one generation it takes 12–33 days. Lower humidity is unfavourable for egg hatching. The life-cycle is completed in 12- 30 days.

Damage : The mites are found under bud bracts, on petiole bases next to buds, beneath bud scales, fruit buttons, etc. Buds in all stages are attacked. The feeding on the buds makes those blackened and are often killed. Continuous feeding results in production of multiple budding on infested twigs, cessation of twig growth and blossom development. Buds infested with mites become thickened, flattened and sometimes rosette growth is seen. Leaves from affected buds assume abnormal shape, blossoms show malformation with aborted floral parts. Fruits also become abnormal shape and drop off prematurely. The oranges become flattened vertically and ridges appear on rind when orange plant is fed by *E. sheldoni* (Dhooria *et al.*, 2005).

Control : Spray of lime sulphur (2%) or Triazophos or light mineral oil will control this mite having no adverse effect on the natural enemies.

Calarus citrifolii Keifer

It infests citrus, peach, papaya.

Distribution : South Africa, India.

Damage : The infestation of this mite produces blotches with concentric rings. Feeding by mite also causes leaf chlorosis. Die back may occur in case of severe infestation. The tree suffers from denudation.

Biology : Eggs are flat, circular, hatch in 3–4 days to first stage nymph, which passing through II stage nymph reaches adulthood. The egg to adult period takes about 15 days.

Cosella fleschneri (K.)

This mite infests citrus and causes deformation of leaves with red lesion marks. This affects growth and yield of citrus.

Aculops pelekassi (K.)

The infestation of this mite causes dislocation of growth and russeting of fruits and leaves.

Euseius kalimpongensis (Gupta)

Gupta, 1978 (*Indian J. Acar.*, **2** : 60–77) recorded this predatory mite on citrus from Orissa.

Amblyseius mcmurtryi Muma

Gupta, 1978 (*Indian J. Acar.*, **2** : 60–77) reported it on citrus from Orissa.

Typhlodromus homalii (Gupta)

Gupta, 1977 (*Indian J. Acar.*, **2** : 1–11) recorded it from Chandmari.

Broad mite : *Polyphagotarsonemus latus* (Banks)

This mite is called yellow mite and is a pest of jute, chilli, tea etc. Adult is glossy, amber coloured, convex, very fast moving. The nymphs remain enclosed within skin of quiescent larvae. Young females are subcircular and less deeply coloured as compared to matured females. Adult male is shorter than female, colourless, initially, becomes rich amber when fully grown and 4th legs with well developed claws. The males are often seen carrying the pharate females by its chelicerae.

Host range and distribution : This is a polyphagous species and occurs on over 30 plant species. Among its different hosts, the plants which are more seriously attacked are jute, chilli, tea, tobacco, potato, citrus, gerbera and some ornamental plants like marigold, etc. The distribution of this mite also is very wide both in temperate and tropical zones.

Biology : Average longevity of female and male is 13.44 days and 12.0 days, respectively. The intrinsic rate of increase is rm = 0.359, with a mean generation time of 10.34 days and net reproductive rate Ro = 41.0. A single generation is completed in 4-5 days during summer, 7-10 days in winter. Average number of eggs laid per female per day is 3.6, laid on leaves or fruit surface. Males often carry the pharate deutonymphs to help in dispersal of the colony.

Damage : The mite feeds young terminal leaves on lower surface causing crinkling and crumpling of leaves. The nursery plants are more seriously affected. Later, the damaged leaves crack, ventral surface becomes bronzed. When the fruits are attacked, the fruit surface becomes silvery white. The stems and flowers are also sometimes attacked. The damage is more acute under hot humid condition which is more favourable for its breeding. The infested leaves become deformed. The fruit surface develops silvery skin. The toxin injected with saliva contributes towards development of deformities. The growth and flowering of the plant are also affected. The fruits start developing symptoms within 4-5 days after infestation.

Chemical control : Propergite, dicofol, carbophenothion, avamectin in their recommended doses can be used.

Natural enemies : Not much is known about the natural enemies especially on citrus.

Dhooria *et al.* (2005) provided the following suggestions for management of citrus mite pests :

- Emphasis should be laid on the use of pathogens and predators in biocontrol.
- Attempt should be made to develop insecticidal resistant strains of phytoseiid mites as has been done in USA and Australia.
- For determining proper time for undertaking plant protection measures, the EIL should be worked out for different citrus species, before application of pesticides.

- Use of broad spectrum pesticides should be avoided.
- Alternate host plants should not be grown in orchards to prevent harbouring of the mites in the off season and perpetuate the attack round the year.
- Proper cultural practices should be adopted to prevent infestation.

2) FIG (*Ficus cunea/F. hispida*)

Euteranychus orientalis (Klein)

Gupta & Gupta 1978 (*Indian J. Acar.*, **3** : 87–91) reported this mite on fig.

Eotetranychus hirsti Pritchard & Baker

This is a very common species which infests in large number on undersurface of fig leaves causing yellowish white discolouration. Those gradually turn brownish. Finally such leaves defoliate.

Seasonal occurrence : Mukherjee *et al.*, (1995, *J. Acarol.*, **13** : 63–68) studied seasonal incidence of fig mite *Eotetranychus hirsti* in relation to weather factors at Varanasi. The study indicated the attaining of peak population of *E. hirsti* during June–July, minimum during October - December. Increase in population was associated with high temperature and low humidity. Temperature was the regulatory factor. Rain did not reduce the population of mites to any great extent, may be because of the fact that mites inhabit the lower surface of leaves.

Eutetranychus caricae Nassar & Ghai

This mite also occurs on fig. The feeding causes yellowing of leaves but the damage is of minor nature.

Aceria sorghi ChannaBasavanna

Ghosh & Chakrabarti 1988 (*Acarologia,* **29** : 379–387) reported the species on *Ficus cunea.*

Dendroptus sp.

This mite has been reported to cause fig leaf gall.

Phytoseius punjabensis Gupta

Gupta, 1977 (*Indian J. Acar.*, **1** : 11–18) recorded this species on fig from Punjab.

The other mites reported on fig as listed in Gupta, 1985 are *Tenuipalpus fici* Maninder & Ghai, *Rhyncaphytoptus ficifoliae* Keifer, *Oligonychus mangiferus* Rahman & Sapra, *Brevipalpus obovatus* Donnadieu, *B. phoenicis* (Geij.), *Eutetranychus orientalis* (Klein), *Eotetranychus irregularis* Nassar & Ghai. However nothing is known about their economic importance on fig tree.

3. PALMYRAH PALM (*Borassus flabellifer*)

Neodialox palmyrae Mohanasundaram

Mohanasundaram, 1982 (*Indian J. Acar.*, **7** : 53–59) described the species collected on this host from South India.

Notostrix flabelliferae Mohanasundaram

On *Borassus flabellifer* (in Gupta, 1985)

***Mackiella borasus* Mohanasundaram**

On *Borassus flabellifer* (in Gupta, 1985)

4. MANGO (*Mangifera indica*)

Oligonychus mangiferus (Rahman & Sapra)

It is dark red mite, occurs on upper surface of leaves. The colony is covered with webbing. It attacks peach, pear, pomegranate, mango. It is known from India, Pakistan, Mauritius and Egypt.

Gupta & Gupta, 1978 (*Indian J. Acar.*, **3** : 87–91) and Rather (1989: *Progress in Acarology*, **2** : 183–189) reported this mite on mango.

Damage : The damage symptoms appear as yellowing of leaves especially along midrib on upper surface of leaves. Later, with the intensity of increase of damage, the leaves turn brownish. The monsoon shower washes away the population. The damage is more severe in young plants during summer season and heavy defoliation may take place.

Biology : Oviposition rate of this mite increased with advancing age of female until reaching 11th date of adult life and decreased thereafter. Mated female had higher rate of oviposition and total fecundity than their unmated counterparts despite enhanced longevity of latter group. The change of host plant from mango to black berry adversely affected egg laying capacity. Daily removal of webbing did not affect rate of oviposition. Its life cycle is completed in two weeks.

Seasonal occurrence : The active period is during March to April.

Control : This can be controlled with dicofol or tetradifon.

Natural enemies : Sadana and Chhabra (1974: *Sci. and Cult.*, **40** : 362–363) reported some predators.

Euseius scutalis Athias-Henriot

This preyed on *O. mangiferus* in Punjab.

Oligonychus biharensis (Hirst)

In India, it infests mango besides litchi and is distributed in Southeast Asia.

Aceria mangiferae (Sayed)

Damage : By inducing *Fusarium oxysporum* to both susceptible and tolerant varities of mango in Egypt, the mango malformation symptom could be produced. The relationship of mite infestation with fungus infection was established along with effect of weather factors (Galal *et al.*, 1989: *Progress in Acarology*, **2** : 101–107). During flowering season, vegetative malformation was more pronounced in young seedlings. Terminal shoots of affected seedlings become greatly shortened and thickened. The internodes and crowded shoots arise from leaf axils giving the shoots a bunchy appearance. In case of floral malformation, the panicles become very compact due to excessive crowding of flowers unlike healthy panicles. Panicles do not bear fruits. (Agrawal & Singh, 1989: *Progress in Acarology*, **2** : 109–114). Axillary buds dry up and are killed due to bud mite infestation. (Rather, 1989: *Progress in Acarology*, **2** : 183–189). This mite causes floral malformation and vegetative malformation. The infestation of this mite in inflorescence results in production of excessive buds and the inflorescence turns into mass of floral buds and those never develop into fruits. In case of vegetative malformation, this mite infests the vegetative shoots which develop into crowded buds. Somchoudhary *et al.* (2010) studied the effect of bioagent (*Aceria mangiferae*) in forecasting the bearing of mango. They reported that this mite had a pronounced impact on the bearing pattern in mango tree. The length of mites feeding on the bearing plants was always smaller than the mites feeding on nonbearing plants. On the other hand, the breadth of the mites feeding on bearing plants was always greater than that of the mites feeding on nonbearing plants. Thus feeding, the authors claim, will pave the way for easy determination of the bearing nature of the plant well ahead of reproductive season.

Seasonal occurrence : The population of the mite was high during April–June, least during rainy season (July–November). Rai *et al.*, (2007: *J. Acarol.*, **16** : 78–79) studied seasonal occurrence of *Aceria mangiferae* and its role in vegetative malformation and reported that the maximum population was in May and minimum was in January. The second peak was attained again in October. Significant positive correlation with temperature and negative correlation with RH and nonsignificant negative correlation with rainfall were observed. Suresh and Mohanasundaram (1995: *Madras Agric. J.*, **82** : 666–669) reported high infestation in May.

Varietal preference : Lucknow, Safeda and Dasheri varieties were most susceptible in U.P. Agrawal & Singh (1989: *Progress in Acarology*, **2** : 109–114).

Keiferophyes guamensis Mohanasundaram & Muniappan

Mohansundaram and Manjunatha (1995) reported this species from Karnataka.

Cisaberoptus kenyae Keifer

It occurs on upper surface of mango leaves and its colony remains covered with a thin silvery white web. A large number of mites will be visible when the web is removed. The damage done is never of any serious nature. Mohanasundaram and Manjunatha (1995) reported it from Karnataka. Ramani & Haq, 1989 (*Progress in Acarology*, **2** : 115–119) screened five varieties of mango against this mite.

Damage : Pandit & Chakraborty (2010) reported this mite causing white coating on upper surface of mango leaf. Its population per leaf reached peak during April–May, declined gradually during rainy season with the increase of humidity and rainfall.

Biology : Life cycle included egg, two nymphal stages and adult. The duration of each stage was around 2-3 days at temperature of 37 ± 1°C and 90 ± 5% RH.

Spinacus agonis K.

Mohanasundaram and Manjunatha (1995) reported it on mango from Karnataka.

Metaculus mangiferae (Attiah)

This is called mango rust mite and causes bunchy top and occurs in Egypt and India (Mohanasundaram and Manjunatha, 1995). It causes russeting of terminal buds and inflorescence which affect the growth of the plant and subsequently dry up. The yield is substantially affected. A mass of malformed flowers are formed in the damaged inflorescence. Vegetative malformation occurs in mango seedling.

Vilaia panithus (Boczek & Chandrapatyan)

This was reported by Pandit & Chakraborty (2010) on mango.

Spinacus lenginquus Huang *et al.*

This was reported by Pandit & Chakraborty (2010) on mango.

Acaphylla sp.

Mohanasundaram and Manjunatha (1995) reported it as new mite from Karnataka.

Tarsonemus sp.

It was also reported on mango.

Fungitarsonemus sp.

It was also reported on mango.

Typhlodromus rhenanus (Oudemans)

Gupta, 1977 (*Indian J. Acar.*, **1** : 11–18) recorded it on mango.

Euseius coccineae (Gupta)

Gupta, 1977 (*Indian J. Acar.*, **1** : 28–37) recorded it on mango.

5. LITCHI (*Litchi chinensis*)

Oligonychus biharensis (Hirst)

This mite often colonizes on under surface of litchi leaf and causes light brownish patches on infested leaves.

Notocaphylla chinensiae Mohanasundaram & Singh

Mohonasundaram & Singh (1989: *Entomon.*, **13** : 259–261) described *Notocaphylla chinensiae* from litch collected from West Bengal.

Aceria litchii (Keifer)

Damage : This mite feeds on young shoots and leaves resulting in production of excessive growth of hairs on under surface of leaves which are brownish and that gives a velvety appearance to the leaves. This velvety growth affects the normal growth of leaves and shoots. During the time of new flush, the infestation becomes more serious.

This mite colonizes on the undersurface of litchi leaf and causes formation of chocolaty brown velvety erineum. The affected leaves become curled, crinkled, dry up and fall off. The growth of flower buds are also affected. It was earlier believed to be due to injection of a toxin in the leaves through mite saliva during feeding. But a group of scientists are of the opinion that the erineum which is formed on the undersurface of leaves is nothing but the algal mycelia of the parasitic algal species *Cephaleurus virescens* (Somchoudhury *et al.*, 1989). However, there are many who do not accept this view.

Biology : The eggs are laid amidst erineum which hatch in a couple of days to first stage nymphs which last for 2–3 days and through final moulting it reaches adulthood. The total developmental period is 11–12 days.

Control : Mechanical removal of affected leaves and spraying of ethion will be useful to control this pest.

Amblyseius largoensis (Muma)

Gupta, 1978 (*Indian J. Acar.*, **2** : 60–77) reported it from Eastern India. Chakraborty (2010) also reported it in association with litchi erineum mite.

Amblyseius herbicolus (Chant)

Chakraborty (2010) reported it in association with litchi erineum mite as predator, in West Bengal.

Euseius coccosocius (Ghai & Menon)

Chakraborty (2010) reported it in association with litchi erineum mite as predator in West Bengal.

Euseius ovalis (Evans)

Chakraborty (2010) reported it in association with litchi erineum mite as predator in West Bengal.

Euseius coccineae (Gupta)

Chakraborty (2010) reported it in association with litchi erineum mite as predator in West Bengal.

Euseius findlandicus (Oudmans)

Chakraborty (2010) reported it in association with litchi erineum mite as predator in West Bengal.

Neoseiulus fallacies (Garman)

Chakraborty (2010) reported it in association with litchi erineum mite as predator in West Bengal.

Agistemus sp.

Chakraborty (2010) reported it in association with litchi erineum mite as predator in West Bengal.

Neocunaxaoides sp.

Chakraborty (2010) reported it in association with litchi erineum mite as predator in West Bengal.

6. BLACK BERRY (*Syzygium cumini*)

Eotetranychus syzygii Gupta & Gupta

Gupta & Gupta, 1878 (*Indian J. Acar.*, **3** : 87–91) reported this species on black berry from MP. No importance as pest is known.

Oligonychus mangiferus (R. & S.)

This mite often attacks mango along with black berry causing minor injury like yellowing of leaves. Srisikar & Nagabhushanam (1988: *Progress in Acarology*, **2** : 47–51) studied the oviposition rate of this species on black berry.

Raoiella macfarlanei Pritchard & Baker

This was also reported to be infesting black berry (Mohanasundaram & Parameswaram, 1991: *Madras Agric J.*, **78** : 76–77) but its economic importance is unknown.

Neoraoiella eugeniae Mohanasundaram

It was collected on *Eugenia* sp. causing slight russeting of leaves Mohanasundaram (1996: *J. Ent. Res.*, **20** : 141–143) but its economic importance is unknown.

Diptilomiopus jevremovici Mohanasundaram

Mohanasunram & Parameswaram (1991, *Madras Agric J.*, **78** : 76–77) reported this mite infesting this host but damage symptoms are not known.

Diptilomiopus cuminis C.

Chakrabarti *et al.* (1992: *Acarologia*, **33** : 75–81) described this species on *Syzygium cumini* but its economic importance is unknown.

Euseius neococcineae (Gupta)

Gupta, 1978 (*Indian J. Acar.*, **2** : 60–77) recorded it on blackberry from Meghalaya.

7. PINEAPPLE (*Ananas comosus*)

Dolichotetranychus floridanus (Banks)

These mites are bright scarlet red, with elongated body. The four pairs of legs are in two groups, the first and second pairs are placed anteriorly, the other two legs placed posteriorly and both the groups are well apart. The mites in colonies will be seen at the basal part of the leaf where they feed on petioles. Secondary microbial infestation develops at the points of feeding which lead to development of reddish scars. Das *et al.*, (1987: *Env. & Ecol.*, **5** : 668–670) studied effect of temperature and RH on development of predatory mite *Cunaxa* sp. infesting *D. floridanus* on pineapple.

Das *et al.* (1991: *Env. & Ecol.*, **9** : 929–933) studied chemical basis of resistance of pineapple against this mite.

Tarsonemus ananus

Das *et al.*, (1987: *Env. & Ecol.*, **5** : 668–670) studed its biology on pineapple.

8. PHALSA (*Grewia asiatica*)

Swarnanychus bandipurensis Mallik & Kumar

Mallik & Kumar 1998 (*Int. J. Acarol.*, **24** : 227–230) described this species on phalsa from South India.

Eutetranychus orientalis (Klein)

Gupta (1985) listed this species on phalsa.

9. MULBERRY (*Morus alba*)

Panonychus ulmi (Koch)

This mite was reported on mulberry from Kashmir valley (Manzoor & Rather, 2010). It is also known on several other temperate fruits.

Eotetranychus suginamensis (Yokoyama)

This mite is a very common one attacking mulberry leaves and builds its colonies on undersurface of leaves causing yellowish discolouration. Nangia *et al.* (1999: *J. Acarol.*, **15** : 29-31) studied biochemical changes in different varieties of mulberry and reported reduction in transpiration rate, total chlorophyll, protein, sugars and amino acid contents in the infested leaves. This caused poor quality silk production when the silkworms were fed with such type of leaves.

Aceria mori (Keifer)

This mite very often occurs as vagarants on undersurface of mulberry leaves doing no noticeable damage.

Agistemus albae Roy *et al.*

Roy *et al.*, (2010: *Entomon.*, **34** : 175-180) described this on this host.

10. Guava (*Psidium guajava*)

Eutetranychus orientalis (Klein)

Gupta & Gupta, 1978 (*Indian J. Acar.*, **3** : 87–91) reported this species on guava from Madhya Pradesh.

Eotetranychus hicoriae (McGregor)

Eotetranuchus hiscoriae is a pest of guava and also attacks pecan, hickory, horse chestnut, oak, red oak and Asiatic and European chestnut. Mites reproduced both sexually and parthenogenetically. Developmental period in case of sexual reporoduction averaged 3.69 days (egg), 1.37 days (larva), 1.60 days (protonymph), 1.50 days (deutonymph), 0.80 days (1 quiescent), 0.81 days (II quiescent), 0.85 days (III quiescent). In case of parthenogenetic reproduction, these periods were 4.29, 1.26, 1.44, 1.40, 0.69, 0.77, 0.76 and 0.85 days, respectively. Mating took 1.0–1.5 minutes. Preoviposition, oviposition, postoviposition and longevity of adult female were 2.23 days, 28.77 days, 3.66 days, and 31.00 days, respectively. Fecundity was 13.77 eggs and 10.55 eggs in case of mated and unmated females, respectively. Sex ratio male: female = 1 : 4.7. The preponderance of female population in the present study was due to short lived nature of male compared to female. The study of life cycle at higher temperature also favoured production of female.

Biology : Mallikarjunappa & Nageshchandra (1989: *Indian J. Acar.*, **10** : 47–51) studied biology of this mite on guava. Further, the same authors in 1989 (*J. Ecobiol.*, **1** : 34–38) studied ecology of this mite with special reference to prey prevalence and plant host relationship.

Seasonal occurrence : The record of the species was made on guava from South India (Mallikarjunappa and Nageshchandra, 1989: *Progress in Acarology*, **2** : 33–37). They reported variation in population with different stages and weather factors. The population was positively correlated with temperature and sunshine hours but negatively correlated with rainfall and RH. Correlation between predator and prey mite was non-significant.

Petrobia latens (Muller)

Chatterjee & Gupta (1995) recorded this mite on guava but no damage was done by this mite.

Brevipalpus deleoni Pritchard & Baker

Chatterjee & Gupta (1995) recorded this mite on guava but no damage was reported.

Brevipalpus obovatus Donnadieu

Chatterjee & Gupta (1995) recorded this mite on guava but no damage was reported by this mite infestation.

Brevipalpus cucurbitae Mohanasundaram

Sadana & Kaur (1992: *Entomol.*, **17** : 95–97) reported this species from guava in Punjab.

Brevipalpus phoenicis (Geij.)

This is a reddish, flat mite with dark spots on dorsal surface of body and having short stumpy legs. These are found in colonies on undersurface of leaves on normal condition but are also common on twigs, fruits and sometimes on upper surface of leaves as well. They are slow movers, suck the sap from the leaves/fruits producing spots which may be seen on the young leaf/fruit surfaces. The damaged fruits develop small scars on fruit surface. In case of severe damage, the fruits stop developing and may drop off. Sarkar & Das, 1991 (*Indian J. Ecol.*, **18** : 83–85) reported that maximum population on guava was during April and decreased in later months. Highest population was on Baruipur variety and lowest was on Banarasi variety.

Kumari & Sadana (1995: *J. Acarol.*, **13** : 55–62) studied seasonal occurrence of *B. phoenicis* and *E. alstoniae* on guava. *B. phoenicis* attained peak during second half of December in 1989, 1988 and 2nd half of December or as late as first half of January in 1987. The population build up on guava started when temperature ranged (11-24°C), RH (56–76%), wind velocity (27 km/PH) and sunshine hours (6–10 hrs), with no or less rainfall, prevailed. *E. alstoniae* population build up was seen when temperature (26.2–29.55°C), RH (56.33–79.83%), wind velocity (3–4.5 km/h) and rainfall 0–42.7 mm prevailed. The influence of rainfall on population fluctuation of *E. alstoniae* was very little as compared to that on *B. phoenicis*. No correlation was seen with population of predatory and prey mites indicating that predatory mite could subsist on some other food. Kumari & Sadana (1995: *J.Acarol.*, **13** : 69–74) studied biology of *B. phoenicis* using *E. alstoniae* on potted guava plants. The time required by the predatory mite to completely eliminate prey mite increased with increase in prey density. *E. alstoniae* could effectively control the prey mite in the entire predator - prey ratios studied by them. Population of prey on control plants increased rapidly except in case where predator-prey ratios of 1 : 10 and 1 : 20 were used. The leaves of control plants at 1 : 30 ratio showed damage symptoms (whitish spots) due to feeding of *B. phoenicis*. Damaged leaves turned yellow, dried up, became brownish and finally fell off. The plants which received predators along with prey mites did not reach upto the stage of leaf drop.

Brevipalpus assamensis Sadana & Rajendra

Sadana & Rajendra 1990 (*Acarologia*, **31** : 357–360) described this species on guava from Assam.

Brevipalpus karachiensis Chaudhri *et al.*

Sadana & Rajendra 1990 (*Acarologia*, **31** : 357–360) described this species on guava from Assam.

Terminalichus psidi Mohanasundram

Mohanasundaram, 1983 (*Entomon.*, **8** : 221–223) described the species on guava from South India.

Terminalichus delhiensis Maninder & Ghai

Sadana & Sidhu (1989: *Entomon*, **14** : 107–108) reported this species on guava from Punjab.

Amblyseius mcmutryi Muma

Gupta, 1978 (*Indian J. Acar.*, **2** : 60–77) reported this species on guava from Orissa.

Euseius meghalayensis (Gupta)

Gupta, 1978 (*Indian J. Acar.*, **2** : 60–77) reported this species on guava from Orissa.

Phytoseius kapuri Gupta

Gupta, 1977 (*Indian J. Acar.*, **1** : 11–18) recorded it from guava from Rajasthan.

Euseius coccosocius (Ghai & Menon)

Gupta, 1977 (*Indian J. Acar.*, **1** : 28–37) recorded it from guava in Punjab.

Euseius kalimpongensis Gupta

This was recorded on guava from Gujarat (Gupta, 1977: *Indian J. Acar.*, **1** : 28–37).

Euseius delhiensis (Narayanan & Kaur)

Gupta, 1978 (*Indian J. Acar.*, **2** : 60–77) reported this species on guava from Orissa.

Euseius finlandicus (Oudemans)

Jagadish *et al.*, 1995 reported this species on guava from Bangalore.

Euseius alstoniae (Gupta)

Kumari & Sadana (1995) reported this species as predator of guava mite *E. hicoriae*.

Paraphytoseius multidentatus Swirski & Shechter

Jagadish *et al.*, (1995) reported this species on guava from Bangalore.

Phytoseius rugosus Denmark

Jagadish *et al.*, (1995) reported this species on guava from Bangalore.

Phytoseius sp.

Sarkar & Das (1991, *Indian J. Ecol.*, **18** : 83-85) mentioned the peak population of this mite on guava in Baruipur variety during July–August.

Typhlodromus darjeelingensis Gupta

Jagadish *et al.*, (1995) reported this species on guava from Bangalore.

Typhlodromus gopali Gupta

Jagadish *et al.*, (1995) reported this species on guava from Bangalore.

Typhlodromus rickeri Chant

Jagadish *et al.*, (1995) reported this species on guava from Bangalore.

Cunaxa sp.

Jagadish *et al.*, (1995) reported this species on guava from Bangalore.

Bdellodes sp.

Jagadish *et al.*, (1995) reported this species on guava from Bangalore.

Cheyletus sp.

Jagadish *et al.* (1995) reported this species on guava from Bangalore.

Pronematus sextoni Baker

Jagadish *et al.*, (1995) reported this species on guava from Bangalore.

Pronematus sp.

This predator on guava mite *B. phoenicis* was reported from West Bengal (Sarkar & Das, 1991: *Indian J. Ecol.*, **18** : 83–85). Its peak population was recorded during April.

Agistemus fleschneri Summers

This predator on guava mite *B. phoenicis* was reported from West Bengal (Sarkar & Das, 1991: *Indian J. Ecol.*, **18** : 83–85). Its peak population was recorded during May.

11. POMEGRANATE (*Punica granatum*)

Brevipalpus phoenicis (Geij.)

Gupta & Gupta, 1978 (*Indian J. Acar.*, **3** : 87–91) reported this mite on pomegranate from MP producing characteristic damage symptoms.

Tenuipalpus punicae Pritchard & Baker

Gupta & Gupta, 1978 (*Indian J. Acar.*, **3** : 87–91) reported this mite on pomegranate from MP, causing discolouration of leaves.

Euseius alstoniae (Gupta)

Gupta, 1977 (*Indian J. Acar.*, 1 : 28–37) reported this on pomegranate from Gujarat.

Oligonychus mangiferus (Rahman & Sapra)

This mite attacks pomegranate in India as well as in Pakistan, Mauritius and Egypt producing damage symptoms similar to that produced on mango. It remains active in field during March to April. It can be controlled by application of dicofol.

Tetranychus puschelii Meyer

This was reported on pomegranate but no damage was done (Sadana & Gupta, 1994: *Entomon.*, **9** : 141–147).

Tenuipalpus guptai Sadana & Gupta

This was reported on pomegranate but no damage was done. (Sadana & Gupta 1994: *Entomon.*, **9** : 141–147).

12. WOOD APPLE (*Aegle marmelos*)

Tetra aegleis Gosh *et al.*

This was reported on wood apple but nothing is known about its damage (Ghosh *et al.*, 1984: *Entomon.*, **9** : 231–237) recorded it on this plant.

Amblyseius largoensis (Muma)

Roy *et al.*, (2008: *Entomon.*, **33** : 119-128) recorded it on this plant.

Agistemus edulis Gupta

Roy *et al.*, (2008: *Entomon.*, **33** : 119-128) recorded it on this plant.

13. PAPAYA (*Carica papaya*)

Panonychus citri (McG.)

This is an important pest of papaya throughout India. It is a large reddish mite with long dorsal hairs borne on tubercles and mostly occurs on upper surface of leaves but may also occur on lower surface, petioles and fruits.

Chatterjee & Gupta (1995) recorded it on papaya from West Bengal.

Biology : This was studied under laboratory condition at 23.6 ± 1° C with 64.5% RH, 26.7 ± 1°C with 51.5 % RH and 30.6 ± 1°C with 48.7% RH. Female laid 24–37 eggs. Incubation period was prolonged with decrease of temperature and conversely it was lowered with rise in temperature. The most favourable condition was 30.6 ± 1° C with 48.7 % RH when egg - adult period was completed in 12.46–14 days. The longevity of male and female was 6–9 days and 7–11 days, respectively. The mite was active in the field during August–March but was scarce during hot summer and heavy rainfall months (Maity & Chakraborti, 1977).

Eutetranychus orientalis (Klein)

Gupta, 1985 listed this species infesting papaya.

Tetranychus puschelii Meyer

Sadana & Gupta, 1993 (*Entomon.*, **8** : 1–6) recorded it on papaya.

Tetranychus urticae Koch

Gupta (1985) listed this species infesting papaya.

Tetranychus fijiensis Hirst

Gupta (1985) listed this species infesting papaya.

Tetranychus neocaledonicus Andre

Nassar & Ghai (1981) reported this species on papaya.

Aponychus sulcatus Chaudhri

The record of the species on papaya was made by Sadana & Chhabra (1980: *Sci. & Cult.*, **46** : 319).

Brevipalpus californicus Banks

Gupta (1985) recorded it on papaya.

Gupta 1985 listed the following species occurring on papaya but their economic importance is unknown :

Calacarus brionesae Keifer

Euseius coccosocius (Ghai and Menon)

Amblyseius largoensis (Muma)

Calacarus citrifolii Keifer

This mite infests papaya along with citrus and peach.

Damage : The infestation of this mite produces blotches with concentric rings. Feeding by mite also causes leaf chlorosis. Die back may occur in case of severe infestation. The tree suffers from denudation.

Biology : Eggs are flat, circular, hatch in 3–4 days to I stage nymph, which after passing through II stage nymph reaches adulthood. The egg to adult period takes about 15 days.

14. JACK FRUIT (*Artocarpus integrifolia*)

Euseius coccineae (Gupta)

It was recorded on jack fruit by Gupta, 1978 (*Indian J. Acar.*, **2** : 60–70).

Tenuipalpus lalbaghensis ChannaBasavanna & Lakkundi

ChannaBasavanna & Lakkundi, 1977 described it collected on jack fruit from Karnataka.

Raoiella indica Hirst

This was recorded on this plant from Kerala producing characteristic brownish spots on leaves. Life cycle is completed in 16 days at 27±1 degree C. the eggs are laid on under surface of leaves.

Gupta (1985) listed the following mites occurring on this host :

Bakerina orissaensis Prasad

Eutetranychus anneckei Meyer

Petrobia harti Ewing

Panonychus ulmi (Koch)

Panonychus citri (McG.)

Neocunaxoides pradhani Gupta

Diptilomiopus artocarpae Mohanasundaram

15. DATE PALM (*Phoenix sylvestri/P. dactylifera*)

Raoiella indica Hirst

This is a common pest of date palm in many parts of India. It builds small colonies on undersurface of leaves covered with dense webs and produces reddish scattered patches wherever it feeds.

Euseius alstoniae (Gupta)

The record of this predatory mite on date palm was made by Gupta, 1977 (*Indian J. Acar.* 1: 28 - 37) from Gujarat.

16. BANANA (*Musa sapientum*)

Oligonychus indicus (Hirst)

This greenish coloured mite builds colonies on under surface of leaves and suck sap from leaves producing whitish patches (De *et al.*, 2010). Sometimes brownish spots are also developed. Its damage on banana is of moderate in nature.

Oligonychus oryzae (Hirst)

Its record on banana has been made by Karmakar & De (2004), De *et al.* (2010). The former report indicated that this species has potentiality to attain serious pest status.

Oligonychus sapienticolus Gupta

Its record was made on banana by De *et al.* (2010). It causes no damage to the host.

Oligonychus mangiferus (Rahman & Sapra)

Its record was made on banana by De *et al.* (2010). No economic importance of this species is known on banana.

Eutetranychus orientalis (Klein)

Its record was made on banana by De *et al.* (2010). No importance is known on banana.

Panonychus ulmi Koch

De *et al.* (2010) recorded it. No importance is known on banana

Tetranychus tumidus (Banks)

Its record was made on banana by Ramose & Rodriguez (1999). No importance is known on banana.

Tetranychus lombardinii Baker and Pritchard

Its record was made on banana by Jones (1978). No importance is known on banana.

Tetranychus urticae Koch

Its record was made on banana by De *et al.* (2010). No importance is known on banana.

Tetranychus piercei McGregor

Its record was made on banana by Zang & Fu (2004).

Petrobia sp.

De *et al.* (2010) reported it on banana but nothing has been mentioned about its economic importance.

Tetranychus neocaledonicus Andre

Its record was made on banana by De *et al.* (2010).

Brevipalpus phoenicis (Geij.)

Gupta (1983) recorded it on banana but nothing was mentioned about its damage. De *et al.*, (2010) also recorded it on banana.

Raoiella indica Hirst

This is also known to occur on banana (Kane & Ochoa, 2006) but the damage done by it is not known. De *et al.* (2010) also reported it on banana from West Bengal.

Phyllocoptruta musae Keifer

Mohanasundaram *et al.* (1989) recorded the species collected on banana but its damage is not known.

Euseius ovalis (Evans)

This is a common predatory mite, occurs on banana in different parts of India and it is considered as an effective predator of spider mites observed to be voraciously feeding on different stages of *O. oryzae*. It may turn out to be a good biocontrolling agent and hence needs to be conserved. Gupta, 1978 (*Indian J. Acar.* **2** : 60–77) reported it on banana from Tripura.

Neoseiulus fallacies (Garman)

Gupta, 1978 (*Indian J. Acar.*, **2** : 60–77) reported it on banana from Tripura.

The other predatory mites recorded on banana are :

Amblyseius largoensis (Muma) - Gupta (1985)

Scapulaseius sapienticola (Gupta) - Gupta (1985)

Paraphytoseius multidentatus Swirski & Shechter – Gupta (1985).

Phytoseius meyerae Gupta - Gupta (1985).

17. BER (*Zizyphus jujuba/Zizyphus mauritiana*)

Eriophyes cernuus Massee

Eriophyes cernuus is ber gall mite and has been reported from J & K, H.P., Punjab, Haryana, Rajasthan. Karnataka, Tamil Nadu. It was seen on ber trees grown on road sides and produced woody galls. Its population was low (3–12/cm^2 of gall area) in February which increased to 15–38 mites/cm^2 gall area in July. The gall associated other mites were the members of Phytoseiidae (*Amblyseius* sp.), Cheyletidae, Cunaxidae, Stigmaeidae (Bhullar & Kaur, 2010):

Larvacarus transitans (Ewing)

This mite poduces lac–like hemispherical dish-shaped closed hollow galls on cortical region of stem of *Zizyphus mauritiana*. A single larva settles on fresh twig and starts forming galls by producing a covering of rusty secretion. Larva matures into a female which lays unfertilized eggs giving rise to males only. One of the males fertilizes the mother producing normal progeny of males and females. The whole process takes place within the galls. No definite relation among mite population and temperature, humidity could be found indicating no direct effect of these factors on biology of this mite. Initially, the male population remains high in galls and later female number increases much more than males. At this stage, the number of female, male per gall becomes 25 and 10, respectively. (Ghai & Baker 1989: *Progress in Acarology,* **2** : 81-89). The number of galls ranged from 20-60 per/ twig while percentage of trees in terms of galls ranged from 29-89 in Jodhpur, (based on average of 16 twigs, 75 cm from apical buds), while Udaipur and Bharatpur had higher intensity of galls numbering 54 and 66, respectively.

Sharma (1991: *Modern Acarology,* **1** : 539-542) reported that this mite incidence commenced on 1st week of October and continued after 1st week of August. Gall intensity and mite population reach maximum in June and thereafter gradually declines. Degree of varietal resistance of ber to this mite was in descending order as Sev, Umran, Mundia, Gola. The same author also studied seasonal incidence of this mite in Rajasthan (Sharma, (1992: *Ann. Arid. Zone,* **31** : 231-232).

Varietal preference : Relative abundance of this mite on 5 varities of ber (Sev, Gola, Jogia, Pawandi and Umran) revealed that the incidence commenced in the 2nd week of October and continued till August. The varietal resistance in descending order was Sev> Jogia > Gola> Pawandi > Umran. (Sharma & Kushwaha, 1989, *Progress in Acarology* 2: 91-93). Latif & Wali (1961: *Pak. Sci. Res.,* **13** : 77-87) correlated emergence of *L. transitans* with onset of monsoon and reported that oviposition and hatching delayed with lower temperature and accelerated with rising temperature.

Bhullar & Kaur (2010) studied varietal preference of *Larvacarus transitans* on 4 varieties of Ber *viz.* Tikkari, Sev, Banarasi-Pawandi and local selection. Incidence commenced in October and continued till May-June. Varietal resistance in descending order was sev > Tikkari > local selection > Banarasi pawandi. Temperature and rainfall did not show any effect on mite population, but humidity adversely affected population. The probable reason for the decrease in the mite population was due to humidity and caused reducing egg production and increased mortality of newly hatched nymphs. Sharma & Kushwaha (1985: *Indian J. Acar.,* **9** : 69-76). Sharma (1992: *Annals arid Zone,* **31** : 231-232) studied seasonal incidence of *L.transitans* on *Zizyphus* in Rajasthan.

Control : Sharma & Kushwaha, 1985 (*Indian J. Acar.,* **9** : 77-87) conducted field and laboratory trials on variety *Banarasi powandi* in Rajasthan with 6 different pesticides among those phosphamidon proved to be most effective followed by dimethoate and dinobutan. The percentage of mortality was minimum after 24 hrs and maximum was achieved after 72 hrs of spray. Pesticides could kill mites within galls and that indicated the penetration of galls by pesticides.

Cheletogenes ornatus (Canestrini & Fanzago)

Sharma & Kushwaha (1983) reported *Cheletogenes ornatus* feeding on *L .transitans* @ 5.60 mites per 12 hrs. Incidence of predator started from 2nd week of June (32 per 10 galls), peak attained in 3rd week of July (230) and abruptly declined (24) in August. Temperature, RH, rainfall had no influence on predatory mite population.

Eutetranychus orientalis (Klein)

Sadana & Gupta (1983: *Entomon.*, **8** : 1-6) reported it from Punjab and Rather (1989: *Progress in Acarology*, **2** : 183–189) reported this mite from Kashmir valley during July. The incidence of damage has not been mentioned.

Eotetranychus hicoriae (Meyer)

This mite was reported on ber in Karnataka (Mallikarjunappa & Nageshachanrda, 1990). *Cunaxa setirostris* Hermann, *Euseius delhensis* (Narayanan & Kaur), *T. tetranychivorus* (Gupta), *Phytoseius swirskii* Gupta, *P. punjabensis* Gupta were recorded as predators of *Eotetranychus hicoriae* infesting Ber.

Paraphytoptus jujubae Mohanasundaram

Mohanasundaram, 1989 (*Entomon.*, **14** : 261–267) described this mite on ber.

18. SAPOTA (*Achras sapota/Manilkera achras*)

Tuckerella kumaonensis Gupta

This is a pest of sapota in India. The mites are bright red with long setae present posteriorly. The setae on dorsal body surface are broad, fan-shaped, whitish. This mite in all stages is found on fruit surface or hides under rough skin. The feeding causes discolouration of fruits often roughening of fruits surface. Such fruits loose its normal taste and the market value is reduced.

Tenuipalpus jagatkhanensis Sadana & Gupta

Sadana & Gupta, 1984 (*Entomon.*, **9** : 141–147) recorded it from Punjab on sapota.

Euseius alstoniae (Gupta)

Gupta, 1977 (*Indian J. Acar.*, **1** : 28–37) reported this mite on sapota in Gujarat.

Euseius delhiensis (Narayanan & Kaur)

Jagadish *et al.* (1995) reported this mite on sapota from Karnataka.

Typhlodromus rickeri Chant

Jagadish *et al.* (1995) reported this mite on sapota from Karnataka.

19. GRAPEVINES (*Vitis vinifera*)

Panonychus ulmi (Koch)

Occasionally, this mite infests grapevine in Kashmir, H.P., Punjab during late summer. The infested leaves become discoloured, bronzed and premature leaf drop occurs. This mostly occurs on the upper surface of the leaves. The time required to complete the life cycle depended upon the prevailing weather condition.

Oligonychus mangiferus (Rahman & Sapra)

In Punjab and Kashmir valley, this mite occurs on grapevine regularly producing characteristic brownish patches on leaves. The infested leaves gradually dry up. Infestation normally occurs during late summer. The leaves suffer from chlorosis and abscission on leaves. Vines become poorly developed and look unhealthy. The varieties Jaoes beli, Kabar ravi, Lamanto-Medelene angevine, Medeline royal, Muscat were less susceptible to this mite attack. In Kashmir, the suscaptible varities are Khalilli>Hussaini>Sahib>Perlette>Thonpson Seedless>Anab-e-Sahi>Heimrod.

Oligonychus punicae (Hirst)

This mite is also known to infest grapevines producing symptoms similar to *O. mangiferus*.

Tetranychus urticae Koch

This is another serious pest of grapevine in Kashmir valley. The infested plant suffers from chlorosis checking growth and yield of vine. Mani *et al.* (2007: *J. Acarol.*, **16** : 47–49) while studying population fluctuation in Maharashtra, reported that 87.9% of mite population could be predicted by 2 variables, *viz.*, minimum temperature and RH. Among these two factors, about 77.2% fluctuation in population was solely due to RH. It was concluded that weather factors chiefly RH influence the mite population on grapevine.

Eutetranychus orientalis (Klein)

This also occasionally infests grapevine.

Eotetranychus truncates Estebanes & Baker

This is another mite known to infest grapevine in Punjab and has been reported on 10 varieties of grapevines. The varierties Angoor kalan, Kishmish charni, Kata kurgan, Perlette were less susceptible to this mite. It has also been recorded from Kashmir (Rather, 1999: *J. Acarol.*, **15** : 18-24) doing severe damage during late summer and autumn.

Colomerus vitis (Pgst.)

This mite causes gall formation on leaves. Sometimes one form of this mite due to feeding, produces felty erineum on lower surface of leaves followed by blister like swellings on upper surface. The erineum patches are whitish at first, later become yellow and finally turn redish brown. They may be abundant during early spring. Another form attacks grape vine buds causing deformation of primordial bud clusters, distortion of basal leaves and stunting at growing points (Keifer *et al.*, 1982).

Caleptrimerus vitis Pag.

This mite causes vine rust in Kashmir (Rather, 1999: *J. Acarol.*, **15** : 18-24).

Brevipalpus phoenicis (Geij.)

Gupta & Dhooria (1972: *Curr. Sci.*, **41** : 824–825) reported this mite on grapevine from Punjab. It attacks lower surface of leaf, near midrib. Heavily infested leaves show yellowish green colouration, particularly around venation (Rather, 1999: *J. Acarol.*, **15** : 18-24).

Brevipalpus californicus (Banks)

Gupta (1985) mentioned the occurrence of this species on grapevine. This mite attacks lown surface of leaves. Infested leaves show yellowish green colouration (Rather, 1999: *J. Acarol.*, **15** : 18-24).

Tenuipalpus ludhianaensis Sadana & Chhabra

Sadana & Gupta (1982: *Int. J. Ent.*, **1** : 65–68) reported this species on grapevine from Punjab.

Euseius delhiensis (Narayanan & Kaur)

Gupta, 1977 (*Indian J. Acar.*, **1** : 28–37) reported this species on grapevines from Punjab.

Neoseiulus cucumeris (Oudemans)

Gupta, 1977 (*Indian J. Acar.*, **1** : 28–37) reported this species on grapevines from Punjab.

20. CASHEWNUT (*Anacardium occidentalis*)

Euseius kalimpongensis (Gupta)

This predatory mite was recorded on cashewnut from Orissa. Gupta (1978: *Indian J. Acar.*, **2** : 60–77).

Euseius coccineae (Gupta)

This predatory mite was recorded on cashew from Orissa. Gupta (1978: *Indian J. Acar.*, **2** : 60–77).

Amblyseius largoensis (Muma)

This predatory mite was recorded on cashew from Orissa. Gupta (1978: *Indian J. Acar.*, **2** : 60–77).

Abacarus anacardiae (Mohanasundaram)

Mohanasundaram (1982: *Indian J. Acar.*, **6** : 9–13) described this new species on *Anacardium occidental* is from within buds and flower bracts of the inflorescence and may cause flower sheding, poor fruit setting, etc.

21. MELON (*Cucumis melo*)

Tetranychus puschelii Meyer

Sadana & Gupta 1983 (*Entomon.*, **8** : 1– 6) reported this on melon and mentioned its occurrence on papaya also.

22. APPLE (*Pyrus malus*)

Panonychus ulmi (Koch)

This is one of the most important pests of apple, peach, pear, cherry and sometimes may also occur on grapes. It is a pest of deciduous fruits in H.P., J. & K. and other apple growing areas in North India. Though this mite is known in India since 1980 but damages are becoming more serious only in the recent years. Adults are brick red coloured, with whitish spots at base of setae. All stages of mites are found on leaves. During winter, it hibernates in egg stage. Overwintering eggs are reddish, partly flat, seen among tertiary branches and vegetative buds. During spring, the buds start bursting, the eggs hatch and mites become active. For development from egg to adult, the time taken is 20–28 days and the number of generations per year is 10–12.

Immatures feed on undersurface of the leaves while adults feed on both the surfaces. Due to feeding, white specks appear. Subsequently, the more damaged leaves turn yellowish brown and finally bronzy. Often the leaf blades may be rolled. In case of severe defoliation, the tree is denuded. All these affect the growth of the apple tree as well as its yield. Excess of chemical fertilizers and some cultivation practices help in rapid multiplication of this pest. Rather *et al.*, (1994: *J. Ecol.*, **6** : 287–291) studied ecobiology and host range and distribution of this mite in Kashmir valley. Rather & Bano (2007: *J. Acarol.*, **16** : 124–126) studied distribution of *P. ulmi* on apple in Kashmir valley. According to the authors, this mite prefers terminal portion of branches of trees perhaps due to more succulent foliage in that region and it was more so in summer. Therefore, that region requires more attention especially during summer in management of this mite on apple. Sharma and Bharadwaj (2007: *J. Acar.*, **16** : 41–42) studied the intratree distribution of overwintering eggs of *P. ulmi* on apple in HP and reported that maximum mean population of overwintering eggs on vegetative spurs (52.97 eggs) and fruiting spurs (112.80 eggs) were on east tree quadrant, followed by west quadrant (48.22 eggs in vegetative and 90.46 eggs in fruiting spurs), in north quardrant vegetative (39.29 eggs) and fruiting spurs (80.07 eggs) and minimum was in south tree quadrant (vegetative - 34.29 eggs, fruiting spurs 73.56 eggs). This indicates that *P. ulmi* prefers to lay eggs on fruiting spurs than on vegetative spurs. They prefer rough surface to lay eggs which provide them protection from vagaries of nature.

Chander *et al.* (1995) reported epidemic outbreak of ERM, *P. ulmi* on apple during 1991 as serious pest in apple orchards in HP. Three categories of orchards were identified viz basing on economic status of orchardists. Progressive orchards with pesticide application score of (a) > 75 %, (b) orchardists with scores between 50-75%, (c) marginal orchardists adopting pesticides application to the extent of 25-50%. Mite density was found to be directly related to the standard of management practices and pesticide scores and inversely proportional to phytoseiid predators. Commercial and well managed orchards gave average of 3000 motile stages of mites per infested leaves during peak infestation. More mites (186) motile stages per leaf were found in the middle strata of the tree with hightest infestation in peripheral region.

According to Rather (1995), P. *ulmi* is a serious pest of apple in J. & K. and also attacks many other plants. Foliage discolouration, bronzing, premature leaf drop, affecting quality of fruits, etc. are the damage symptoms. The other hosts were *Prunus domestica, P. persica, P. armeniaca, P. amyagdalus, P. avium, Pyrus communis, Morus alba, Rubus* sp. *Lycopersicum esculentum*, etc. Activity of this mite is from early spring to late autumn.

According to Kakar and Chander (1995), *P. ulmi* appeared in epidemic form in Kulu apple growing areas. The commercial cultivars were more proned to attack with 30-40 mites per leaf in apple orchards compared to pollinizing cultivars (18 mites/leaf). It overwinters in egg stage in twigs deposited in autumn. Summer eggs are pale and green laid on underside of leaves. Eggs hatch in April. Nymphs are of variable colours. They start feeding immediately after hatching. Regular pest management is needed with acaricides to suppress pest population. Spraying with miscible oil during dormant stage is effective which will keep mite population at low level during following spring.

Distribution : It is worldwide distributed.

Damage : All stages of this mite feed on undersurface of the leaf. Damaged leaves turn brown and defoliate. The yield becomes severely affected when plant is heavily infested.

Biology : Eggs are laid at the base of the buds. The time taken to complete the life cycle will depend upon prevailing temperature and duration is shorter at higher temperature and longer at lower temperature.

Seasonal Occurrence : Rather & Shah (2007: *J. Acarol.*, **16** : 88-90) studied role of abiotic factors on abundance of mites in apple orchard and reported positive significiant correlation with temperature, significant negative correlation with rainfall and R.H. The occurrence of peak population during summer in Kashmir valley was attributed to high temperature, optimum moisture content and good food availability during that period. Low population in winter was due to sub - zero temperature and water logging and poor food. Rather *et al.*, (1994: *J. Ecol.*, **6**: 287-291) - studied ecobiology, distribution and host range of *Panonychus ulmi* in Kashmir. Kumar & Bhalla (1993: *Curr. Sci.*, **64**(10) : 709) reported sudden outbreak of *P. ulmi* on apple in Himachal Padesh.

Control : Tetradifon, dicofol may be recommended to control this pest.

Rangrez and Rather (2007, *J. Acarol.*, **17** : 103–104) evaluated botanical pesticides against apple mite, *P. ulmi* in Kashmir and reported superiority of neem oil (1%, 1.5%) 144 hrs after treatment registering 51.98% and 53.01% mortality, respectively.

Bhardwaj & Bhardwaj (2010, p. 110-111) reported higher concentration (1%) of MaK all season, orchol - 13, Orches - 796 suppressed mite population while lower concentration (0.05%) could not provide adequate control. HP summer oil (1%, 0.05% servo all season oil (1%, 0.5%) also were effective for control of this mite.)

Kumar (1999: *J. Acarol.*, **14** : 34–35) reported higher population of *P. ulmi* and lower population of predators (*Chrysoperla* sp./*Typhlodronus* sp./*Amblyseius* spp./ *Zetzellia* sp.) in commercial well manged orchards as compared to neglected and poor managed orchards. Bhagat *et al.*, (1993) reported *Scymnus gracilis* as predator of *P. ulmi.*

Oligonychus (Oligonychus) yothersi (McG.)

It is also an important pest of fruit trees like apple, grapes, avocado with wide distribution (Tropical Asia, USA, S. America). It also attacks other plants like mango, litchi.

Damage : Due to feeding on the upper surface of leaves, white spots develop which later turn reddish brown.

Control : Any commonly available acaricide will control the pest.

Oligonychus (Oligonychus) punicae (Hirst)

This infests grapes and avocado and occasionally apple in India. The infested leaves are covered with cast off skins.

Eutetranychus orientalis (Klein)

This is called oriental citrus mite, is a major pest of citrus and also attacks a number of other plants like pear, peach, apple

Distribution : Mostly in tropical and subtropical world.

Tetranychus urticae Koch

This is a most injurious polyphagous mite in apple orchard in Kullu valley and Kashmir as well as in many apple growing areas in the world. It causes yellowing and drying of leaves.

Control : Rangrez and Rather (2007: *J. Acarol.*, **17** : 103-104) evaluated *in vitro*–efficacy of entomopathogenic fungi on *T. urticae* infesting apple. Initially, 24 hrs after treatment, the mortality with various fungi was poor but that increased with time and maximum was with *Hirsutella thompsonii* (41.10%) after 72 hrs and 59.99% after 144 hrs. *B. bassiana, M. anisopliae and V. lecanii* caused. 42.22%, 33.33%, 23.33% mortality after 144 hrs at a spore concentration of 1.0×10^8 spores/ml $^{-1}$, respectively. *Paecilomyces fumosoroseus* was least effective at both concentrations. Pionar and Pionar,

1998 (ARE, **43** : 449–469) also reported that *H. thompsonii* showed considerable success in controlling many mite species. Plants treated with two sparys of dicofol (0.05%) at petal fall and fruits development stages recorded minimum population of mites (12.4 mites/leaf) as compared to control (85.2 mites/leaf). Wettable sulphur was the least effective chemical in all schedules (spraying at pink bud, petal fall, Fruit Development Stage I and Fruit Development Stage II). Three sprays at petal fall, FDS I and FDS II stages recorded minimum population of mite per leaf (3.4–8.4) as compared to one or two sprays. Author recommended spray of dicofol (0.05%) at petal fall and fruit development stage I for managing the mites on apple. Bhardwaz & Sharma (2010, p. 81–83) evaluated seven modern pesticides against *T.urticae* on apple in HP and reported that hexithiazox 0.0025%, 0.005%., abamectin 0.01%, fenzaquin 0.001% and propergite 0.05% gave exellent control of *T. urticae*. Price & Nagle (2007 ISHS *Acta Horticulture*: 842), Longhurst *et al*., (1992, *Pest & Diseases*, Brighton, November 23–26 pp. 51–58) also reported abamectin and hexithiazox providing significant reduction of *T. urticae*.

Bryobia rubrioculus Scheuten

Rather 1987 (*Indian Sci. Cong. Assoc.*) reported this mite on apple in Kashmir valley and studied its bionomics.

Oligonychus yothersi (McGregor)

It is an important pest of apple along with grapes and avocado. The feeding on upper surface of leaves causes production of white spots which later develop into reddish brown patch.

Control : Any commonly available acaricide will control this pest.

Kumar & Kumar (1999: *J. Acarol.*, **14** : 32–33) and Kumar (1999: *J. Acarol.*, **14** : 34–35) reported a number of predatory mites on apple orchard in HP. Those belong to *Typhlodromus* spp., (including *Typhlodromus pyri*), *Amblyseius* sp., *Zetzellia* spp. as well as some predatory insects like *Chrysopa* sp. and the authors were of opinion that these predators may help in suppression of pest mite. It was reported that these predators were more in neglected orchards than in well managed orchards.

23. CHERRY (*Prunus cerasus/Prunus avium*)

Rather, 1989 (*Progress in Acarology*, **2** : 183–189) reported *Phytoptus pyri* on cherry during July in Kashmir valley.

Banerjee, (1989) mentionted *Panonychus ulmi* Koch on cherry causing browning of leaves followed by defoliation.

Gupta, (1985) recorded *Euseius finlandicus* on this host.

24. APRICOT (*Prunus armeniaca*)

Rather, 1989 (*Progress in Acarol.*, **2** : 183–189) reported the following species on this host from Kashmir valley.

Brevipalpus pulcher (C. & F.)

This appears in September–October in Kashmir valley and is considered to be most destructive species. Hibernation occurs underneath bud scale. Female becomes active in first week of April. It feeds on young leaf buds, lower surface of leaves and fruits. Leaves become bronzy and fruits turn rusty. Heavily infested trees become stunted, deformed and yield becomes severely affected.

Panonychus ulmi (Koch)

This occurs during August and causes injury to the plants as explained in case of apple.

Cenopalpus sp.

This mite also occurs during September and does minor damage.

Tetranychus urticae Koch

This has been recorded on this host in Kashmir valley. The profuse webbing serves as traps of fungal spores as well as dust. This affects normal physiological activity of the plant.

Apart from the above phytophagous mites, the predatory mites recorded on this host are *Eusieus insanus, E. prasadi, E. finlandicus, Typhlodromus hadii, Typhlodromus umbratus* and *Typhloctonus prunus*. However, their predatory importance is unknown. The author pointed out that when the predatory mites are present in the field, the spraying should be done with caution to avoid elimination of predators (Rather, 1989).

25. PLUM (*Prunus domestica/Prunus salicina*)

Rather (1989) reported the following phytophagous mites on this plant :

Brevipalpus pruni Maninder & Ghai

This species was recorded in September. No information on damage is available.

Brevipalpus pulcher C. & F.

This mite was recorded in August. It causes the appearance of characteristic damage symptoms of this species.

Cenopalpus sp.

This was recorded during August.

Eotetranychus pruni Oudemans

This was reported to be most destructive mite pest on this host. Its infestation was seen during August. Other mites recorded on this host are :

Eutetranychus orientalis - Gupta (1985) reported this.

Bryobia praetiosa - Gupta (1985) reported this.

Panonychus ulmi - Gupta (1985) reported this.

These mites were recorded on this host doing the typical damage symptoms for these species. It is known from Uttarakhand, Jammu & Kashmir, Himachal Pradesh occurring on this host. Some of the predatory mites recorded on plum are :

Amblyseius indirae Gupta

A. largoensis (Muma)

Euseius delhiensis (Narayanan & Kaur)

E. finlandicus (Oudemans)

Typhlodromus pruni Gupta

Typhlodromus rickeri Chant

However, their potentiality as predators is unknown.

26. HUDSON ALMOND (*Prunus bokhariensis*)

Brevipalpus pulcher (C. & F.)

It was recorded on this host during October from Kashmir valley (Rather, 1989).

27. ALMOND (*Amygdalus communis/Prunus amygdalus*)

Bryobia rubrioculus Scheuten

Rather (1989) reported this mite causing serious damage on almond in Gilgit and Ladakh regions. Infestation was heavy during August-September.

Pannonychus ulmi (Koch)

Rather (1995) recorted it on this host during early spring to late autumn.

Eutetranychus orientalis (Klein)

Occasionally, this mite infests almond tree but does not do significant damage

28. PEACH (*Prunus persica*)

Brevipalpus pulcher (C. & F.)

It was recorded on this host during September from Kashmir valley (Rather, 1989).

Eutetranychus orientalis (Klein)

Gupta & Gupta (1978) recorded it on peach. This mite occurs on upper surface of leaves. A heavy webbing envelops the leaves where dust particles adhere and that affects normal physiological activities of plant. The leaves turn yellowish brown and dry up.

Eutetranychus africanus (Tucker)

This mite attacks peach in India and Africa. The infestation causes heavy defoliation.

Panonychus ulmi (Koch)

This mite also attacks peach along with several other temperate fruits. All stages of mite feed on undersurface of leaves. Damaged leaves turn brown and defoliate. The yield is severely affected. It has been recorded from Uttar Pradesh, Jammu & Kashmir, Himachal Pradesh (Rather, 1989, 1995).

Bryobia praetiosa Koch

This mite infests peach as well as pear and is distributed in Asia, Africa, USA. The infested leaves become yellow and then turn bronzy. Such plants suffer defoliation. The growth and yield are affected. Gupta *et al.*, (1975: *Sci. & Cult.*, 41) reported good performance of Galecron (0.05%), Binapacryl (0.04%), tetradifon(0.04%), Oxydemeton methyl and Dimethoate in controlling this mite.

Oligonychus magiferus (R. & S.)

This mite attacks peach along with several other fruit trees and is known from India, Pakistan, Mauritius, Egypt. It infests upper surface of leaves. Active period of this mite is March–April.

Calacarus citrifolii K.

This mite infests peach along with citrus and papaya. The infestation of this mite produces blotches with concentric rings. Cholorosis of leaves and dye - back are also common symptoms.

Biology : The eggs are flat, circular, hatch in 3–4 days to larva and that after passing through nymph I and nymph II stages reach adulthood. Egg - adult period takes about 15 days.

Neoseiulus reticulatus (Oudemans)

This predatory mite was recorded on peach from Punjab (Gupta: 1977, *Indian J. Acar.*, **1** : 28–37).

Tetranychus kanzawai Kishida

Its record was made on this host from Kashmir valley during August (Rather, 1989).

29. HOPS (*Humulus lupulus*)

Tetranychus urticae Koch

Rather, 1995 reported this mite to attack hops along with other plants and some fruit trees, sunflower, cotton, ornamental plants, etc., in Jammu & Kashmir during early summer till late spring. The damage caused by this mite is reported to be serious. Weeds like *Datura stramoneum, Solanum nigrum, Lathyrus sativa, Forsythia japonica*, forest trees like *Morus alba, Salyx babylionica, Ailanthus altissium*, etc. served as alternate hosts.

30. WATER MELON (*Citrullus vulgaris*)

The species *Tetranychus neocaledonicus* and *T. macfarlanei*, infest this plant producing characteristic chlorosis of leaves. It never causes any serious damage.

31. LOQUAT (*Eriobotrya japonica*)

Tetranychus urticae Koch

Occasionally, it infests this plant but never attains any serious form.

Gupta (1985) reported the following mites on this host but their economic importance is unknown :

Schizotetranychus tephrosiae Guitierrez

Eutetranychus nagai Nassar & Ghai

Tetranychus neocaledonicus Andre

Bryobia praetiosa Koch

Oligonychus biharensis (Hirst)

O.mangiferus (R. & S.)

Brevipalpus californicus (Banks)

B. obovatus Donnadieu

32. CLOVER

Bryobia praetiosa Koch

This is a dark brown mite with 1st pair of legs much longer than other legs. The feeding causes the leaves to become yellowish brown and start drying. This mite overwinters at egg stage and some hibernate in adult stage.

Tetranychus urticae Koch

This mite also occurs on clover causing yellowing and drying of leaves.

33. AVOCADO (*Persea americana*)

Oligonychus punicae (Hirst)

This mite occasionally attacks avocado in India. The infested leaves become covered with cast off skins.

34. STRAWBERRY (*Fragaria nilgerrensis/F. vesca*)

Polyphagotarsonemus latus (Banks)

Infestation of this mite was noticed on this plant but the damage was never of any serious nature.

Paraamblyseius fragariae Gupta

This predatory mite was recorded on this plant.

35. MUSKMELON (*Cucumis melo*)

Tetranychus urticae and *T. neocaledonicus*

These species occasionally attack this plant. In case of severe attack, the entire leaf becomes pale yellowish with brownish small patches.

36. PEAR (*Pyrus cmmunis*)

Panonychus ulmi (Koch)

This mite regularly attacks pear and due to sucking of plant sap from under surface of leaves, those become yellowish, later turn bronzy and finally the plants suffer defoliation. The mite remains active during early spring to late autumn.

Oligonychus mangiferus (R. & S.)

This mite occasionally infests pear producing similar type of damage symptoms as it produces on other plants. Its active period is during March–April.

Eutetranychus orientalis (Klein)

Gupta (1985) listed this species infesting pear. It causes same type of damage as it does on other hosts.

Bryobia praetiosa Koch

This is one of the most injurious pests of pear and in case of severe infestation all the leaves turn brown, wither and their petiolear attachment becomes so loose that a simple touch to the leaf causes defoliation.

Tenuipalpus solanensis Sadana & Rajendra

Sadana & Rajendra (1990: *Acarologia*, **31** : 357–360) recorded this mite on pear.

Tenuipalpus pyrusae Maninder & Ghai

Gupta (1985) listed this mite under this host, but it does no serious damage.

Tenuipalpus kesari Sadana & Rajendra

Sadana & Rajendra (1990, *Acarologia*, **31** : 357–360) recorded this mite on pear.

Tenuipalpus decus Sadana & Sidhu

Sadana & Rajendra (1990: *Acarologia*, **31** : 357–360) recorded this mite on pear.

Phytoptus pyri (Pag.)

This mite attacks pear causing blemishing and twisting of leaves.

Some of the predatory mites known to occur on this plant are :

Euseius prasadi, E. bambusae, E. kodaikanalensis, E. alstoniae, Amblyseius neorykei, E. finlandicus, E. delhiensis, Typhlodromus himalayensis Typhlodromus communis, Typhlodromus kodaikanalensis, Neoseiulella transitans. However, their predatory importance is unknown

37. MALAY APPLE (*Eugenia malaccensis*)

Oligonychus mangiferus (R. & S.)

This mite occurs on upper surface of leaf. The damage is of no serious nature.

38. CUSTARD APPLE (*Anona squamosa*)

Oligonychus mangiferus (R. & S.)—Gupta (1985) listed it on this host.

Brevipalpus phoenicis (Geij.)—Gupta(1985) listed it on this host.

39. CUCUMBER (*Cucumis sativus*)

Tetranychus neocaledonicus (Andre)—Gupta (1985) listed it on this host.

T. macfarlanei Baker & Pritchard—Gupta (1985) listed it on this host.

T. urticae Koch—Gupta (1985) listed it on this host.

Brevipalpus californicus (Banks)—Gupta (1985) listed it on this host.

The above mites occasionally attack cucumber. However, the damage of none of those barring *T. neocaledonicus* is of serious nature.

40. WALNUT (*Juglans regia*)

Eriophyes erineus (Nal.)

It is a major pest causing galls on upper leaf surface and produces dense hairy outgrowth on the lower surface, affecting the yield seriously (Rather, 1989). The infested trees bore less fruits.

Eriophyes tristiatus (Nal.)

This mite causes yellow bead-like blisters on leaves along midrib and veins. Heavily insfested trees bore no fruits. Predatory mites, *Euseius vignus, E. insanus, Kuzinellus kuzini, Typhlodromus denmarki, T. tarbatejamae* were also recorded in association with this mite (Rather, 1989).

3.7. VEGETABLES

India is next only to China in area and production of vegetables contributing to 13.88 % in the world production. India occupies first position in cauliflower, second in onion and third in cabbage production in the world. West Bengal, Orissa, Uttar Pradesh, Bihar and Maharashtra are the major vegetable growing states in India covering 35.80 lakhs ha. and contributing 61.07 % of the total production (Chadha, 2010). About 40 types of vegetables belonging to Solanaceous, Cucurbitaceous, Leguminous, Cruciferous, root crops and leafy vegetables are grown in Indian tropical, subtropical and temperate regions. The important vegetable crops are potato, onion, tomato, brinjal, peas, beans, okra, chilli, spinach, cabbage, cauliflower, pumpkin, bottlegourd, cucumber, carrot, radish, etc. and mites infesting those crops along with other vegetables are discussed in this chapter.

1. INDIAN BEANS (*Dolichos lablab/Lablab purpureus*)

Tetranychus ludeni Zacher

This is a polyphagous species and occurs on over 150 hosts throughout the world. Green vegetables are most attacked.

Diagnosis : Adult females are carmine with red legs.

Distribution : India, South Africa, Europe, New Zealand.

Nature of damage : The feeding by this mite causes first yellowing of leaves and then necrotic patches encompass. Such leaves dry up. In case of severe infestation, the entire leaf gets enveloped with webs which further affect normal physiological activities of the plants. In some cases the leaves curl, twist and fall off.

Biology : The reproduction is by both through parthenogenesis and sexually. In case of former, the offsprings are males only and in case of latter it is of both sexes. Normally the life cycle is completed in 8-10 days depending upon the prevailing temperature which may be lengthened at lower temperature and shortened at higher temperature. A number of studies have been done on biological aspects of this mite and those have been reviewed in Gupta (1985). Nitrogen fertilizer increases population of this mite. Malviya & Rai (1995) studied biology of this mite on Indian beans at average temperature (21.28°C) and 48.5%RH and reported that life cycle took 7.28±0.62 days (male) and 7.58±0.80 days (female) with fecundity of 53.05±10.79 eggs (mated female).

Seasonal occurrence : This mite occurs in the field throughout the year. Population is dependent on less rainfall, low RH and high mean temperature.

Control : Sannaveerappanavar & ChannaBasavanna (1989: *J. Acarol.*, **11** : 83–89) conducted experiment for control of this mite on beans. It was reported that sublethal doses of HCH, Carbaryl, DDT, Dicofol, Endosulfan did not stimulate oviposition of *T. ludeni.* Fecundity was reduced by dicofol and endosulfan. Test chemicals had no effect on adult female longevity. DDT and carbaryl changed the sex ratio making it female biased. DDT at 0.1% produced highest percent (80.79%) of female progeny compared to 71.04% for untreated check. Increased proportion of females contributed to mite resurgence in the field after the treatment and that also caused elimination of natural enemies.

Control : Onkarappa & Ashok Kumar (1995: *Bangalore Symposium*, p. 78) evaluated synthetic pyrethroids like deltamethrin, fenpropathrin, cypermethrin and fenvalerate. These induced higher reproductive potentiality of *Tetranychus urticae* on French bean. Highest increase in fecundity was (30.62%) over control as was seen in deltamethrin at 0.00084%, followed by fenpropathrin (86.26%) at 0.0015%, cypermethrin (66.92%) at 0.00019%, deltamethrin (64.99%) at 0.00042%, fenpropathrin (53.92%) at 0.003%, fenvalerate (26.82%) at 0.003%.

In another study, Malaviya & Rai (1995), (Bangalore Symposium, p. 80), reported dicofol 0.04% and monocrotophos 0.04% to be most effective. Further, plant products like Neemate 0.05%, Replin 1% were as effective as conventional pesticides. These pesticides not only caused mortality of *T. ludeni* on Indian beans but also had no adverse effect on predators.

Srinivasa & Chandrasekhara (1999: *J. Acarol.*, **15** : 6–9) studied role of synthetic pyrethroids in causing pest resurgence on Indian beans. The females when sprayed with synthetic pyrethroids (Cypermethrin, fenvalerate, deltamethrin) had shown excess production of eggs indicating that these pesticides stimulated reproductive capacity directly specially at the sublethal doses (hormoligosis). The flare up of mite population following pesticidal application may be attributed to elimination of natural enemies consequent upon direct effect of synthetic pyrethroids when used in sublethal doses (hormoliogosis) or indirectly through changes in host plant nutritional satus (trophobiosis) and reduced interspecific competition due to dispersal behaviour (Hall & Thacker, 1993, *J. Econ. Ent.* 86: 537-543). The present findings of sublethal doses ascertained that the mechanism of resurgence of mites in the absence of effective predators is due to reproductive stimulation by small quantities of synthetic pyrethroides.

Natural enemies : Gupta, 1977 (*Indian J. Acar.*, **1** : 28–37) reported *Euseius ovalis* (Evans) on beans.

Tetranychus urticae Koch

This mite also infests French beans. Usha *et al.* (1999: *J. Acarol.*, **15** : 25–28) reported that population development of *T. urticae* was higher on plants under moderate moisture stress (50% FC) than on plant under slight stress (75% FC) or plant under severe stress. The contents of total sugar, reducing sugar, non reducing sugar and proline of the leaf increased with stress but moisture content reduced. Hence, according to this study, the increases of above factors favour its multiplication but after a point, moisture becomes limiting factor for the mites to assimilate the nutrients.

Tetranychus neocaledonicus Andre

This spider mite infests beans throughout India. It preferred middle aged leaves as compared to old ones. Peak population was attained during September, November, March and was low during rainy season.

2. SPONGE GOURD (*Luffa acutangula*)

Brevipalpus obovatus Donnadieu

This is a flat, pale to dark red mite with various pattern of dark pigmentation over it. The pigmentation depends upon the type of food taken by the mite. This mite has been recorded on this host (Goyal *et al.*, 1985: *Indian J. Acar.*, **9** : 63-68) doing damage to this crop. The authors reported that the *Luffa acutangula* is a suitable host on which the life cycle is completed within 14-18 days and fecundity was 10-12 eggs/female.

3. BRINJAL (*Solanum melongena*)

Tetranychus neocaledonicus Andre

This produces damage syndromes very similar to those of *T. urticae.*

Control : Saradamma *et al.* (1983) reported fish oil, insecticidal soap, neem extract, tobacco decoction, dicofol, malathion, etc. which provided effective control of *T. neocaledonicus* on brinjal both under laboratory and field conditions.

Varietal screening : Sharma (1984: *Indian J. Acar.*, **8** : 100–103) screened 4 varieties of brinjal, viz, black beauty, pusa purple long, PÉ, Pusa purple round in Rajasthan. The incidence was maximum on variety black beauty followed by Pusa purple round. No appreciable differences were seen between population of various stages during October–January but population of various stages significantly varied according to season. Adult, immature and egg population varied significantly according to variety.

Tetranychus macfarlanei Baker & Pritchard

Application of Abamectin, hexithiazox, difenthiuron, fenazaquin and propergite recorded after 2nd spray significant reduction in mite population on brinjal recording 0.10, 0.15, 0.20, 0.40 and 0.40 mites per 4 sq cm area. The increase in yield was highest in hexithiazox. (Prasanna *et al.*, 2007: *J. Acar.*, **17** : 79–80). Patel & Nandihalli 2007 (*J. Acar.*, **17** : 100–102) evaluated biorationals against *T. macfarlanei* on brinjal and reported that neem oil (2%) caused maximum inhibition of egg hatching

(55.18%), while dicofol (0.046%) registered highest ovicidal action (98.33%). The other sprayings like Nemazol F 5AZ, sweet flag rhizome extract, Econeem plus and turmeric rhizome extracts were also tried.

Tetranychus ludeni Zacher

Varietal preference : Reddy & Daskaran (*Mysore J. Agric Sci.*, **25** : 331–334) studied biology of *T. ludeni* and its varietal preference on 4 varieties of brinjal.

Influence of fertilizers : Puttaswmy & ChannaBasavanna (1982: *Indian J. Acar.*, **6** : 64–71) studied influence of fertilizers on incidence of *T. ludeni* on brinjal and reported that mite population was at higher level when nitrogenous fertilizers were used and thus established a direct relationship with plants and nitrogen supply.

Seasonal occurrence : Puttaswamy & ChannaBasavanna (1981: *Indian J. Acar.*, **5** : 69–79) reported the occurrence of this mite on brinjal throughout the year. It started building of population from April and reached peak in May–July. The increase of population was associated with less rainfall, low RH and higher mean temperature.

Predators : *Stethorus pauperculus* Weise, *Oligota oviformis* (Casey) and *Scolothrips sexmaculatus* (Pers.) were found associated with this mite.

Life cycle : On brinjal, it took 9.24 days to complete the life cycle laying 71 eggs/ female and lived for 14.13 days (Puttaswamy & ChannaBasavanna, 1981).

Control : Ramaraju *et al.*, 1995 evaluated plant products against *T. ludeni* towards development on brinjal and the descending order of efficacy was neem oil (5%), *Vitex negundo* leaf extract (5%), *Prosopis juliflora* leaf extract (5%), NSKE (5%), *Vitex negundo* (3%), Neem leaf extract 5% and 3%, *Eichhornia crassipes* (5%), *P. juliflora* (3%), NSKE (3%), *E. crassipis* (3%). The development prolonged (12 to 17.25 days) on plants treated with neem oil (5 %), *Vitex negundo* leaf extract (5%), *Prosopis juliflora* (5%) as against 10.25 days in untreated check.

Tetranychus puschelii Meyer

Sadana & Gupta (1983: *Entomon.*, **8** : 1–6) reported this mite attacking brinjal along with Okra and chilli.

Tetranychus urticae Koch

This is a polyphagous species and has a wide host range of over 150–200 species all over the world but the vegetables are its major hosts where this mite occurs throughout the year having peak population during summer months. They mostly make their colonies on undersuraface of leaves and cover the colonies with thick webs. The webbing in case of servere infestation may be covering the entire plant affecting its normal physiological activities.

Damage : Initially, on the points of mite puncturing on leaves the cholophyll gets damaged and yellow spots appear, which subsequently coalesce to form yellow patch. Later, the leaves dry up, defoliate and that in turn, reduces the growth and vigour of the plant. The damage may vary from 30-80%.

Biology : The eggs are laid both asexually and sexually. The progeny in case of former is males only while in case of latter, the progeny is of both sexes. The egg - adult period takes about 8-10 days and the post egg stages are larva - protonymph - deutonymph - adult each of 2-3 days while in case of male the deutonymphal stage is missed.

Cultural control : Bhullar and Bhatt (2007: *J. Acarol.*, **16** : 52-54) studied effect of cultural practices on population of *T. urticae* on brinjal and reported that plants grown with polythene mulch recorded maximum mite population (20 mites/2cm^2 leaf areas) followed by straw mulch (19.3 mites/2cm^2). Control plots recorded lowest mite population. Differences were nonsignificant.

Chemical control : For control of this mite on brinjal, plictran & dicofol were more effective. (Shah *et al.*, 1989: *Progress in Acar.*, **2** : 433-437), dicofol (0.05%) was safe to predator and effective against *T.urticae* (Pal *et al.*, 1989: *Progress in Acar.*, **2** : 453-459). Endosulfan (0.075%) was both effective and safe to predators while monocrotophos and dicofol were toxic to predators (Rai *et al.*, 1995). Thangaraju *et al.* (1995) reported percentage of resurgence as 20.51% in methyl demeton, 15.70% in quinalphos, 65.29% in acehpate, 82.93% in carbaryl, 56.38% in carbosulfan and 22.5% in fenvalerate. Three sprays of fenvalerate, dimethoate and acephate resulted in increased resurgence percentage of 329.16% in fenvalearte, 198.84% in dimethoate and 171.65% in acephate. Dicofol (0.04%), monocrotophos (0.04%) and endosulfan (0.075%) were highly effective against this mite as compared to tetradifon (0.1%), triazophos (0.05%), replin (1%), wettable sulphur (0.25%), margocide ck (0.1% and neemark (0.5%) which were found less effective (Vora and Rai,1995). Nicotin was reported to be more toxic with LC_{50} value of 3.58 followed by neem oil (3.84), garlic (4.33), NSKE (6.57) and Nochi (7.15) (Veeravel *et al.*, 1995). Propergite 57 EC (750 and 1000 ml/ha), Spiromesifen 240 SC (300 and 400 ml/ha), Fipronil 5 SC (45 gm ai/ha), Fenazaquin 10EC (125 gm ai/ha), Milbemectin 1 EC (3.5 g ai/ha), Dicofol 18.5EC (2.5 ml/L) and Chlorfenafyr 10 SC (75 g ai/ha) were very effective in reducing mite population(Onkarappa *et al.*, 2007, *J. Acarol.*, **17** : 81-83). Mallik *et al.* 2010 also reported that spiromesifen 24% SC @ 300 and 400 ml/ha on *T. urticae* on brinjal could provide total control. Sedma 50 SC(fenpyroximate) @ 1000 ml/ha was highly effective and better than fenazaquin 10% EC, propergite 57% EC,fenpropathrin 10% EC, dicofol 18.5% EC and profenophos (50% EC).

Varietal preference : Misra *et al.* (1990: *Indian J. Agric. Sci.*, **34** : 172-185) studied incidence of *T.urticae* on some selected accessions of brinjal with special reference to physical basis of resistance. Brinjal variety ABH - 1, had maximum density of *T.urticae*, followed by Morvi - 42 and M - 36. ABH - 2 had shown least incidence followed by Pusa purple long and Ringan Gulabi. ABH was highly resistant (Vora & Rai, 1995). Leaf sheath width, thickness and number of hairs had no relation with resistance/tolerance agaist mite (Rai *et al.*, 1995)

Alternate hosts : Some wild plants like *Ageratum conyzoides, Cannabis sativa, Spergula arvensis* acted as alternate hosts (Pal *et al.*, 1989).

Predators : *Paraphytoseius multidentatus, Cunaxa setirostris* were found as predators. Rai *et al.* (1995) reported *Phytoseius rachelae* and *Pronematus fleschneri* as effective predators.

Seasonal occurrence : The population of *T.urticae* on brinjal was directly related to temperature, humidity and rainfall. Temperature, RH and wind velocity were positively correlated with incidence of mite. Mean number of mite on pure brinjal crop was 12.6 per leaf and in mixed crop it was 5.3/leaf (Veeravel *et al.*, 1995). Morphological features of leaves in relation to mite incidence, leaf width, length, number of hairs, veins, depth of middle vein, groove and thickness of leaf had no bearing on imparting resistance/tolerance against spider mite (Pal *et al.*, 1989). Rai *et al.* (1995) also reported positive correlation of this mite with temperature and RH and negative with rainfall.

Brevipalpus phoenicis (Geij.)

Gupta & Gupta (1978: *Indian J. Acar.*, **3** : 90) reported occurrence of this mite from MP on brinjal.

Paraphytoseius multidentatus S. & S.

Gupta (1978 *Indian J. Acar.*, **2** : 66–77) reported this mite on brinjal.

Phytoseius kapuri Gupta

Gupta (1977: *Indian J. Acar.*, **2** : 1–11) reported this mite on brinjal from Gujarat, Meghalaya.

Neoseiulus bindrai Gupta

Gupta (1977: *Indian J. Acar.*, **1** : 28–37) reported this mite on brinjal from Punjab.

Aceria lycopersici (Wolff.)

Host & distribution : This mite occurs abundantly on brinjal and less on tomato in India. It is wide spread in distribution.

Field identification : It is a light brownish mite, occurs on undersurface of brinjal leaf as vagarants.

Damage : It produces excessive growth of hairs (erineum) on leaves and stems. The affected plants look greyish white.

Seasonal occurrence : *Aceria lycopersici* occurs on brinjal throughout the year but more common during June to November. The prevalence of this mite is more on top canopies of leaves and less on middle and bottom canopies.

Control : Spraying of monocrotophos or dicrotophos @ 0.015% will control this mite.

4. OKRA (*Abelmoschus esculentus*)

Tetranychus ludeni Zacher

This mite infests okra throughout India and elsewhere, producing damage symptoms characteristics of spider mites i.e yellowing and drying of leaves.

Initially, *T. ludeni* influenced development of *T. neocaledonicus* on okra as evident from the fact that when *T. neocaledonicus* population was alone, its population was much higher as compared to when mixed with infestation of *T. ludeni*. After 3 weeks, the population of both suffered reduction due to competition among two species population.

Rai *et al.* (1999, *J. Acarol.*, : **14** : 105–108) worked out effect of date of sowing, weather factors, natural enemies and role of botanicals on *T. ludeni* on bhendi. Mite population was positively correlated with abiotic factors. *T. ludeni* appeared in April and peak was attained during May. Crops sown during 6 November–21 December escaped mite damage while those sown during 21 January-21 February were seriously affected.

Control : Kumar & Sharma (1993: *Ind. J. Pl. Prot.*, **21** : 68–71) studied biology and control of mite on okra. Dicofol (0.04%), monocrotophos (0.04%) and methyl-o-demeton (0.025%) were highly effective.

Predators : *Euseius alstoniae* (Gupta) and *Scolothriprs indicus* were found to be effective predators and had shown significant positive relation with population of *T.ludeni* on okra (Rai *et al.*, 1999).

Tetranychus puschelii Meyer

Sadana & Gupta 1983 (*Entomon.*, **8** : 1-6) reported this mite on okra.

Tetranychus urticae Koch

Sivakumar & Hariprasad (1999, *J.Acarol.*, **14** : 116–118) reported polytrin C 44EC (1.0, 1.5, 2.0 L/ha), Cypermethrin 10 EC (0.8L/ha), Nuvacron 10 EC (0.625L/ha) and dicofol 18.5EC (1.5L/ha) when tested on okra against *T. urticae* could reduce population within 2 days after spraying but population increased in all the treatments 8 days after spraying. Maximum increase was in cypermethrin.

The bioefficacy of all acaricides was affected when water with high electrical conductivity (WHEL) and high pH (WHpH) were used (Duripandian & Raghupathy 1999: *J. Acarol.*, **13** : 81–85). Tudu *et al.*, (2010) also got excellent control with spiromesifen against this mite which also gave significant increase in yield.This observation conformed with those of Roffeni *et al.* (2008: *Fitopathologiche*, **1** : 29-34; Cloyd *et al.*, 2009: *Hort. Sci.*, **44** : 476–480 and Srinivasa *et al.*, 2003, *J. Pl Prot.*, **31** : 146-147). Acrex 30 EC (Dinobutol) 0.09% gave 88.16% mortality of *T. urticae* on Okra (Kumar and Kareem, 1989). Pande *et al.* (1996: *J. Ad. Zool.*, **17** : 7–11 (reported loss of okra due to infestation of *T. urticae*. Kumaran *et al.*, (2007, *Indian J. Acar.*, **17** : 4–

6) estimated damage and yield loss due to infestation of *T. urticae* on okra. The vegetative stage of crop was more proned to damage and yield loss is more when infestation occurs at early stage of crop because at this stage it gives sufficient loss in time gap available for population build up than to flowering and fruiting stages resulting in more yield reduction than the mites infesting at later stage. Lower yield loss was 60 DAS might be due to high plant vigour which helped plant tolerance. This strongly provides an insight as to when to apply chemicals for management of this mite. Feeding sites of *T. urticae* on Okra was in the following descending order mature leaves,young leaves, fruits, flowers, buds.

Seasonal occurrence : Pande *et al.* (1996: *J. Ad. Zool.*, **17** : 7-11) studied seasonal occurrence of this mite on okra. According to Chinniah *et al.* (2007: *J. Acarol.*, **16** : 45-46) significant positive correlation existed with maximum temperature and negative correlation with RH and rainfall in respect of *T. urticae* on okra. Negative correlation with population also was seen with minimum temperature.

Control : Dicofol 0.04%, neem oil (5%), *Vitex negundo* extract (5%), NSKE (5%), neem oil (3%) were reported to be highly effective against *T. urticae* infesting okra after first spray which was 45 days after sowing and second spray 15 days later (Ramaraju *et al.*, 1995). Singh & Mukherjee (1995) reported wettable sulphur (0.25%), NSKE (0.23%) and fenvalerate (0.005%) were good for control of *T. urticae* on okra and were safe to predatory mite, *Neoseiulus longispinosus* while dicofol (0.04%), ethion (0.05%), monocrotophos (0.05%) gave maximum mortality. Balaji *et al.* 2007 (*J. Acarol.*, **17** : 38-39) reported that NSKE 60 kg/ha + *Paecilomyces fumosoroseus* ($1x10^8$ colonies per gram) recorded maximum mortality of *T.urticae* (adult + eggs) infesting okra. Profenophos 50% EC @1% used as check recorded highest reduction of mites + eggs. Diafenthuron 50 SC, buprofezin, diafenthuron 50 WP, fenazaquin and fenpyroximate significantly reduced mite population after two rounds of sprays with increase in yield compared to control.According to Kumaran *et al.*, (2007), Azadirachtin 3 ml/L, *Vitex negundo* dry leaf extract (50g/l) and TNAU neem oil (C) 60 EC (30 ML/L) were effective against *T. urticae* on okra due to high antifeedant activity. Dicofol was superior to neem products and neem oil was superior among neem products and was most effective (Umamaheswari *et al.*, 1999: *J. Acarol.*, **14** : 79)

Tetranychus macfarlanei Baker and Pritchard

This mite damages okra crop in the same manner like other spider mites producing speckled appearance on leaves. Gradually, the leaves become yellow, later brown and finally dry up. Infested plants become droopy. This mite seriously infests okra when grown as summer crop in Gujarat. Population was correlated with minimum temperature. This mite first appear on okra crop 15 weeks old (45 days after sowing) and reached peak during 22nd week (May). No significant relation was seen on top, middle and lower canopies. This mite preferred lower surface of leaves. (Rai *et al.*, 1991: *Modern Acar.*, **1** : 571-580).

Control : Dicofol (0.04%) was most effective in controlling this mite. Under laboratory condition dicofol, monocrotophos, fenpropathrin, endosulfan, performed as acaricides while tetradifon, ethion, dicofol, fenpropathrin acted as good ovicide. Wettable sulphur, endosulfan and monocrotophos had no ovicidal action (Rai *et al.*, 1991, *Modern Acarology*, **1** : 571–580). The high effectiveness of tetradifon 0.05%, 0.1%, dicofol 0.02%, 0.04%, wettable sulphur (0.25%, 1.25%) against *T. macfarlanei* was also reported by Patel *et al.*, (1995: *V. Nat. symp.*, : p. 81). Srinivasa & Sugeetha (1999: *J. Acarol.*, **15** : 1-5) reported aqueous seed extract of Mohua, Pongamia and Mahogany at 4-6% conc. caused 66-74% , 64-86%, 78-90% mortality, respectively of larvae of *T. macfarlanei* on okra while methanol extracts from leaves of Clerodendron and Vitex at 4-6% killed 62-86% and 70-80%, respectively. The corresponding adult mortalities were 67-84%,68-91%,62-70%, 54-84% and 68-76%, respectively. They concluded that integration of botanical and synthetic pesticides is possible.

Varietal preference : Sugeetha & Srinivasa (1999: *J. Acar.*, **15** : 10–14) reported differential preference for different okra varities in different cropping seasons and no varity was free from infestation. Pusa Sawani, Prabhani Kranthi and GOH-1 were suscetible during summer, while line-199, Hybrid-7, Arka Anamika and Prabhani Kranthi were susceptible during Kharif in the order as mentioned.

Amblyseius manipurensis Gupta

Gupta (1978) *Indian J. Acar.*, **2**(2) : 60–77 reported it from Manipur.

Tetranychus yusti (McG)

This is also known to occur on okra (Banerjee, 1989).

Tetranychus urticae Koch

Bhaskaran *et al.* (2010) estimated yield loss due to attack of *T. urticae* as 53.23% over unprotected control. The protection was provided by spraying fish oil, Rosin soap (FORS 25g/L), fenazaquin 10 EC 1ml/L and dicofol 18.5 EC 2.5 ml/L.

Varietal screening : Debnath *et al.*, (2010) screened okra varieties against *T.urticae* at Kalyani. Field evaluation of 18 okra varieties revealed that variety P - 7 had lowest infestation (7 mites/leaf) followed by DSW – 1 (8.33/leaf) and maximum mite population was on var. MBORH 913 followed by DSN – 1. The maximum yield was obtained from var. P - 7 (8.38 t/ha) followed by JNDOL 031 (6.21 t/ha) and lowest yield was from MBORH 913 (1.82 t/ha). This is a major pest of okra in Punjab (Ghai *et al.*, 2003: *Agr. Bio. Res.*, **8**(1): 69–71) and in Himachal Pradesh (Singh & Joshi, 2003: *Insect Environment*, **9**(4): 173–174).

In Gujarat, this mite appeared on okra on 9th week (1st week of September) after sowing, increased rapidly, reaching peak in the 12th week after sowing (last week of September), with population of 18–20 mites/leaf.

Singh *et al.* (1990: *J. Int. Ento.*, **52**(1) : 57–62) studied seasonal incidence of this mite. The yield loss due to infestation of *T. urticae* on okra has been reported as 17.66% (Dhote *et al.*, 2010: *Abst. Int. Symp. Cum-Working*, p. 45).

5. POTATO (*Solanum tuberosum*)

Polyphagotarsonemus latus (Banks)

This is a serious pest of potato along with several other vegetables, fruits, trees, ornamentals and pulses throughout tropics and temperate regions.

Diagnosis : This is light yellowish, glossy, tiny, fast moving,convex mite occurs on undersurface of leaves. Often males are seen carrying female deutonymphs with their chelicerae.

Nature of damage : On potato, this mite attacks young terminal leaves and causes longitudinally curling and crinkling of leaves which is called Tambera disease of potato in Maharashtra. First, oily looking blackish spots appear on undersurface of young leaves. Later, the spots turn reddish and extend to the entire leaf surface. All such leaves become bronzy and crinkling starts from margin (Gupta, 1993), Sontakke *et al.*, (1989: *Env. Ecol.*, **7** : 391–349) and Nandhihalli *et al.*, (1996: *Mysore J. Agric. Sci.*, **30**(2): 138–146) reported infestation of this mite on potato. The affected plants become stunted and in case the attack is severe, the yield loss may be very high. Srinivasa *et al.*, (2007: *J. Acar.*, **16** : 130–131) studied distribution pattern of yellow mite on potato and found distinct relationship between number of mites on the leaflets and the total number on the corresponding compound leaf. As the total number of mites on the compound leaf increased, the number of mites on leaflets specially on terminal leaflets increased. Hence, they suggested that the terminal leaflets from the compound leaves at the top canopy should be sampled for reliable and precise population estimation.

Aculops lycopersici (Massee)

Banerjee (1989) listed this mite occurring on potato.

Tetranychus ludeni Zacher

This mite has also been recorded on potato (Banerjee, 1989). The damage symptoms on potato are very similar to those produced by this mite on other crops.

6. CHILLI : (*Capsicum frutescens / C. annuum*)

This crop is attckde by a number of mites as below :

Polyphagotarsonemus latus (Banks)

For diagnosis and nature of damage, those given in case of potato may be refered to. The infestation on chilli causes serious yield loss.

Biology : Karuppuchamy & Mohanasundaram, 1987 (*Ind. J. Pl. prot.*, **15** : 1–4) and Borah (1989: *Thesis abstract HAU.*, **14**(4) : 357–358) studied biology of this mite. Life cycle took 8.47 ± 6.67 days, fecundity - 28.7 ± 6.91 eggs and adult longevity was 8.66 ± 1.57 days. Hosamane *et al.*, (2007: *J. Acar.*, **16** : 70–71) reported the duration of different developmental periods as incubation - 32.32 ± 1.35 hrs, larva - 21.80 ± 1.56 hrs, quiescent - 23.80 ± 1.75 hrs. total life cycle in case of male in June 2008 and January 2009 took 72.35 ± 2.10 hrs and 80.30 ± 2.70 hrs, respectively and the corresponding figures for female were 89.75 ±2.90 hrs and 99.20 ± 2.30 hrs, respectively. Sreeramalu (1976) (*Arecanut spices* Bull 7: 65–68) and Sanap & Nawale (1985, *Maharashtra Agr. Univ. J.*, **10** : 352–353) also contributed on this mite.

Seasonal occurrence : Population of yellow mite showed negative significant correlation with maximum and minimum temperatures. Rainfall also had negative correlation as excessive rainfall washed away the population. In Varanasi condition, the population increased from 1st fortnight of March 2008 (3.50 mites) reaching peak in December 2008 (21.30 mites). Similar trend was noticed in 2009 though population was very low and in that case the population increased from second fortnight of June (2.60 mites) and reached 12.30 in November 2009. Correlation of population with RH was significant at 5% level in both the years (Singh & Singh, 2010 : *Abst. Int. Symp-Cum-Workshop-Acar.*, p 5).

Nature of damage : The feeding causes downward curling of leaves in an inverted boat shaped manner and elongation of petiole takes place. Histochemical and histological studies reveal that reduction in leaf thickness and size and number of starch grains altered. Protein and RNA content increased in leaf tissues (Ravi & Puttaswamy, 1995: *Abst. V, Nat. Symp. Acar.*, : 38–39). Infestation .at early flowering stage caused bud and flower sheding, leaf curling and twisting. (Dhote *et al.*, 2010: : 45). Yield loss due to yellow mite on chilli ranged from 37-52%.

Varietal screening : Ghosh *et al.*, (2010: *Abst. Int. Symp.-Cum-Workshop-Acar.*, p. **61**) screened 38 locally available chilli germ plasms against *P. latus* in West Bengal. The population started from March, attained peak in mid - May (2.99 mites/sq cm area) and during this time the damage incidence was also very high. The germplasms Suryamukhi - 4, Caning Suryamukhi - 6 and 7, Suryamukhi Bullet - 5, 6, Caning Bullet - 3, BC-CH-SL-4, Black Cluster, CH-1, K-1, CO-3 and 4 were moderately resistant where very low mite population was recorded. Germplasms like Caning Suryamukhi - 8, Suryamukhi Bullet - 1, Biadaggy kaddy and Biadaggy dubby and Cluster Suryamukhi were highly susceptible to yellow mite where less fruits were set.

Control : Manjunatha & Lingappa (1995: *Abst. V. Nat. Symp. Acar.*, : 84-85) reported acephate (1g/L), dicofol (2ml/L) as effective for control of this mite. Similar result was obtained by Thangaraju *et al.* (1995, p. 86). The latter report indicated increase in yield by 10,283 kg in dicofol (0.25%) and 9850 kg in ethion (0.25%). Apart from dicofol, the other effective chemicals were Fenbutatin oxide (0.1%), avermectin (0.1%), bifenthrin (0.05%) and monocrotophos (0.1%) (Anil & Shetty, 1995 *Abst. V. Nat. Symp. Acar.*, 85-86). Propergite 57 EC @ 850 gm ai/ha was also quite effective giving mortality above 95%. Omite (0.228%) combined with Dhanuvit (0.1%), a surfactant, were also good to give effective control (Jeyarani *et al.*, 2007, *J. Acarol.*,

17 : 87–89). Application of lamda – Cyhalothrin under field condition reported to be more effective against yellow mite than endosulfan, fenvalerate. Efficacy increased with concentration (30> 15> 7.5 gai/ha) (Mathirajan & Natarajan, 1999: *J. Acarol.*, **14** : 8–9; Vishwakarma *et al.*, 2010: p. 78) reported maximum reduction of *P. latus* on chilli with Milbemectin 1% EC when used @ 0.00050% followed by Fenzaquin 10% EC (75.74%) @ 0.005%, dicofol 18.5% (72.84%) @ 0.005%, Neem spray Aza 3000 EC (65.77%)@ 0.0012% and DC Tron plus. (59.43%) @ 0.6% concentration. Methanol extract of *Acorus calamus* and petroleum ether extract of *A.calamus* were ineffective against *P.latus*. The cost benefit ratio was highest (19.52 : 1) when dicofol was used at 0.002%, followed by Fenazaquin 10% EC (17.28 : 1) at 0.001% concentration. The HPLC analysis revealed that grain chillies can be consumed 5 days after spraying of pesticides like flubendiamide 24% + thiacloprid 24% - 480 SC(W/V) at recommended dose (Hudait & Banerjee, 2010, p. 80). Spiromesifen 24% SC (W/V) when used with insecticides, fungicides and fertilizers against yellow mite on chilli, no flocculation, sedimentation or separation was observed in any of the treatments in bioefficacy study and all combination of spiromesifen reduced mite population satisfactorily upto 15 days after treatment. No sign of necrosis, epinasty, hyponasty, leaf tip injury, wilting, vein clearing were recorded. Spiromesifen is compatible with triazophos, imidacloprid, carbendazim and urea and can be used as tank mixture (De *et al.*, 2010, p. 84-85). Hexithiazox 5. 47 EC was also found to be effective against yellow mite and at the same time safe to natural enemies.The acaricidal and ovicidal effects of diafenthuron and fenazaquin were reported by Senapati *et al.*, (2010, p. 95) while effectiveness of abamectin, fenazaquin and propergite against chilli mite was also reported by Nayak *et al.*, (2010). Boom Tet + diafenthiuron, Boom Tet + garlic extract, Redux +azadirachtin NSKE, Commercial azadirachtin formulations, CHA 2062@ 14.4 and 16.2g ai/ha are the other products found effective against this yellow mite (Patel *et al.*, 2010 p. 97; Adhikhary *et al.*, 2010 p. 98; Debnath & Baidya, 2010 p. 105-106).

Tetranychus puschelii Meyer

Sadana & Gupta (1983: *Entomon.*, **8** : 1–6) reported *T. puschelii* on chilli.

T. urticae Koch

Sadana & Gupta (1982) (*Int. J.Ent. India*, **1**(1) : 65–68) reported this mite on chilli.

Nature of damage : This mite causes light specklings or localized pale yellow spots on the upper surface of leaves. Leaves become bronzy, dry up and fall off.

Amblyseius largoensis (Muma)

Gupta, 1978 (*Indian J. Acar.*, **2**(2) : 60–77) reported this on chilli in Meghalaya.

Euseius alstoniae Gupta

Gupta, 1977 (*Indian J. Acar.*, **1** : 28–37) reported this on chilli in Gujarat.

T. neocaledonicus Andre

Manjunatha & Puttaswamy (1983: *Abst. II All India Symp. Acarology, Pune* 21-22) reported this mite on chilli. It took longer time to complete life cycle on chilli (13.05 days) followed by tomato (12.92 days), bottle gourd (9.44 days), pumpkin (8.72 days), brinjal (8.24 days). Egg laying on chilli was 9.20 per female and longevity was 13.50 days. Chilli was less preferred host than other vegetables.

7. ONION (*Allium cepa*)

Steneotarsoemus furcatus

This is a white tiny mite found on undersurface of onion leaves. This mite has been reported as a damaging pest of onion in Tamil Nadu (Mohanasundaram & Karappuchamy 1988 *Entomon.*, **13** : 315–316). Other important damage causing mites are *Petrobia latens*, causing wilting, *Tetranychus urticae* and *Baerina orissaensis*.

8. CAULIFLOWER (*Brassica oleracea*)

Tenuipalpus kesari Sadana *et al.*

Sadana *et al.* (1985) described this new species collected from *Brassica oleracea*. Not much is known about its damage symptoms.

9. SEEM (*Vicia faba*)

Eutetranychus orientalis (Klein)

Though this mite is a pest of mostly fruit trees and ornamental plants but occasionally it attacks other crops and Sadana & Gupta (1983) recorded it on. *Vicia faba* doing insignificant damage.

10. CUCUMBER (*Cucumis sativa*)

Tetranychus puschelii Meyer

Sadana & Gupta (1983) recorded this mite on cucumber.

Tetranychus neocaledonicus Andre

This mite often attacks cucumber throughout India. It builds colonies on underside of leaves and sucks sap from there. The infested leaves become brown, ,dry up and fall off.

11. CUCURBITS

T. neocaledonicus Andre

This is a very common species infesting various cucurbitaceous plants along with over 100 hosts throughout the world.

Diagnosis : Adult females are reddish carmine with proto and deutonymphs being green with dark specks on dorsum.

Damage : It is almost similar to other tetranychids. Apart from producing typical damage symptoms, the feeding causes reduction in vitality and growth, ultimately affecting yield. Sometimes webbing may be so profuse that the entire plant remains covered which further affect normal physiological activities of the plants. Sharma & Pande (1987: *Ind. J. Zool.*, **14** : 68–65) studied relationship between population of *Tetranychus neocaledonicus* and external characteristics of cucurbitaceous leaves.

Tetranychus urticae Koch

Rather (1995) reported this mite on cucurbitaceous vegetables in Kashmir.

12. *Luffa aegyptica*

Brevipalpus karachiensis Chaudhri *et al.*

Sadana & Gupta (1982: *Int J.Ento.*, **1**(1) : 65–68) reported the occurrence of this mite on *Luffa aegyptica.*

Brevipalpus rugulosus Chaudhri *et al.*

Sadana & Chhabra (1980, *Sci. & Cult.*, **46**(10) : 369) reported this species on *Luffa aegyptica.* Sadana & Sharma (1989 : *Progr. in Acarology,* **2** : 95–99) studied influence of temperature on development of *Brevipalpus rugulosus* on *Luffa aegyptica.* It was maximum at 30 ± 1°C, and minimum was at 20 ± 1°C.Temperature of 15 ± 1°C and 35 ± 1°C proved unsuitable for development of all stages of mites. Fecundity and daily rate of egg production were maximum at 30 ± 1°C and minimum was at 20 ± 1°C. Temperature of 30 ± 1°C was most suitable for rapid development, fecundity, daily rate of egg production and hatching.

13. FRENCH BEAN (*Phaseolus vulgaris*)

Among the mite species which occur on French beans are :

Tetarnychus ludeni Zacher

This mite attacks, often seriously, French bean plants. The feeding produces white stipplings resulting in drying and defoliation of leaves. The dispersal was effected by contact of plant to plant.

Biology : Mallik (1983: *Indian J. Acar.*, **8** : 1–12) studied life cycle of this species on French bean and duration of different stages was egg - 106 hrs, larva - 32.5 hrs, proto - 34.5 hrs, deuto - 49 hrs. Female and male took a total of 222 and 200 hrs., respectively to complete the developmet. In case of life table, the rm was 0.3103, Ro - 123.73, T - 15.53 and finite rate of increase - 1.36. According to Puttarudriah & ChannaBasavanna (1981, *Indian J. Acar.*, **5** : 80–84), the life cycle took 9.34 days, laid greater number of eggs when this mite fed on French bean and Okra and lived longer (21.08 days) as compared to other hosts like okra, castor, brinjal, etc.

In the study on effect of temperature and humidity on development, oviposition of *T. ludeni* at constant temperatures (20 ± 1°C - 35 ± 1°C) and 5 RH (55 ± 3%-

95±3%), the optimum condition for development and maximum survival of eggs was between 32± 1 and 35± 1°C , 65 ± 3 % and 75 ± 3% RH, whereas for development of immatures, optimum conditions were 30± 1 to 35 ± 1°C and 55 ± 3% - 75 ± 3% RH. The shortest preoviposition period was noted at 32 ± 1°C followed by 35± 1°C. lowest number of eggs was laid at 20± 1°C. The high humidity reduced egg production (Puttarudriah & ChannaBasavanna, 1980: *Indian J. Acar.*, **4**(1) : 31–40).

The life cycle on French bean under field condition (10. ± 3°C - 28.4°C, 53 - 88% RH), the female took 12.48 ± 0.16 days and male took 11.96 ± 0.38 days to complete life cycle. The oviposition period was of 22.83 ± 4.56 days during which it laid 165.88 ± 47.04 eggs and lived for 27.41 ± 4.75 days. Puttaswamy & ChannaBasavanna (1980: *Indian J. Acar.*, **4**(1) : 41–48). Sex ratio was 1: 10 (male : female) (Manjunatha & Puttaswamy (1989, *J. Acarol.*, **11** : 35–40).

Control : Monocrotophos, dicofol, tetradifon and endosulfan proved good in reducing mite population and also registered higher yield than control (Manjunatha & Puttaswamy (1999: *J. Acarol.*, **13** : 91–94). Monocrotophos also gave highest grain yield with highest net income against attack of *T. ludeni* on French bean (Manjunatha & Puttaswamy) 1983: *Abst. II All India Symp. Acar., Pune,* : 62–63).

14. TAPIOCA (*Manihot esculenta*)

T. ludeni Zacher

This mite occassionaly attacks Tapioca in South India producing characteristic damage symptoms.

Biology : Its biology on Taiopca was studied by Puttaswamy & ChannaBasavanna (1982: *Indian J. Acar.*, **6** : 72–76) and reported that it took longer time on tapioca (12.11 days) than castor (10.20 days) and mulberry (10.14 days). The mites feeding on castor and mulberry laid greater number of eggs, 209.83 eggs (castor), 185.33 eggs (mulberry) than *Amaranthus* (147.42 eggs). Females feeding on tapioca laid least number of eggs (37/female). Its longevity on French bean was 16.62 days which was much shorter than castor (26.32 days), Amaranthus (27.69 days) and mulberry (23.55 days).

15. CARROT (*Dacus carota*)

This plant is relatively free from mite attack. However, Gupta (1977: *Indian J. Acar.*, **1** : 28–37) recorded the following species :

Neoseiulus bindrai Gupta

Gupta (1979) recorded it on carrot in Punjab.

16. POINTED GOURD (*Trichosanthes dioica*)

Tarsonemus sp.

This mite attacks pointed gourd.

Fungitarsonemus sp.

This also attacks pointed gourd.

T. urticae / T. neocaledonicus

Both these mites attack pointed gourd, mostly its older leaves.

Nature of damage : The affected leaves become yellow and with the increasing population the yield is affected. Often the fruits are also damaged and consequently they loose market values. Anon. (2009) reported crop loss of pointed gourd, to the extent of 18.35%.

Control : In an attempt to control *T. urticae* infesting pointed gourd by IPM, it was reported that basal treatment with carbofuran and foliar application with propergite were very effective followed by dicofol with propergite in alternate spray in foliar treatment. Root - deep with carbosulfan + Vermicompost + *Paecilomyces lilacinus* in basal treatment were also effective. The effect of propergite prolonged upto 14 days after spraying. It was concluded that spraying thrice with propergite 7.5% was most effective in controlling incidence of mite population of summer pointed gourd and alternate spraying with dicofol and propergite gave good control (Barma & Jha, 2010, p119). Similar observation indicating effectiveness of propergite in controlling *Tetranychus* spp. was also reported by Kirk *et al.* 1995 (*Proc. Beltwibe Cotton Conf. San Antonio, TX, USA, Jan.*, 4-7, Vol. **2** : 1448-1450).

17. COW PEA

Polyphagotarsonemus latus (Banks)

This mite is reported from Kashmir valley on cowpea (Rather, 1995) and West Bengal (Majumdar *et al.*, 2010).

Nature of damage : Apart from causing yellowing and drying of leaves, it causes stunting of apical growth and dropping of flowers and buds. This mite starts attacking during early seedling stage (maximum mite 2/sq cm) in susceptible variety (Pusakamal) during 1st week of September and persists till November. Pusakamal is the most susceptible variety while Lola and Shweta were tolerant.

Tetranychus urticae Koch

This mite also frequently attacks cowpea in South India producing typical damage symptoms for this species.

Control : Sreerama Kumar & Singh (2007: *J. Acarol.*, **17** : 29-31) attempted control of this mite on cowpea with fungal pathogen *Hirsutella thompsonii* and reported that the infested mites produced disease symptoms like cessation of feeding, restlessness, wriggling, sluggish movement, etc. This was caused due to proliferation of hyphal bodies inside haemocoel and that spread throughout the body. Finally, the host was killed due to physical damage of the organs, nutritional depletion and toxicosis. After the host body was full of fungal biomass, the hyphae emerged out from cadavers through the mouth, anal aperature, genital opening, leg joints and through body wall from all sides.

18. TOMATO (*Lycopersicum esculentum*)

This crop is attacked by the following mite species :

Tetranychus evansii Baker & Pritchard

This mite attacks tomato, and brinjal and is distributed in Mauritius and Brazil.

Damage : The attacked leaves become yellow and with the increase in infestation the russeting symptoms occur. Finally, when the attack is very severe, the plant dies.

Biology : The light to deep orange eggs are laid on undersurface of leaves which hatch after 3 days to larva and the same after passing through nymphal stages, which take 3–4 days, reach adulthood. This mite takes 7–9 days, depending upon temperature, to complete the life cycle.

Control : Monocrotophos at the recommended dose will control this pest.

Tetranychus lombardinii Ptirchard & Baker

This mite also attacks tomato apart from other crops and is known from India and Africa. The infested leaves develop reddish brown spots at the points of feeding.

Biology : This mite completes the life cycle as egg, larva, protontmph, deutonymph and adult and the time which it takes is about 8–10 days.

Tetranychus urticae Koch

This is another notorious pest of tomato and is worldwide in distribution. The damage done by this mite is characteristic of this species as produced on other crops.

Control : A study on relative toxicity of *T. urticae* on tomato, reported that the LC_{50} values of, milbemectin and abamectin were more toxic to adults with corresponding median lethal conc. values of 1.05 and 1.44 ppm. Next in order of toxicity on adults was fenpyroximate (20.82 ppm) and fenazaquin (32.75 ppm). Milbemectin also has ovicidal effect (LC_{50} = 3.77 ppm (Aji *et al.*, 2007: *J. Acarol.*, **17** : 84–86).

Polyphagotarsonemus latus (Banks)

This is another very important pest of tomato throughout India and besides tomato it attacks several other crops like vegetables, fruit trees, fibre crops, pulses, etc.

Damage : This mite prefers young apical leaves and, as in chilli, the infested leaves become crinkled, curl up, turn boat shaped, become bronzy and subsequently dry. When the infestation is very serious, the plants look sickly, droopy and finally die. In several cases, the entire crop may be lost due to this attack.

Control : Dicofol, monocrotophos will prove effective for its control.

Tetranychus urticae Koch

Evaluation of bioefficacy of fenazaquin 10 EC (125g.ai/ha and 150 g ai/ha against *T. urticae* on tomato revealed that 125g ai/ha gave excellent control of this mite and also registered higher yield as compared to dicofol 18.5 EC (Misra, 2010. p 94).

Aceria lycopersici (Wolff.)

This is a tiny mite occurs on undersurface of tomato leaves. Apart from tomato, it is also known to attack brinjal.

Damage : It produces no noticeable damage symptoms barring production of excessive growth of hairs on undersurface of leaves and on stem. The affected plants look greyish white.

Control : Murthy (2010) studied bioefficacy of fenpyroximate 5% EC (Mitigate) for control of this eriophyid mite on tomato and reported that fenpyroximate 50 EC @ 500-625 ml/ha found to be more effective in controlling this mite registering higher cost benefit ratio compared to dicofol 18.5% EC@1375 ml/ha. Srinivasa *et al.* 2003 (*J. Pl. Prot.*, 31 : 146-147) studied bioefficacy of Fenpyroximate 5 SC against *T. urticae* on okra and reported similar results.

19. SPONGE GOURD (*Luffa aegyptica, L. acutangula*)/SWEET GOURD (*Cucurbita maxima*)/PUMPKIN (*Benincasa cerifera*)/RIDGE GOURD (*Cucurbita moschata*)/BITTER GOURD (*Mmordica charantia*)/SNAKE GOURD (*Trichosanthes cucumerina*)/BOTTLE GOURD (*Lageneria vulgaris*) /ROUND GOURD (*Citrullus vulgaris var. fistulosus*)

Tetranychus ludeni Zacher

Chatterjee & Gupta (1995) reported *T.ludeni* on sponge gourd (*Luffa acutangula*). In their study on biochemical changes on sponge gourd due to infestation of this mite, they reported that minerals like Zn, Si, Cr, Fe, inorganic compounds like nitrates/nitrites and organic compounds like chlorophyll were depleted due to infestation of this mite.

T.macfarlanei Baker & Pritchard

This mite attacks pumpkin. Kumar & Singh (2003: In : *Resistant Pest Management Newsletter*, **13** : 1-5) conducted chemical trial against this mite.

T. neocaledonicus Andre

This mite attacks ridge gourd (Manjunatha & Puttaswamy, 1999 : *J. Acarol.*, **13** : 91 - 94), bottle gourd (Murthy, 2010, p. 100).

Control : In an experiment for control of *T. neocaledonicus* infesting ridge gourd several chemicals like tetradifon (0.02%), monocrotophos (0.04%), endosulfan (0.07%) and methyl parathion (0.05%) were tested. It was reported that all these registered high moratlity compared to untreated checks. Monocrotophos, dicofol, tetradifon and endosulfan proved superior.

Murthy (2010) reported that fenpyroximate 50% EC@500-625 ml/ha found to be effective in controlling this mite on bottle gourd.

Brevipalpus obovatus Donnadieu

This mite was reported on sponge gourd (Goyal & Sadana, 1989: *J.Acar.*, **11** : 41-49). While studying biology of this mite on some other hosts along with *L. aegyptica*, it was reported that Golden rod (*Solidago cannadensis*) was better food than *L. aegyptica* as on this host the development took shorter time, had longer oviposition period, higher fecundity and maximum hatchability.

22. GARLIC : (*Allium sativum*)

Aceria tulipae Keifer

This mite attacks bulb of garlic, apart from wheat and tulip. This has been reported from several other countries outside India. From Australia, this has been reported by Halliday & Knihiniki, 2004: *Internat. J. Acarol.*, **30**(2) : 113-118.

Seasonal occurrence : It infests garlic bulb during second fortnight of December and attains peak during February and dwindles thereafter in March. The population remains low during March, mainly because of crop maturity. With the increase of temperature, this mite congregates at the leaf base. Courtin *et al.*, (2000) (*Annals Appl. Biol.*, **137** : 207-211) studied effect of temperature and RH on eggs and nymphal development of this mite.

Varietal preference : The varieties Brendabati and Kati were reported to be tolerant against this mite while Gangajali and Goldana were more susceptible.

Damage : In garlic, this mite lives between layers of bulbs causing curling of leaves. On wheat, it causes wheat streak mosaic and wheat spot mosaic disease. It also attacks various grasses, tulip and corn.

Control : Dicofol 18.5 EC and wettable sulphur in their recomended doses were quite good for satisfactory management of this mite.

21. ARUM (*Colocasia antiquorum*)

The plant feeding mites like *Brevipalpus californicus* (Banks), *Bryobia eharai* Pritchard & Keifer and predatory mites like *Scapulaseius suknaensis* (Gupta), *Euseius coccineae* (Gupta), *Neoseiulus fallacies* (Garman), *Typhlodromus homalii* Gupta are known to infest this plant but none is of any economic importance.

22. *Amaranthus* spp.

Among phytophagous mites, *Tetranychus urticae* Koch is known to attack this plant causing serious damage.

23. GREEN PLANTAIN (*Musa paradisica*)

The plant feeding mites recorded on this host are *Oligonychus mangiferus* (R. & S.), *T. urticae, T. neocaledonicus, E. orientalis* but none causes any serious damage.

24. SPINACH (*Spinacea oleracea*)

The common phytophagous mite species recorded on this host are *T. urticae* and *T. ludeni* and predatory mite *Euseius ovalis* are known to infest this plant having no known economic importance.

25. SUGARBEET (*Beta vulgaris*)

The phytophagous mites *T. urticae* and *T. neocaledonicus* infest this plant but never attain any pest form.

26. RADISH (*Raphanus sativus*)

The mites recorded on this plant are *T. urticae* Koch, *T. neocaledonicus* Andre, *Brevipalpus karachiensis* Chaudhri *et al.*, *B. obovatus* Donnadieu and *Petrobia harti* (Ewing) but none causes any serious damage.

27. TURNIP (*Brassica campestris*)

T. urticae, T. neocaledonicus and *B. californicus* have been recorded on this plant. None is of any economic importance.

28. CABBAGE, CAULIFLOWER, KNOL-KHOL (*Brassica oleracea* - different varieties)

Occasionally, *T. urticae, T. neocaledonicus* and *T. ludeni* occur on these plants but no appreciable damage is caused.

29. COWPEA (*Vigna anguiculata*)

In north and south India, this plant is very seriously attacked by *T. ludeni* causing yellowing, browning and drying of leaves, seriously affecting growth and yield. *Neoseiulus longispinosus* and *E. ovalis* are common and effective predatory mites on this crop./

30. SWORDBEAN (*Canavalia ensiformes*)

Polyphagotarsonemus latus (Banks) and *T. neocaledonicus* Andre occasionally attack this plant producing characteristic damage symptoms.

31. CELERY (*Apion graveolens*)

Excepting the occurrence of one tarsonemid and one tydeid mite, no other mite is known to infest this plant.

32. SWEET POTATO (*Ipomoea batatas*)

Petrobia harti (Ewing) and *Tegonotus convolvuli* (ChannaBasavana) have been recorded on this host. The attack of the former causes pale yellowish turning of leaves which later dry up.

33. KARAMCHA (*Carissa carandas*)

Phytoptus carissae Mohanasundaram is known to infest this plant.

34. KAKROL (*Momordica cochinensis*)

T. urticae casually attacks this plant but causes no serious damage.

35. SCARLET GOURD (*Coccinea grandis*)

T. ludeni among plant feeding mites and *E. coccineae, A. largoensis* and *Cunaxa* sp. among predatory mites are in records on this host. *A. largoensis* feeds on all stages of *T. ludeni.*

36. GARDEN PEA (*Pisum sativum*)

This is often attacked by *T. urticae* and *T. neocaledonicus* but infestation rarely attains any seriously form.

3.8 MEDICINAL PLANTS

A large number of Medicinal plants are attacked by mite pests in India and those are as below :

1. CINNAMONE : (*Cinnamomum zeylanicum*)

Aceria docleri

This eriopryid mite induced both hypophyllous and epiphyllous galls on petioles and stems of Cinnamone in Kerala. Galls are 5 cm in diameter and each had 800-1000 mites. The duration of different stages was Incubation - 4-5 days, nymphs - 2-3 days, quiescent stage 1.5 days. The total developmental period - 11-13 days (Haq, 1995, Bangalore Symp. p. 45).

Monotrimacus ocellatus Mohanasudaran & Ramaraju

This species was described as new by Mohanasundaram & Ramaraju, 2010, collected on this plant (*Abst. Int. Symp.-cum-Workshop Acar.,* p. 15) from Nilgiri Hills in Tamil Nadu.

Colopodacus cinnamomae Mohanasundarum

Mohanasundarum (1980) described this species, on cinnamomum sp. from Tamil Nadu. No information on damage, done, if any, is known.

2. *Cinnamomum camphora*

Brevipalpus deleoni, B. euphorbiae - occasionally attack comphor plant causing scorching of leaves.

Oligonychus biharensis (Hirst)

Often this mite attacks camphor plant but never does any major damage.

3. Mentha : (*Metha arvensis /M. piperata*)

Tetraychus urticae Koch

This mite infests *Mentha arvensis* var MAS - I, MAH - 77 and MAPV - I. Pippermint had maximum attack followed by Japanese mint, Spearmint and Water mint (Premsagar, 1995, *Bangalore Acarology Symp.*; p. 46). The infestation of this mite is seen during October - November. The infested leaves first become yellowish and then turn brown (Gupta, 2005).

Biology : *T. urticae* took 4-5 days to complete development on *Mentha arvensis* and *M. piperata* while it took 4-6 days on *M. spicata* and 4 days on *M. citrata*. The percentage mortality during development on *M. arvensis, M. piperata, M. spicata and M. citrata* was 33.33, 43.33, 76.67 and 96. 67%, respeclively. Oviposition period was 4-16, 5-14, 2-17 and 5 days, respectively while fecundity was 0-46, 33-77, 0-29 eggs in *M. arvensis, M. piperita, M. spicata* and 10 days in *M. citrata*. (Dhooria & Sagar, 1989: *Progress in Acarology*, **2** : 39–41).

Tetranychus neocaledonicus Andre

Gupta (1985) recorded it on mentha.

Eutetranychus orientalis (Klein)

The occurrence of this species on *Mentha piperata* doing minor injuries was reported in Gupta (1985).

Polyphagotarsonemus latus (Banks)

This is one of the major mite pests of Mentha and remains abundant in the field throughout the year. The population remains maximum during September - December when presence of several hundred mites per leaf may not be uncommon (Gupta, 2005). This species becomes more abundant after disappearance of *T. urticae.*

Brevipalpus karachiensis **Chaudhri** *et al.*

This mite attacks Mentha causing yellowing and browning of leaves (Gupta, 2005).

Brevipalpus obovatus Donnadieu

The record of this mite on Mentha was made by Gupta (2005) causing yellowish brownish patches on leaves.

Euseius alstoniae (Gupta)

This predatory mite was found in association with *P. latus* on undersurface of leaves but its predation was not noticed.

4. *Pongamia glabra/P. pinnata*

Aceria pongamiae ChannaBasavanna

This mite produces elongated pouch galls on leaves.

Nature of Damage : Manjunatha *et al.*, (1989: *Progress in Acarology*, **2** : 141–146) studied morphological, histochemical and biochemical aspects of Pongamia galls. They reported that the galls were poor in starch, RNA but was richer in protein content. The leaf gall affected growth of the plants due to reduction in leaf area and that, in turn, hampered photosynthesis (Devraj *et al.*, 2007: *J. Acarol.*, **17** : 21-23). Regarding biochemical constituents, gall tissues had lower amount of free total sugar, reducing sugar, free amino acid, phenol, tannin compared to young leaf tissues. Amino acid profile of galls, young leaves and matured leaf tissues exhibited qualitative and quantitative changes in their composition, the number of aminoacids detected in the respective tissues being 15, 15 and 16, respectively. The presence of high amount of free sugar, especially reducing ones in galls provided nutritional superiority of galls over matured leaves and also this sugar may help in detoxification of harmful secondary metabolites. No notable disparity was noted between tannin content of galls and matured leaf tissues which respectively were 0.9705 and 1,2495 mg/gm tissue.

Control : Umapathy and Mohanasundaram (1995: *Bangalore Symposium*, : 87-88) evaluated effectiveness of synthetic chemical pesticides on *Aceria pongamiae* and reported the effectiveness in decreasing order as dicofol > wettable sulphur > endosulfan > monocrotophos > dimethoate > quinalphos > methyl parathion > phosphamidon > fenvalerate.

Eriophyes cheriani Massee

Mani (1933: *Ann. Mag. Nat. Hist.*, **12** : 138–139) reported this mite causing green cephalic galls on the leaves of *Pongamia glabra.* The galls are of ½ inch in size and are present on upper surface of leaves and occasionally on lower surface of leaves as well. Often the galls are of oblong or kidney shaped with or without opening on lower side (Mohanasundaram, 1990: *J. Acarol.*, **12** : 15 : 88). The galls caused by this mite have also been reported from Delhi region (Joshi *et al.*, 1992: *Annals of Ent.*, **10** : 1-6).

5. DRUM STICK (*Moringa oleifera*)

Aculus menoni ChannaBasavanna

The record of this mite has been mentioned in Gupta (2005). This mite is a leaf vagrant doing no damage to its host.

Tetranychus neocaledonicus Andre

Sangeetha & Ramani 2007 (*J. Acarol.*, **17** : 12-14) reported this mite as a serious pest of *Moringa oleifera*.

Damage : The infestation causes loss of chlorophyll, like 3.97 ± 0.17 in chlorophyll-a and 2.32 ± 0.05 in chlorophyll-b in heavily infested cases. The corresponding figures in moderately infested and uninfested were 6.89 ± 0.066 and 6.03 ± 0.021 and 8.77 ± 0.03 and 6.82 ± 0.05 mg/gram tissue, respectively. Due to actively feeding, large quantities of black coloured faecal pellets were produced which got entangled in a large amount of dust in webs and that further reduced photosynthesis process due to preventing absorption of light. Feeding also induces mechanical injury to epidermal and mesophyll tissues.

6. ASHWAGANDHA (*Withania somnifera*)

Tetranychus urticae Koch

This is a notorious pest of Ashwagandha producing characteristic mite damage symptoms (Gupta, 2005).

Rolania & Sharma (2007: *J. Acarol.*, **16** : 50-51) studied seasonal occurrence of this pest. The correlation matrix indicated that the key abiotic factors did not have a bearing on population fluctuation. Rai and Singh (1999: *J. Acarol.*, **14** : 1-3) also made similar observation at Varanasi with regard to build up of population of *T. urticae* on Ashwagandha. Correlation coefficient of temperature and RH. showed a nonsignificant positive relation with both the factors, and hence RH and rainfall, were not very conducive for population build up.

Tetranychus macfarlanei Baker & Pritchard

This mite infests Ashwagandha occasionally causing characteristic damage symptoms (Gupta, 2005).

Eutetranychus orientalis (Klein)

The infestation of this mite on Ashwagandha has been mentioned in Gupta (2005).

Polyphagotarsonemus latus (Banks)

Occasionally, this mite infests young leaves causing characteristic crinkling of leaves (Gupta, 2005).

Brevipalpus phoenicis (Geij.)

Occasionally, this species infests on the undersurface of leaves (Gupta, 2005). When the infestation is very high, small brownish patches appear.

Neoseiulus longispinosus (Evans)

This species has been recorded on Ashwagandha (Gupta, 2005). It fed on all stages of *B. phoenicis*.

Paraphytoseius multidentatus S. & S.

Gupta (2005) recorded it on this host plant.

Typhlodromus divergentis (Chaudhri *et al.*)

Gupta (2005) reported the occurrence of this predatory mite on Ashwagandha.

7. BLACK PEPPER (*Piper nigrum*)

Polyphagotarsonemus latus (Banks)

This has been reported to infest sweet pepper (Reddy *et al.*, 2007: *J. Acarol.*, **16** : 65 - 67). The study on seasonal incidence under protected and open field conditions indicated that mite population was maximum during March (55.05–104.65 mites/leaf) when average temperature and humidity were 33°C and 66%, respectively.

8. NISHINDA (*Vitex negundo*)

Anthocoptes vitexae Mohanasundaram

This has been reported by Mohanasundaram (1981: *Entomon.*, **6** : 347). Nothing is known about damage done, if any. Sheeja & Ramani (2007: *J. Acarol.*, **16** : 132-134) studied spatial distribution of eggs and that revealed significant differences with respect to age group of leaves. Maximum number of eggs was on middle-aged leaves which coincided with the presence of adults also.

Tegolophus vitexis Mondal & Chakrabarti

Mondal & Chakrabarti (1981: *Acarologia*, **23** : 42) described this species from West Bengal collected on this host. No information is available about damage done by this mite.

Brevipalpus deleoni Pritchard & Baker

This has been recorded on *Vitex negundo* (Gupta, 2005)

Amblyseius largoensis (Muma)

Gupta (2005) recorded this predatory mite on this host but nothing is known about its predatory nature.

9. COUNTRY MALLOW (*Abutilon indicum*)

Tetranychus neocaledonicus Andre

Gupta (2005) reported this mite on this host. When infestation is very high, the leaves and fruits become yellow and then turn brownish. Those ultimately wither and die. The young leaves are mostly attacked.

Aculops abutiloni Mondal & Chakrabarti

This mite has been reported from undersurface of leaves causing no appreciable damage to this plant (Gupta, 1985).

10. APANG (*Achyranthes aspera*)

Aceria achyranthi Mohanasundaram

It was described as new species by Mohanasundaram, 1990 (*J. Acarol.*, **12** : 15–88). This mite is a leaf vagrant and causes russeting of leaves.

Aceria justicae ChannaBasavanna

Gupta (2005) reported this on this host.

Bryobia praetiosa Koch

The record of this species from this plant was made by Gupta (1985). The damage done by this mite is unknown.

Eotetranychus syzygii Gupta & Gupta

This is known to occur on this host without causing any damage (Gupta, 2005).

Brevipalpus californicus (Banks)

Gupta (2005) reported it on this host but no damage is done by it.

Amblyseius largoensis (Muma)

Its record on this host was made by Gupta (2005).

Paraphytoseius multidentatus S. & S.

Gupta (2005) reported it on this host feeding on eggs of *E. syzygii*.

Pronematus sp

Its record on this host was reported by Gupta (2005) feeding on eggs of *Brevipalpus californicus*.

11. BER (*Zizyphus jujuba*)

Eriophyes cernuus causes wood galls on this host in northern and western India (Detailed discussion of this species has been made under fruit trees).

12. SISHUM (*Dalbergia sissoo*)

Aceria dalbergiae ChannaBasavanna

This mite occurs in bud scales (Mohanasundaram, 1990). This mite causes pale green or whitish yellow warty patches on leaf surface. These patches later turn brown (ChannaBasavanna, 1966).

13. POMEGRANATE *Punica granatum*

Discussed under fruit trees

14. SUGARCANE (*Saccharum officinarum*)

Discussed under cash crops.

15. SOAPNUT (*Sapindus saponaria*)

Aceria sapindi ChannaBasavanna

Mohanasundaram (1990) reported this mite on this host as leaf vagrant and under bud scales. It is of no known economic importance (Gupta, 2005).

16. THORN APPLE (*Datura metel*)

Phyllocoptruta daturae Mohanasundaram & Ranganath

Mohanasundaram (1985: *Indian J. Acar.*, **9** : 1–10) recorded this on *Datura.*

Tetranychus urticae Koch

This mite attacks seriously during October-December and again during February -April. The infestation results in producing characteristic damage symptoms for this species (Gupta, 2005).

Polyphagotarsonemus latus (Banks)

This mite occurs throughout the year and its feeding especially on the top young leaves causes crinkling and curling. In severe cases of infestation, the leaves get curled, dry up and often the plants may also die (Gupta, 2005).

The other phytophagous and predatory mites recorded by Gupta (2005) on this host plant are as below :

PHYTOPHAGOUS

Tetranychus ludeni Zacher – occurs during summer months.

Eotetranychus syzygii Gupta & Gupta – occurs in summer months.

Brevipalpus deleoni Pritchard & Baker – This species occurs throughout the year. When the infestation becomes very severe, brownish spots appear on leaves.

PREDATORY

Amblyseius largoensis (Muma) – feeds on all stages of *B. deleoni*

Neoseiulus longispinosus (Evans) – Voraciously feeds upon eggs and nymphs of *T. urticae*

Scapulaseius suknaensis (Gupta) – feeds on all stages of *B. deleoni*

Cunaxa setirostris (Hermann) – Importance is unknown

Dactyloscirus sp. – No importance is known

Lasioseius terrestris Menon & Ghai – No importance is known

FUNGAL FEEDERS

***Acarus* sp.** – No importance is known

Lepidoglyphus destructor – No importance is known

17. *Barleria acuminata*

Paraphytoptus cristatae Mohanasundaram

This mite causes white velvety erineal growth on both sides of leaf.

18. RUDRAKSHA *(Elaeocarpus recurvatus)*

Paraphytoptus elaeocarpae Mohanasundaram

This mite has been reported as vagrant on flower buds.

19. CORIANDER (*Coriandrum sativum*)

Petrobia latens Muller

Jain & Yadav (1988: *Ind. J. Ento.*, **50** : 396) recorded this mite as pest of coriander. It produces yellowish spots on leaves. Such leaves become bronzy. This mite attacks during first week of March and continues till end of March.

Tetranychus urticae Koch

This mite often attacks this plant leading to devitalization and stunting of growth (Gupta, 2005).

Tetranychus neocaledonicus Andre

This mits causes same symptoms as done by *T. urticae* (Gupta, 2005).

20. PALMAROSA/CITRONELLA *(Cymbopogon flexuosus) / C. martinii / C. palmarosa / C. winterianus)*

Schizotetranychus cajani Gupta

This mite builds colonies on undersurface of leaves in longitudinal rows on either side of mid rib and its feeding causes appearance of yellowish stipplings (Gupta, 2005).

Oligonychus oryzae (Hirst)

It is a whitish mite, occurs on undersurface of leaves. The feeding of this mite causes whitish spots on the leaves at the points of feeding (Gupta, 2005).

Oligonychus indicus (Hirst)

This greyish green or white mite with black dorsal blotches, occurs on undersurface of leaves. The feeding produces whitish patches on leaves.

Neoseiulus baraki (Athias-Henriot)

Gupta (2005) recorded it on *C. martinii*.

Paraphytoseius multidentatus Swirski & Shechter

Gupta (2005) reported it on this host.

Tydeus sp.

Its record on *Cymbopogon* has been made by Gupta (2005).

Eriophyes cymbopogoni Mohanasundaram

This mite was described collecting specimen from *C. martinii.*

Biology : Naidu & ChannaBasavanna (1989: *Progress in Aearlogy*, **2** : 129–133) reported that the life stages were egg - protonymph - deutonymph - adult. Incubation period was 60 hrs., protonymphal period - 38 hrs., deutonymphal period - 36 hrs.

Seasonal occurrence : The population of this mite started increasing from January, attained peak in April (12847 eggs + mobile stages/tiller), the second peak was attained in June (12719 mites/tiller). The population of predatory mite (*Neoseiulus baraki*) was highest during May (1979). Highly significant correlation was seen with mite population and temperature (with max temperature r = 0.0659, with minimum temperature r = 0.605). In general, with daily maximum temperature of 30°C, minimum temperature of 20°C and RH less than 20%, the mite population tended to increase while at lower temperature and higher RH tended to population reduction (Naidu and ChannaBasavanna, 1989, *Progress in Acarology*, p. 129-132).

Ecology & Control : Naidu (1987 thesis Abst - HAU 13 (D: 23-24) studied ecology and control of this mite, a pest of *C. winterianus.*

21. MALABAR NUT (*Justicia adhatoda*)

Tetranychus urticae Koch

This mite seriously infests undersurface of leaves during summer months and with the increase of infestation, the leaves get enveloped with dense webs. The infested leaves become yellow and dry up.

Brevipalpus karachiensis Chaudhri *et al.*

Gupta (2005) listed it infesting this host. A huge population was seen during May-June.

Brevipalpus obovatus Donnadieu

Goyal *et al.* (1985) recorded it on this host.

Brevipalpus phoenicis (Geij.)

Kinathi & Ramani (2010: *Abs. Int. Symp.-Cum-Workshop, Acarology* : 31) recorded it on this host causing chlorosis.

Anthocoptes adhatodae ChannaBasavanna

ChannaBasavanna (1966) described this species collecting on Vasak.

25. *Ocimum grattisimum / O. sanctum / O. basilicum / O. kilimandscharicum O. tenuiflorum, Ocimum* spp.

Polyphagotarsonemus latus (Banks)

Several hundred members of this mite attack a single leaf especially the apical young leaves, producing characteristic crinkling and curling of leaves. This mite starts infesting after disappearance of spider mites (Gupta, 2005).

Tetranychus urticae Koch

Serious infestation of this mite occurs during December onwards till March producing the characteristic damage symptoms.

Tetranychus neocaledonicus Andre

This mite also sometimes infests *Ocimum* spp. (Gupta, 2005). It occurs during December - March and disappears with onset of rainy season.

Brevipalpus karachiensis Chaudhri *et al.*

This mite infests *Ocimum* spp. very often but no serious damage is caused by this mite barring production of crinkled leaves.

Brevipalpus phoenicis (Geij.)

Prabheena & Ramani (2010, p. 68) recorded this species on *Ocimum grattisimum* and reported that it caused drastic reduction of chlorophyll "a" and "b" and was responsible for "phoenicis blotch". In case of moderate infestation, the loss of chlorophyll 'a' was 17.04%-31.63% . The loss of chlorophyll "b" in case of moderately and heavily infested plants was 19.37-26.27 % and 86.61-88.54%, respectively. Due to this heavy reduction in photosynthesis, the general health of the plant suffers. That, in turn, affects the medicinal properties of plants.

Brevipalpus obovatus Donnadieu

This mite was recorded on basil (Goyal *et al.*, 1985: *Indian J. Acar.*, **9** : 63-68).

Bakeriella ocimis Chakrabarti & Mondal

This has been recorded on *Ocimum* but no damage by this mite was reported (Gupta, 2005).

Paraphytoseius multidentatus Swirski & Shechter

Gupta (2005) recorded this predatory mite on *Ocimum* spp. feeding upon different stages of *Brevipalpus karachiensis.*

26. CAMEL'S FOOT PLANT (*Bauhinia variegata / Bauhinia acuminata / Bauhinia purpurea*)

Eutetranychus orientalis (Klein)

Lakshman Lal & Mukherjee (1980 *Ind. J. Acar.*, **4** : 61-67) reported this species on these hosts. High temperature, low humidity and high sunny days were favourable for this species.

29. ARJUN (*Terminalia arjuna*)

Ectomerus chebulae Mohanasundaram

Mohanasundaram (1980: *Indian J. Acar.*, **4** : 1-9) described *Ectomerus chebulae* on this host.

Eutetranychus orientalis (Klein)

Anon., 2003 reported it from West Bengal.

Euseius coccineae (Gupta)

Anon., 2003 reported it from West Bengal.

Eriophyes terminalae ChannaBasavanna

It was described on specimen collected on *Terminalia catappa* (ChannaBasavanna, 1966). Young leaves are worst affected.

Abacarus arjunalis Mondal *et al.*

This was described from *Terminalia arjuna* and was reported to cause curling of leaf margins and formation of ventral erineum (Gupta, 2005).

Terminalichus karachiensis Anwarullah & Khan

This was collected on *Terminalia arjuna* and causes no economic damage (Gupta, 2005).

Euseius coccineae (Gupta)

Its record on this host has been made by Gupta (2005). No economic importance is known (Gupta, 1978).

Euseius coccosocius (Ghai & Menon)

Gupta (2005) recorded it on this host but its economic importance is not known.

Euseius ovalis (Evans)

This predatory mite has been reported on this host (Gupta, 2005).

Phytoseius roseus Gupta

This predatory mite is known to occur on this host from Orissa (Gupta, 1977; Gupta, 2005).

30. CARDAMOM (*Amomum subulatum* (small cardamom)

Tetranychus neocaledonicus Andre

It infests lower surface of leaves causing stippling and drying of leaves. Due to sucking from leaf tissues, the plants loose vigour. The upper surface of damaged leaves show yellowish speckled effect. Those later coalesce to form a patch and leaves dry up. Leaf lamina also rolls up. The young leaves are worst sufferers.

Biology : This mite takes 20.08 days in female and 21.71 days in male to complete the life cycle on this host under laboratory condition (*Prog. in Acar.*, **2** : 173-176). The duration of different stages for female is egg - 4.54 days, larva - 2.02 days, protonymph – 3.14 days, deutonymph - 10.14 days, total period 20.08 days, longevity - 23.01 days. The corresponding figures for males are 4.66 days, 2.18 days, 2.49 days, 10.38 days and 20.13 days, respectively.

Dolichotetranychus floridanus (Banks)

This is an elongated mite, found inhabiting concealed niches on cardamom plants, between ligule and leaf sheath and between leaf sheaths of pseudostem.

Damage : The feeding induced production of characteristic reddish discolouration on the damaged parts. Inner face of leaf sheath showed the presence of longitudinal, reddish, blister-like deformed corky tissue in the form of irregular and small cracks due to feeding of mites. Each blotch harboured all stages of mites. The reddish tinge also appears on outersurface of pseudostems. The leaves also showed characteristic pale green to yellowish blotches which extend to the margin. The colour changes ultimately to bronzy. The spindle also becomes brittle and breaks off. This is also an important pest of cardamom in Florida, Guatemala, Cuba, Hawaii, Mexico and Formosa (Siddapaji *et al.*, 1989 *Progress in Acarology*, **2** : 173-176).

31. CINCHONA (*Cinchona officinalis*)

Anystis baccarum (Linn.) : Roy *et al.*, (2008) collected it on cinchona.

Erythraeus cinchoni Roy *et al.* : Roy *et al.*, (2008) described this new species collected on cinchona.

Amblyseius herbicolus (Chant) : Roy *et al.*, (2008) collected it on cinchona.

32. LATA KASTURI (*Abelmoschus moschatus*)

Tetranychus neocaledonicus Andre

This occasionally occurs on this host producing characteristic yellowish spots. The damage is never of serious nature. Some predatory mites like *Typhlodromips syzygii* (Gupta) and *Lasioseius terrestris* Menon & Ghai also have been reported but their feeding potentiality is too poor.

33. NEEM (*Azadirachta indica*)

Eutetranychus orientalis (Klein)

This mite sucks the plant sap causing reduction in plant vitality producing characteristic damage symptoms. This occurs on upper surface of leaves throughtout India.

Schizotetranychus hindustanicus (Hirst)

This occurs throughout India normally on upper surface of leaves but may occur on lower surface as well producing characteristic yellowish stipplings.

Several species of predatory mites have also been recorded on this plant which are *Amblyseius largoensis* (Muma), *A. channabasavannai* (Gupta & Daniel). The former species is known to feed on eggs of *S. hindustanicus* (Gupta, 2005).

34. BRAHMI (*Bacopa monnieri*)

Brevipalpus phoenicis (Geij.)

This mite occurs throughout the year on the under surface of leaves and its population is more during the winter months. Its infestation causes yellowing of leaves.

35. HEMP (*Cannabis sativa*)

Tetranychus urticae Koch

This plant is seriously attacked by *Tetranychus urticae* and its infestation besides producing the characteristic mite damage symptoms also often causes death of the plant.

Eutetranychus orientalis (Klein)

Occasionally, this mite also attacks this plant.

Brevipalpus obovatus* Donnadieu & *B. rugulous Chaudhri *et al.*

These two species have been recorded on this plant but rarely they do any serious damage.

36. BUTTERFLY PEA (*Clitoria ternatea*)

Tetranychus urticae Koch

It seriously infests this plant throughout the year. Hundreds of mites are seen on undersurface of leaves producing yellowing and drying of leaves.

Tetranychus ludeni Zacher

Occasionally, this mite attacks this host producing characteristic damage symptoms.

37. KULTHI (*Dolichos biflorus*)

Tetranychus neocaledonicus Andre

It attacks very seriously during February-May. All the affected leaves may have over 100 mites/leaf and desapping causes yellowing and drying of leaves. All the affected plants become sick, dry up and many ultimately die.

Tetranychus urticae/Polyphagotarsonemus latus

These two mites also attack causing often serious damage.

38. KURCHI (*Holarrhena pubescens*)

Eutetranychus orientalis (Klein)/***Eotetranychus syzygii*** Gupta & Gupta/ ***Schizotetranychus baltazari*** Rimando

These mites infest the leaves during summer months. Of these, *Eutetranychus orientalis* and *S. baltazari* infest the upper surface of leaves producing yellowish white stipplings and the other one infests the lower surface of leaf causing discolouration and chlorosis. In cace of heavy infestation the leaves dry up.

Euseius alstoniae (Gupta)

This predatory mite also is known to occur on this plant but its importance, if any, is not known.

39. INDIGO (*Indigofera tinctoria*)

Schizotetranychus cajani Gupta

It is the major pest during September-February. The occurrence of as many as 40-50 mites on each leaf may not be uncommon. The infested leaves become yellow, remain underdeveloped and dry up (Gupta, 2005).

Tetranychus ludeni Zacher

Occasionally, this mite also attacks this host.

40. CURRY LEAF (*Murraya koenigii*)

Tetranychus urticae Koch / ***T. neocaledonicus*** Andre / ***Schizotetranychus baltazari*** Rimando

The first two species occur on lower surface of leaves causing chlorosis and the other one on the upper surface producing chlorotic spots, with white stipplings. The heavily infested leaves dry up and fall off.

The predatory mites like *A. kulini* Gupta, *Scapulaseius eucalypticus* (Gupta) are known to feed upon eggs of spider mites and thereby may help in reducing pest mite population.

41. OLEANDER (*Nerium indicum*)

Eutetranychus orientalis (Klein)

This mite attacks upper surface of leaves. *Aceria nerii* ChannaBasavanna and *Tegolophus nerii* Mondal & Chakrabarti also are known to occur as vagrants on undersurface of leaves but they cause no damage.

Amblyseins largoensis **(Muma)**/***Gynaeseius eharai*** (Gupta)

These predatory mites live amidst colonies of *Eutetranychus orientalis* and feed very voraciously on all stages of the prey.

42. AMRUL (*Oxalis corniculata)*

Petrobia harti (Ewing)

This mite very seriously infests this plant. The infestation starts during December and reaches the peak during April-May. Hundreds of this mite may be seen on both sides of leaves and petioles and mites fall down from leaves with slighest jarking. All the infested plants become yellowish white and subsequently those turn brown and dry up.

43. OPIUM POPPY (*Papavar somniferum)*

Tetranychus urticae Koch

This mite infests this plant very seriously immediately after disappearance of aphids and remains in the field till April. The infested plants look unhealthy.

44. ASHOK (*Saraca asoca)*

Brevipalpus californicus occasionally attacks this plant but never poses any serious threat.

In addition, two predatory mites *Pronematus fleschneri* Baker and *Euseius alstoniae* (Gupta) also were reported on this plant found feeding on eggs and nymphs of *B. californicus*.

45. BAHERA (*Terminalia bellirica)*

Eutetranychus orientalis (Klein)

Gupta (2005) recorded this mite on upper surface of leaf. No economic importance is known.

46. HARITAKI (*Terminalia chebula)*

Ectomcrus chebulae Mohanasundaram and *Brevipalpus* sp. have been recorded. No damage is done. One predatory mite, *Amblyseius herbicolus* also has been recorded.

Paraphytoseius multidentatus Swirski & Shechter, *Typhlodromips syzygii* (Gupta) : also have been reported on this plant.

47. BAN VASHYA (*Wissadula periplocifolia*)

Tetranychus urticae Koch

Many a times this mite seriously attacks this plant and its feeding produces characteristic mite damage symptoms.

Eotetranychus syzygii Gupta & Gupta

Gupta (2005) recorded this mite on this host. *Ambhyseius largoensis* (Muma) and *Pronematus elongatus* Baker are the predatory mites recorded on this host.

48. HARSINGHAR (*Nyctanthes arbortristis*)

Eotetranychus fremonti Tuttle & Baker

This mite forms colonies on undersurface of the leaves and due to sucking sap, the leaves become discoloured.

Cunaxa sp. : This predatory mite often occurs on this plant.

Anystis sp. : This predatory mite often occurs on this plant.

Brevipalpus californicus (Banks) : Occasionally, this mite infests undersurface of leaves.

The other predatory mites recorded on this host are *Agistemus gambli* Gupta, *Dactyloscirus bengalensis* Gupta, *Phytoseius indicus* Bhattacharyya but no predation has been observed in field.

49. VANILLA (*Vanilla fragrans*)

Brevipalpus sp. : This mite has been recorded on vanilla but does no damage

Pronematus sp. : This predatory mite was also recorded on this host but its predation was very poor.

50. JASMINE (*Jasminum officinalis*)

Discussed under Ornamental plant chapter.

51. MARIGOLD (*Tagetes erecta/T. patula*)

Discussed under Ornamental plant chapter.

52. *Michelia champaca*

Discussed under Ornamental plant chapter.

53. CHINA ROSE (*Hibiscus rosa sinensis*)

Discussed under Ornamental plant chapter.

54. LATKAN (*Bixa orellana*)

Oligonychus mangiferus (Rahman & Sapra) : Occurs on upper surface of leaves, causing chlorosis.

Typhlodromips syzygii (Gupta), ***A. herbicolus*** (Chant), ***A. paraaerialis*** Muma, ***Octobdellodes*** sp. also recorded on this plant having no known economic importance.

55. MEHENDI (*Lawsonia inermis*)

Brevipalpus sp. and ***Amblyseius paraaerialis*** Muma have been recorded but none is of any economic importance.

56. GARLIC (*Allium sativum)*

Aceria tulipae (Keifer) is becoming an important pest of this plant. The details are given under vegetable chapter.

Tetranychus urticae Koch : This is a minor pest doing occasional damage.

57. CLOVE (*Syzygium aromaticum*)

Euseius ovalis (Evans) is the only mite collected on this host.

58. RED SANDAL WOOD (*Pterocarpus santalinus)*

Tetranychus neocaledonicus Andre occasionally infests the undersurfaces of leaves.

59. WHITE SANDAL WOOD (*Santalum album*)

Only one predatory mite, *Euseius coccineae* (Gupta) is known to occur on this host.

60. FENUGREEK (*Trigonella foenum-graecum*)

Brevipalpus phoenicis (Geij.) is the only mite known to occur on this plant.

61. PIPUL (*Piper longum*)

Tetranychus urticae Koch : Sometimes infestation of this mite is seem on this host but never attains any serious status.

Brevipalpus deleoni Pritchard & Baker : This mite also occasionally infests this plant at a very low level and hence causes no damage. A predatory mite *Amblyseius largoensis* (Muma) has been recorded on this host but is not known to have any importance.

62. BAY LEAF (*Laurus nobilis*)

Only one *Pronematus* sp. has been recorded on this host.

63. DALCHINI (*Cinnamomum zeylanicum)*

Steneotarsonemus sp. and *Euseius alstoniae* (Gupta) are the only mites known to occur on this host.

64. BALA (*Pavonia odorata*)

Only two phytophagous mites, *Tetranychus ludeni* Zacher sucking plant sap from undersurface of leaves and *Polyphagotarsonemus latus* (Banks) on apical young leaves have been recorded on this plant.

65. *Barleria cristata*

Paraphytoptus cristatae Mohanasundaram- It causes white velvety erineal growth on both sides of leaf (Mohanasundaram, 1984, *Indian J. Acar.*, **8** : 78-86).

3.9 AROMATIC PLANTS

The demand for aromatic herbs in India is quite high both as raw material as well as in value added form.These herbs are widely used in food preparations, as flavours, pharmaceutical concerns, herbal cosmetics, perfumery and beauty aids.

In India, at the present moment, the availability of these herbs is rather limited and irregular and hence a lion's share for our consumption is being imported from outside this country. The domestic market consumption alone is about 200 tones/ year while only 60 tonnes are produced within the country. Bulk of these herbs (188 tonnes) are used for culinary purposes and about 12 tonnes for Medicinal and cosmetic purposes. India, having a vast area of land with varied climatic conditions, is ideally suited for cultivation of aromatic plants. The foreign exchange earned by India from export of these plants and plant products is about US $3000 million/ year and the countries where those are exported are Europe, USA, Japan. The demand for these plants is increasing both in developed and developing countries. The annual export of the derivatives of aromatic plants is to the tune of 100 -700 million rupees .The plants which are considered under this category are Sheuli, Citronella grass, Citrus plants, Rose, Latakasturi, small cardamom, Vanilla, Jasmine, Marigold, Black pepper, Camphor, Champa, Pepper mint, Basils, Garlic, Sandal wood (red & white), geranium, etc.

Many of these plants are infested by both phytophagous and predatory mites and those are discussed in this chapter plant -wise summarizing the available information.

The following mite species have been recorded on different aromatic plants in India. Since in most of the cases, the damages caused by them have been discussed in this book under different other chapters, those are not repeated here, excepting listing the mite species.

1. *Nyctanthes arbortristis* : Beng. Sheuli

Plant feeding - *Eotetranychus syzygii* Gupta & Gupta, 2) *E. sexmaculatus* (Riley), 3) *Brevipalpus phoenicis* (Geij.).

Predatory : *Agistemus* sp., *Pronematus ubiquitus* Baker, *Tydeus* sp.

2. *Cymbopogon palmarosa* : Palmarose

Plant feeding : *Oligonychus indicus* (Hirst)

3. *Cymbopogon flexuosus/C. winterianus*

Plant feeding : *Oligonychus oryzae* (Hirst)

4. *Citrus limonum* : Lemon

Plant feeding : *Panonychus citri* (McGregor), *Eutetranychus orientalis*

Predatory : *Euseius ovalis* (Evans), *E. alstoniae* (Gupta)

5. *Rosa damascena, R. centifolia, R. indica, R. alba* : Roses

Discussed in Ornamental plant chapter.

6. *Abelmoschus moschatus* : Latakasturi

Discussed under Medicinal plant chapter.

7. *Elettaria cardamomum* : Cardamom

Discussed under Medicinal plant chapter.

8. Vanilla

Discussed under Medicinal plant chapter.

9. *Jasminum sambac / J. officinalis* : Jasmine

Discussed under Ornamental plant chapter.

10. *Tagetes patula* : Marigold

Discussed under Ornamental plant chapter.

11. *Piper nigrum* : Black pepper

Discussed under Medicinal plant chapter.

12. *Cinnamomum camphora* : Camphor

Discussed under Medicinal plant chapter.

13. *Michelia champaca* : Champa

Discussed under Medicinal plant chapter.

14. *Mentha arvensis* : Mentha

Discussed under Medicinal plant chapter.

15. *Ocimum* spp. : Lemon Tulsi

Discussed under Medicinal plant chapter.

16. *Ocimum tenuiflorum* : Krishna Tulsi

Discussed under Medicinal plant chapter.

17. *O. grattisimum* : Ram Tulsi

Predatory : *Euseius ovalis* (Evans), *E. eucalypti* (Ghai & Menon)

18. *Allium sativum* : Garlic

Discussed under vegetable plants chapter.

19. *Pavonia odorata*

Discussed under Medicinal plant chapter.

20. *Santalum album* : Sandal wood

Discussed under Medicinal plant chapter.

21. *Pterocarpus santalinus* : Red sandalwood

Discussed under Medicinal plant chapter.

22. *Palargonium graveolens* : Geranium

Plant feeding : *Tetranychus urticae*

23. *Syzygium aromaticum* : Clove

Discussed under Medicinal plant chapter.

3.10 DYE YIELDING

1. *Hibiscus rosa-sinensis* : China rose

Discussed under Ornamental plant chapter.

2. *Nyctanthes arbortristis* : Sheuli

Discussed under Ornamental plant chapter.

3. *Indigofera tinctoria* : Indigo

Discussed under Medicinal plant chapter.

4. *Clitoria ternatea* : Aparajita

Discussed under Medicinal plant chapter.

5. *Tagetes patula*

Already mentioned

6. *Cocos nucifera*

Mentioned under Plantation crops

7. *Bixa orellana* : Latkan

Discussed under Medicinal plant chapter.

8. *Aegle marmelos* : Bael

Discussed under Forest trees

9. *Lawsonia inermis* : Mehendi

Discussed under Medicinal plant chapter.

10. *Terminalia chebula*

Discussed under Medicinal plant chapter.

11. *Punica granatum* : Pomegranate

Discussed under fruit trees

12. *Acacia catechu* : Babla

Discussed under Medicinal plant chapter.

13. *Justica adhatoda* : Vasak

Discussed under Medicinal plant chapter.

3.11 NARCOTIC

1. *Nicotiana tabacum* : Tobacco

Plant feeding : *Oligonychus* sp.

2. *Datura metel* : Datura

Discussed under Medicinal plant.

3. Tea

Discussed under Plantation crop.

4. HEMP : *Cannabis sativa*

Discussed under Medicinal plant.

3.12 SPICES

Spices constitute an important group of horticultural crops and are defined as vegetable products or mixture thereof, free from extraneous matter and used for flavouring, seasoning and imparting aroma in food. Since ancient time, India is considered as home of spice crops producing wide variety of spices like black pepper, cardamom (small & large), ginger, garlic, turmeric, chilli, and a variety of tree and seed spices. Major spice growing states are Andhra Pradesh, Kerala, Gujarat, Rajasthan, Maharashtra, West Bengal, Karnataka, Tamil Nadu, Madhya Pradesh and Sikkim. The area covered under spices in the country is estimated to be valued at 7000 crores (1998-99) (Chadha, 2010).

The crops considered under this category are Pipul, French basil, black pepper, chilli, cinnamone, turmeric, coriander, cumin, fennel, etc. The mites occurring on these plants have been reported and discussed.

1. *Piper longum* : Pipul

Discussed under Medicinal plant.

2. *Ocimum basilicum* : French basil

Discussed under Medicinal plant.

3. *Piper nigrum* : Black pepper

Discussed under Medicinal plant.

4. *Capsicum* spp. : Chilli

Discussed under Vegetable.

5. *Cinnamomum zeylanicum* : Dalchini

Discussed under Medicinal plant.

6. *Curcuma longa* : Turmeric

No phytophagous mite attacks, only *Amblyseius largoensis* has been recorded.

7. *Coriandrum sativum*

Discussed under Medicinal plant.

3.13 CONDIMENTS

1. *Murraya koenigii* : Curry leaf

Discussed earlier under Medicinal plant.

2. *Trigonella foenum-graecum* : Fenugreek

Discussed earlier under Medicinal plant.

3. *Nigella sativa* : Black cumin

Brevipalpus phoenicis is the only mite known to infest this plant.

4. *Melilotus alba* : White methi

Tetranychus urticae rarely infests this plant, but never reaches at alarming stage.

5. *Foeniculum vulgare* : Fennel

Paraphytoseius multidentatus Swirski & Shechter, predatory mite was collected on this plant. No phytophagous mite damages this plant.

6. *Cuminum cyminum* : Cumin

Euseius alstoniae (Gupta), a predatory mite, is known to occur on this plant but no phytophagous mite damages this plant.

3.14 ORNAMENTAL AND FLORICULTURAL PLANTS

Flowers in India have immese values in socio-cultural and religious lives of Indian people.Ornamental plants and floricultural plants have recently become viable business in India generating income and employement opportunities. Apart from these, this sector is involving women leading to the women empowerment and finally India is capturing a good portion of international market by exporting flowers and ancillary products.The leading states in India are Tamil Nadu ,Andhra Pradesh, Karnataka, Maharashtra, West Bengal, Sikkim, and Jammu & Kashmir. The area under flower cultivation is 2,32,540 ha with production of 4,59,156 tones of loose flowers and 15,613 cut flowers having stems (Chadha, 2010). About 50 types of flowering plants are discussed in this chapter with regard to the mites infesting those plants.

1. JASMINE (*Jasminum sambac*)

Aceria jasmini ChannaBasavanna

This mite is called Jasmine erineum mite and attacks jasmine throughout India but more so in South India. The mites are seen on undersurface of leaves. The feeding induces extensive growth of erineum both on leaves and shoots. The attack retards plants growth and flower production to the extent of 5-60%. Infested leaves had lower concentration of chlorophyll, nitrogen, phosphorous and potassium contents compared to healthy plants. Chlorophyll content is reduced to half as compared to that of healthy one. The erineum growth reduces photosynthesis (Jose *et al.*, 1999: *J. Acarol.*, **14** : 45-46). Ravi and Puttaswamy (1995: *Bangalore Symposium,*

: 38-39) made histological and histochemical studies of jasmine leaves infested with this mite and reported the reduction in size of mesophyll tissues, which in turn, resulted in thickness in leaves. Size and number of starch grains were reduced. Protein content increased but RNA content was not altered.

Control : For control of this mite, spraying of monocrotophos, phosalone and sulphur was significantly good in reducing damage (Udayagiri and Mohan, 1983 *Abst. II All India Symp. Acarology, Pune* : 64). Umapathy and Mohanasundaram (1995, Bangalore Symposium, p.86) evaluated different pesticides against this mite and reported dicofol, wetable sulphur, endosulfan, monocrotophos induced only 0-5% erineum formation and were superior to others. Difenthiuron (0.1%) was found to be most effective followed by bromoprophylate (0.1%), dicofol (0.1%) (Jose *et al.* 1999: *J. Acarol.,* **14** : 41-44). Foliar application of monocrotophos (0.05%), wetable sulphur (0.14%), phosalone (0.07%) not onl;y gave good mortality but also were cost effective as cost of 6 applications of monocrotophos, sulphur and phosalone was Rs. 3621.56, Rs. 1047.00 and Rs. 2664, respectively, while the cost of 4 applications of aldicarb, as recommended by Letchoumanane and Subramaniam (1979: In : *Contributions to Acarology in India,* p. 215-221), was 4019.00. Three foliar applications of wetable sulphur was best and economical (Udayagiri and Mohan, 1989, *J. Acarol.,* **11** : 91-94).

Calcarus jasmini Chakraborti & Mondal

Chakrabarti and Mondal (1978: *Indian J. Acar.,* **3** : 71-76) described this species collected from *Jasminum sambac* in West Bengal. The infestation of this mite produces white yellowish patches on leaves. The maximum population was seen during April-June and was again seen during October-November.

Tetranychus neocaledonicus Andre

This mite also attacks jasmine producing characteristic mite damage symptoms which affected growth and yield. Sudharma *et al.,* (1995: *Abst.V Nat. Symp. Acarology, Bangalore* : 14) also reported this species seriously infesting jasmine in Kerala.

Brevipalpus nangalensis Sadana & Kaur

Sadana and Kaur (1992: *Entomon.,* **17** : 95-97) described this species from *Jasminum sambac.* No information is available about its economic importance.

Brevipalpus obovatus Donnadieu

Karmakr *et al.,* (2010: p.40-41) reported this mite from West Bengal on *Jasminum multiflorum.*

PREDATORY MITES

Euseius kalimpongensis (Gupta)

This predatory mite was reported on Jasmine in Bihar (Gupta, 1978: *Indian J. Acar.,* **2** : 60-77).

Amblyseius paraaerialis Muma

This predatory mite has also been reported on Jasmine feeding upon *Tetranychus macfarlanei* infesting Jasmine (Karmakar *et al.*, 2010).

2. ROSE (*Rosa centifolia, R. damascena, R. alba*)

Tetranychus urticae Koch

Nature of Damage : It is a serious pest of rose and does considerable damage (Karmakar *et al.*, 2010, Dhooria, 1999a). The population may be as high as 50 mites/ leaf. The damage caused by feeding of this mite may be upto 53% (Dhooria 1999). It attacked 7 varieties of rose, viz., First Red, Golden Yellow, Mercedes Long, Pavarroti, Prophyta, Saphire and Vivaldi grown in polyhouse in Punjab.

Onkarappa *et al.* (1999: *J. Acarol.*, **15** : 44-46) while studying spatial distribution of *T. urticae* on rose cultivated in open, reported that proximal leaves of each canopy level and terminal leaflets of each compound leaves harboured more number of eggs, nymphs and adults. Rose being a shrub, senescence of leaves is much slower compared to French bean. Hence, the leaves at the bottom of the canopy remain suitable for feeding by mites for a longer period.

Control : Better reduction of *T. urticae* on rose grown in polyhouse was obtained with mixture of monocrotophos (0.036%) + hippe (*Madhuca latifotea* oil 0.04%) and dicofol (0.027%) + hippe oil (0.04%). This was followed by monocrotophos (0.018%) + pongamia oil (0.04%), dicofol (0.027%) + pongamia oil (0.04%) (Onkarrappa *et al.*, 1999, *J. Acarol.*, **15** : 47-50). In another experiment, the same authors reported difenthiuron (300, 450, 600 g ai/ha) was most effective against *T. urticae* on rose in polyhouse condition over profenophos (500 g ai/ha) and dicofol (740g ai/ha) which was at per with untreated control (Onkarappa and Puttaswamy, 1999: *J. Acarol.*, **15** : 51-54).

Cha2062 (Coded product of M/S Cheminova India Ltd., Mumbai) @ 18 g ai/ha was very efficient causing significant reduction of this mite. Abamectin (18 g ai/ ha) was also very good and safer to predators. Both CHA 2062 and Abamectin had similar efficacy pattern. Abamectin (1.9% EC) @ 2 ml/10lt. of water also reported to be best against *T. urticae* infesting rose giving 97.09% reduction in mite population followed by propergite (57% EC @ 1 ml/lt of water) registering 96.22% reduction after 14 days of spray (Senapati *et al.*, 2010: 97). Sridhar and Jhansi Rani (2007: *J. Acarol.*, **17** : 48-60) while studying resistance in this mite collected from different polyhouses to dicofol and wettable sulphur reported differences in susceptibility of *T. urticae* to those chemicals. This may be attributed to different selection pressures and different mechanisms. Field population of *T. urticae* had shown maximum resistance against dimethoate (31 folds). Resistance development to dicofol in the four populations ranged from 372.92 folds to 1780 folds. Among organophosphates, maximum resistance was noticed in dimethoate with 547.38 folds followed by dichlorvos, monocrotophos and profenophos in decreasing order of resistance (Shaila and Mallik 2007, *J. Acarol*, **17** : 54-56). Abamectin 1.8 EC @ 13.5 g ai/ha was very effective in controlling *T. urticae* on rose giving maximum yield of 11,25,000 and 7,31,250 flowers/ha in Chinnamettupalayam and Vellakinaru respectively (Bhaskaran *et al.*, 2007, *J. Acarol*, **17** : 92-94).

Tetranychus neocaledonicus Andre

This mite has also been recorded on rose doing damage characteristic to other spider mites.

Oligonychus biharensis (Hirst)

Nature of damage : The rose plants which have high export value are very seriously attacked by this mite causing infested rose leaves to become discolored from green to rusty red leading to reduction in flower formation.

Control : Sterilisation of mites by lower dose of 0.25 kd, prevented production of subsequent generations. The sterilization with low dose and cold temperature can disinfect rose from mites as well as increased vase life. This, in turn, will benefit flower trading, both at national and international levels (Majumder and Bhuiya, 1995: *Abst. V Nat. Sem. Acar.*, : 77-78).

Eutetranyhcus orientalis (Klein)

Gupta and Gupta (1978: *Indian J. Acar.*, **3** : 90) reported this mite on rose from M.P. It occurs on upper surface of leaves and since a thick cover of dust accumulates on the leaves, the physiological activities get hampered. Chatterjee and Gupta (1995) also reported it on rose from West Bengal.

Oligonychus mangiferus (Rahman & Sapra)

This was recorded on rose in W. Bengal (Anon., 2003).

Bryobia praetiosa Koch

Gupta (1985) recorded this species on rose.

Brevipalpus californicus (Banks)

Its record on rose was made in Gupta (1985).

Brevipalpus phoenicis (Geij.)

Its occurrence on rose was listed by Gupta (1985).

PREDATORY MITES

Several predatory mites are in record on rose and those are :

Neoseiulus longispinosus (Evans)	Gupta, 1978: *Indian. J. Acar.*, **2** : 66-77 from Bihar
Euseius ovalis (Evans)	Gupta (1985)
Amblyseius largoensis (Muma)	Anon. (2003)

Amblyseius herbicolus (Chant)	Karmakar *et al.* (2010) from West Bengal
Paraphytoseius multidentatus S. & S.	Gupta (1985)
Phytoseius macrosetosus Gupta	Gupta (1977: *Indian J. Acar.*, **1** : 11-18) from M.P.
Tyrophagus putrescentiae (Schrank)	Anon. (2003)

3. Coleus (*Coleus aromaticus, C. forskohlii*)

Brevipalpus obovatus (Donnadieu)

Goel and Sadana (1983: *Indian J. Acar.*, **8** : 22-30) reported this as an injurious pest of *Coleus* and studied the effect of feeding on biochemical components of *Coleus* as below :

Sl. No.	Components	Control	Heavily infested
1.	Chlorophyll	63-22 mg/m^2	15-22 mg/m^2
2.	Sugar	29.50	12.70
3.	Reducing sugar	24.76 mg/g	11.60 mg/g
4.	Non reducing sugar	4.74 mg/g	1.10 mg/g
5.	Protein	1.15 mg/g	0.72 mg/g
6.	Free amino acid	0.28 mg/g	0.21 mg/g
7.	Starch	13.37 mg/g	7.80 mg/g
8.	Nitrogen	18.00	14.50
9.	Phosphorous	0.232	0.195
10.	Potassium	2.175	0.70
11.	Sodium	0.047	0.039
12.	Sulphur	4.75×10^{-3}	3.98×10^{-3}

The presence of appreciable amount of carbohydrate, nitrogen, phosphorous and potassium in *Coleus* sp. made it a suitable host for *B. obovatus*.

2. *Aculus colei* ChannaBasvanna : ChannaBasvanna (1966) described this species collected on *Coleus amboinicus*.

4. BOUGAINVILLEA (*Bougainvillea spectabilis*)

***Eriophyes ladakhensis* Rishi and Rather :** Rishi and Rather (1981: *Indian J. Acar.*, **6** : 14-16) reported this species on *Bougainvillea* sp. from Kashmir valley. Nothing about its importance is known.

***Euseius ovalis* (Evans)** : Gupta (1978: *Indian J. Acar.*, **2** : 60-77) recorded it on *Bougainvillea* from Meghalaya.

Brevipalpus californicus (Banks) : Gupta (1985) reported its occurrence on this host.

Euseius ovalis (Evans) **:** Its occurrence on this host was reported in Gupta (1985).

5. *Bauhinia acuminata/Bauhinia purpurea* : Mountain Ebony

Euseius prasadi Chant & Denmark : This was reported by Gupta (1978: *Indian J. Acar.*, **2** : 60-77) from Tripura on *B. acuminata.*

Amblyseius largoensis (Muma) **:** Gupta (1985) listed this species on this host.

Agistemus macrommatus Gonzalez-Rodriguez : Gupta (1985) listed this species on this host.

6. PALM TREE

Typhlodromus gopali Gupta : Gupta (1977: *Indian J. Acar.*, **1** : 11-18) reported it from palm tree from Rajasthan.

Euseius alstoniae (Gupta) **:** Gupta (1977: *Indian J. Acar.*, **1** : 28-37) recorded it on palm tree in Gujarat.

7. CHRYSANTHEMUM *(Chrysanthemum coronarium/C. morifolium)*

Bryobia eharai Pritchard & Keifer **:** This mite regularly occurs on *Chrysanthemum* specially in North India. It is yellowish brown mite found normally on upper surface of leaves.

Damage : Feeding causes yellowing of leaves which later turn brown. This reatards growth of young plants (Menon and Ghai, 1968, *Indian J. Ent.*, 30: 88-89). It occurs in the field throughout the year. It overwinters in egg stage in foliage. This mite is more active during April to July and population dwindles with monsoon rain (Gupta, 1985). After rain, the population reappears and remains until November.

Distribution : Maharashtra, Punjab, UP, Delhi, Karnataka, Jammu & Kashmir.

Tetranyhcus urticae Koch **:** Its occurrence on this host was mentioned in Gupta (1985).

Tetranyhcus macfarlanei Baker & Pritchard **:** Karmakr *et al.* (2010) mentioned this as important pest.

Brevipalpus karachiensis Chaudhri *et al.* **:** Sadana and Gupta (1982) recorded it on *Chrysanthemum* in Punjab.

Paraphytoptus chrysanthemi Keifer **:** It causes malformation of shoot, witche's broom effect, stunting of growth and backward curling.

Neoseiulus aceriae (Gupta) **:** Gupta (1977: *Indian J. Acar.*, **1** : 28-37) collected it on *Chrysanthemum* from Gujarat.

***Neoseiulus cucumeris* (Oudemans)** : Manjunatha *et al.* (1995: Banglore Symposium, 1995 : p. 25), collected this mite on *Chrysanthemum* and conducted its olfactory behaviour by Pettersson's four way olfactometer. As per their report, this mite significantly responded to volatiles of *Chrysanthemum.* Germacrene-D 42.2 (ng µL) elicited maximum olfactory response in the predators than other volatiles and the increase in response corresponded with increase in concentrations upto 50 ng/ µL for time spent in the olfactometer trteated arms. Ethyl nicotinate attracted the predator at 100, 250 and 500 ng/µl. The tritrophic interaction with *Chrysanthemum,* western flower thrips and predatory mite, *N. cucumeris* was discussed.

Amblyseius channabasavannai Gupta & Daniel **:** Gupta (1985) mentioned its occurrence on *Chrysanthemum.*

Amblyseius neorykei Gupta : Gupta (1985) listed it under this host.

***Eusieus ovalis* (Evans)** : Its occurrence on this host also was mentioned in Gupta (1985).

Brevipalpus karachiensis Chaudhri *et al.* : Sadana and Gupta (1982) reported it on this host.

Tetranychus macfarlanei Baker & Pritchard **:** Karmakr *et al.,* (2010) mentioned it as important pest.

Typhlodromus neosoleiger Gupta **:** Gupta (1977: *Indian J. Acar.,* **1** : 11-18) recorded it on *Chrysanthemum* from Gujarat.

8. OLEANDER (*Nerium indicum/N. odorum*)

The following mites have been collected on this plant :

Eutetranychus orientalis (Klein) **:** This mite occurring on upper surface of leaves produces characteristic damage symptoms (Gupta, 1985) (Karuppuchamy and Mohanasundaram, 1987: *Entomon.,* **12** : 89-94).

Tenuipalpus punjabensis Maninder & Ghai **:** Maninder and Ghai (1978: *Oriental Insects,* **12** : 111-113) described it on *Nerium indicum.* No economic importance is known (Gupta, 1985).

Brevipalpus californicus (Banks) **:** Gupta (1985) listed this on this host.

Brevipalpus phoenicis (Geij.) **:** Gupta (1985) listed this on this host.

Aceria nerii ChannaBasavanna **:** ChannaBasvanna (1966) described this species collected from *Nerium indicum.* No economic importance is known (Gupta, 1985).

Euseius alstoniae (Gupta) **:** Gupta (1977: *Indian J. Acar.,* **1** : 28-37) recorded it on this host from Gujarat.

Amblyseius largoensis (Muma) **:** Its listing under *Nerium* has been mad by Gupta Gupta (1977: *Indian J. Acar.,* **1** : 28-37) from Gujarat.

Euseius ovalis (Evans) : Gupta (1985) listed this mite occurring on *Nerium*.

Tegolophus nerii Mandal & Chakraborti : Mondal and Chakrabarti (1979, *Entomon.*, **4** : 376-377) described it on *N. odorum*.

9. Waxflower (*Tabernaemontana coronaria*)

The following mites have been reported but none has any economic importance:

Eutetranychus orientalis (Klein) : Gupta (1985).

Brevipalpus californicus (Banks) : Gupta (1985).

Brevipalpus rugulosus Chaudhri *et al.* : Gupta (1985)

Calepitrimerus tabernaemontanis Mandal & Chakraborti : Mandal and Chakrabarti (1983).

Neoseiulus longispinosus (Evans) : Gupta (1985)

Amblyseius largoensis (Muma) : Gupta (1985)

Euseius coccineae (Gupta) : Gupta (1985)

Euseius ovalis (Evans) : Gupta (1985)

***Euseius alstoniae* (Gupta)** : Gupta (1977: *Indian J. Acar.*, **1** : 28-37) recorded it from Gujarat.

Cunaxa setirostris (Hermann) : Gupta (1985).

10. NIGHT JASMINE (*Nyctanthes arbor-tristis*)

The following mites have been collected on this plant :

Brevipalpus deleoni Pritchard & Baker : Gupta (1985)

Brevipalpus phoenicis (Geij.) : Gupta (1985)

Amblyseius crotalariae Gupta : Gupta (1978, *Indian J. Acar.*, **2** : 60-67, recorded it from Tripura)

11. FLAME OF THE WOOD/TORCH TREE (*Ixora parviflora, I. coccinea*)

The following mites have been collected on this plant :

Eutetranychus orientalis (Klein) : Chatterjee and Gupta (1995), p. 13, reported this species on *I. coccinea.*

Tenuipalpus ixorae (Maninder & Ghai) : Maninder and Ghai, 1978: *Oriental Ins.*, **12** : 254-255, described this species collected on *Ixora parviflora* from UP.

12. ZINIA (*Zinnia elegans/Z. pauciflora*)

The following mites have been collected on this plant :

Tetranychus urticae Koch : Chatterjee and Gupta (1995).

Brevipalpus phoenicis (Geij.) : Gupta (1985) listed it under *Zinia* sp.

Brevipalpus karachiensis Chaudhri *et al.* : Gupta (1985)

Brevipalpus rugulosus Chaudhri *et al.* : Gupta (1985)

Polyphagotarsonemus latus (Banks) : Gupta (1985) listed it under *Zinia* sp.

Euseius alstoniae (Gupta) : Gupta (1985)

Neoseiulus longispinosus (Evans) : Gupta (1985)

13. *Poinsettia pulcherrima*, CACTUS (*Euphorbia pulcherrima, E. antiquorum, E. geniculata*)

The following mites have been collected on these plants :

Tetranychus neocaledonicus Andre : Gupta (1985) listed it under *E. geniculata.*

Tetranychus urticae Koch : Chatterjee and Gupta (1995) reported it on *E. pulcherrima.*

Brevipalpus californicus (Banks) : Gupta (1985)

14. *Codaeum* sp.

The following mites have been collected on this plant :

Brevipalpus sp. : Infested *Codaeum* (Karmakar *et al.*, 2010)

Euseius ovalis (Evans) : Fed on *Brevipalpus* sp. infesting *Codaeum* sp. (Karmakar *et al.*, 2010).

15. PINK CASSIA (*Cassia* sp.)

Schizotetranychus lechrius

Dhooria (1985), reported this species on Pink cassia in Punjab. Infestation caused rusty red color on ventral surface of leaves. The eggs are yellowish, white, round. Incubation period was 7.59 days, larval, protonymphal and deutonymphal periods-avareaged 4.24, 3.61 and 3.71 days, respectively. The combined nymphal period took 15 days. Female : Male was 59 : 41, the longevity of male and female was 10.67 and 12.75 days, respectively.

16. CYCLAMEN

Tetranycus urticae Koch

This mite severely damages Cyclamen grown in glass house in Shimla region. Mite feeding produces irregular chlorotic spots on lower leaf surface, making those brown and plants wither thereby loosing their natural look. Obviously, this reduces the market value. Mit - 50 EC (Ethion 0.1%) gave effective control followed by Kelthane 18.5 EC @ 0.05%. Verma (1995, *V Nat. Symp. Acarology, Bangalore*, p. 78).

17. CARNATION (*Dianthus caryophyllus*)

Tetranyhcus urticae Koch

These are important cut flowers and are attacked by *T. urticae* in polyhouse affecting flower production. The average tolerance limit of the plant was 12.15-14.43 mites/leaf. However, with the exceed of this limit (20 mites/leaf) the quality of flower becomes medium and above that level, the harvested flowers show complete damage. The percentage of bad quality flowers was more in variety Kartina (20.75) followed by Grafitti (19.23), Feyenoord (18.9), Grafield (18.36), Cabaret (17.80), Desio (16.49), Navajo (15.60) and Furlano (14.28). The highest percentage of good quality flowers was recorded in variety Grafitti, followed by varieties Rirandello (71.30), Furlano (69.52), Navajo (69.50), Desio (68.04), Cabaret (64.38), Grafield (62.24), Feyenoord (61.26), and Karina had the lowest percentage (60.32) good quality flowers. Highest percentage of monetary loss was recorded in variety Kartina (29.80) and Feyenoord (28.41), Grafield (27.60), Cabaret (26.34), Desio (23.90), Grafitti (22.92), Furlano (22.05). Var. Rirandello recoded lowest percentage of monetary loss (Rajashekharappa and Mallik, 2007, *J. Acarol.* 17: 1-3). Among the varieties like Domingo, Solar, Madam callatte, Master on which the mite *T. urticae* infestation was assessed on middle leaves and flower buds, Madam callatte recorded less number of mites on leaves (4.8) and flower buds (3.8) compared to other varieties. Domingo var. recorded more number of mites (47.2 mites/flower bud and 21.8 mites/leaf) compared to other varieties (Prasad Kumar, 2007: *J. Acarol.*, **16** : 55-56). As regards distribution of *T. urticae* on carnation grown in polyhouses it was reported that the population was high at top canopy leaves followed by middle and bottom canopy leaves. Within leaves, the upper surface harboured more mites (all stages) compared to lower surface in the bottom canopy. So, the upper surface should be considered for mite sampling as the co-efficient of variation was low. The leaves of the middle and lower canopies reach senescence early and therefore, the mites avoid those leaves and like the top canopy leaves. A similar phenomena occurs in rose grown in polyhouse as reported by Vidya (1999, M.Sc. Thesis) (Rajshekharappa and Mallik, 2007: *J. Acar.*, **16** : 121-123). Three sprays of *Hirsutella thompsonii* @ 10^8 CFU/ml (average 5.0 mites/flower bud) were found to be statistically superior followed by *Verticillium lecanii* (Ave. 5.6 mites/flower bud). Spraying Abamectin @ 0.5 ml/lt thrice at 15 days interval was most effective in suppressing *T. urticae* population (Anon. 2009-2010, AICRP on biocontrol of crop pest. NBAII, Bangalore, p. 217).

18. RHODODENDRON

Acaricalus darjeelingensis

This mite was collected and described on rhododendron from Darjeeling as vagrants on ventral surface of *Rhododendron* leaves.

Gupta (1985) listed the following species on Rhododendron but none of these are of any economic importance.

Brevipalpus lewisi McG.

Euseius rhododendroni (Gupta)

Typhlodromus rhododendronis (Gupta)

19. GOLDEN CHAMPA (*Michelia champaca, M. grandiflora*)

Paraphytoptus champacae Mohanasundaram

Mohanasundaram (1984: *Indian J. Acar.*, **8** : 73-86) described this species collected on this host. It inhabited vegetative buds. Damage done by this mite is unknown.

Tetranychus macfarlanei Baker & Pritchard

(Karmakar *et al.*, 2010) mentioned this as important pest of this host plant.

20. TUBER ROSE (*Polyanthea tuberosa*)

Tyrophagus putrescentiae (Schrank)

Its report on tuber rose was made by Ganguly *et al.* (1993: *Curr. Nematology*, **4** : 113-116). It formed tunnels between cortex and stele due to disappearance of some particle cells which might have been eaten away/dissolved by mites. In this disease syndrome, the roots were primarily infected by the root knot nematode (*M. incognita*). The roots get secondarily infected by mites. Plant suffers from heavy injury.

Tetranychus urticae Koch

It is also known to infest tuber rose occasionally.

Scapulaseius polyantheae (Gupta)

Gupta (1985) listed this predatory mite on this host but its economic importance is unknown.

21. CHINA ROSE (*Hibiscus rosa-sinensis*)

Gupta (1985) listed the following mites on this host :

Eutetranychus maximae Nassar & Ghai : Anon (2003)

Brevipalpus californicus Banks : Causes occasional infestation

Brevipalpus phoenicis (Geij.) : Causes occasional infestation

Euseius delhiensis (Narayanan & Kaur) : predatory mite

Amblyseius largoensis (Muma) : Predatory mite of *Brevipalpus*

Euseius ovalis (Evans) : As above

Walzia indiana Smith-Meyer & Ueckermann : Very common predatory mite, feeds on eggs of *Brevipalpus* sp.

22. MARIGOLD (*Tagetes patula, T. erecta*)

Tetranychus urticae Koch

This mite very often seriously attacks the leaves and envelops the leaves with webs. The leaves become yellow, then brown, spotted and finally dry up. The infested plants look unhealthy.

Tetranychus ludeni Zacher

Karmakar *et al.* (2010) recorded this mite on this host in West Bengal.

Polyphagotarsonemus latus (Banks)

This mite often infests the apical young leaves. Those become brown, crinkled, curled and dry up (Gupta, 1985). Heavy infestation has been noticed on this plant in Bengal and Punjab where the whole plant was totally enveloped by webs and leaves had shown brownish patches. Such leaves defoliate (Sadana & Chhabra, 1981, *Sci. & Cult.*, **47** : 172-173).

Brevipalpus sp.

An unidentified *Brevipalpus* mite occasionaly occurs on undersurface of leaves.

Euseius coccineae (Gupta)

This predatory mite was recorded on this host.

23. *Canna indica*

Brevipalpus rugulosus Chaudhri *et al.*

Gupta (1985) listed it on this host.

24. QUEEN OF THE NIGHT/HASNA HANA (*Cestrum noctrum*)

Brevipalpus californicus (Banks)

Gupta (1985) listed this species on this host. No damage is known.

Brevipalpus phoenicis (Geij.)

Sadana and Rajinder (1990: *Acarologia*, **13** : 357-360) recorded it on this host. No damage is caused by this mite.

25. *Dahlia variabilis*

Gupta (1985) recorded the following mite species on this host plant :

Petrobia latens (Muller)

Tetranychus urticae Koch

Tetranychus ludeni Zacher

Brevipalpus deleoni Pritchard & Baker

Brevipalpus phoenicis (Geij.)

Amblyseius channabasvannai Gupta & Daniel

Phytoseius wainsteini Gupta

26. GERANIUM (*Geranium* sp.)

Gupta (1985) recorded the following mite species on this host :

Tetranychus neocaledonicus Andre

Brevipalpus phoenicis (Geij.)

27. SUNFLOWER (*Helianthus annuus*)

The following mite species are known to infest this plant (Gupta, 1985) but nothing is known about their economic importance :

Tetranychus urticae Koch

Eutetranychus orientalis (Klein)

Brevipalpus californicus (Banks)

Brevipalpus obovatus Donnadieu

Brevipalpus phoenicis (Geij.)

Typhlodromus confusus Narayanan *et al.*

Paraphytoseius multidentatus Swirski & Shechter

28. *Lagestroemia indica*

The following mites have been recorded on this plant (Gupta, 1985), but their economoic importance is unknown :

Oligonychus mangiferus (Rahman & Sapra)

Brevipalpus californicus (Banks)

Brevipalpus karachiensis Chaudhri *et al.*

29. *Murraya exotica*

The following is the mite species recorded on this host (Gupta, 1985) :

Brevipalpus californicus (Banks)

30. *Petunia alba/P. hybrida*

Gupta (1985) listed the following species on this host :

Tetranychus urticae Koch

Bevipalpus karachiensis (Sadana and Gupta (1982) reported it on this host).

31. TEMPLE TREE (*Plumeria aculifolia/P. alba*)

Brevipalpus phoenicis (Geij.) : Gupta (1985).

32. YELLOW OLEANDER (*Thevetia neriifolia*)

Brevipalpus californicus (Banks) : Gupta (1985)

33. *Clerodendrum inerme* (Bon Jui)

Aceria clerodendronis Farkas

ChannaBasavanna (1966) recorded this species on this host. As a result of attack, violet coloured warty patches are produced on the upper surface of leaves (Bindra & Singh, 1970).

34. *Dalbergia sissoo*

Aceria dalbergiae ChannaBasavanna

ChannaBasavanna (1966) described this species collected on this host. The attacked leaves develop pale green or whitish yellow warty patches, which later turn brown.

Aceria erythrinae ChannaBasavanna

ChannaBasvanna (1966) described this species collected on this host.

35. *Cassia fistula*

Eutetranychus orientalis : Bindra and Singh (1970) recorded it on *Cassia fistula.*

36. *Dodonea viscosa*

Bindra and Singh (1970) listed *T. neocaledonicus* on this host.

37. GLADIOLUS

Tetranychus urticae Koch : Bindra and Singh (1970) listed this species on this host.

38. COSMOS

Tetrancyhus ludeni : Bindra and Singh (1970) listed this species on this host.

39. HOLLYHOCK

Tetranychus urticae : Bindra and Singh (1970) listed this species on this host.

T. neocaledonicus : Anon.

40. *Crossandra undulaefolia*

Bindra and Singh (1970) listed *T. neocaledonicus* on this host.

41. GERBERA (ZERBERA)

Agistemus sp., ***Brevipalpus deleoni, B. phoenicis*** are the mites which have been recorded on this host but nothing about their importance is known (Gupta, 1985).

42. TIGER LILLY

Agistemus sp.

43. *Mussandra corymbosa*

Amblyseius largoensis (Gupta, 1985)

44. TULIP (*Thespesia populnea*)

Polyphagotarsonemus latus (Banks) : Sometimes occur on this plant

Tetranychus urticae Koch : Occasionally infest this plant

45. CHANGEABLE ROSE (*Hibiscus mutabilis*)

Infestation of *Eutetranychus orientalis* (Klein) is often seen on the upper surface of leaves causing yellowish specks and accumulation of heavy dust particles. The damage is of no serious nature.

46. BOTTLE BRUSH (*Callistemon speciosus*)

Two species of tenuipalpid mites, *Brevipalpus californicus* (Banks) and *B.karachiensis* Chaudhri *et al.* ., occur on under surface of leaves doing discoloration of leaves. No serious damage is caused .

47. *Thevetia nerifolium*

Only one Tenuipalpid mite, *Brevipalpus californicus* (Banks) is known to occur on this host causing desapping of leaves leading to appearance of brownish patches .The damage is of very insignificant nature.

48. BIGNONIA (*Bignonia venasta*)

Occasionally, *Brevipalpus phoenicis* (Geij.) attacks this plant but no damage of serious nature is caused.

49. RAJANIGANDHA (*Adantheria pavoniana.*)

A predatory mite, *Phytoseius kapuri* Gupta, has been reported on this host. No plant feeding mite has so far been reported.

50. GANDHARAJ (*Gardenia florida/G.jasminoides*)

Tetranychus urticae Koch and *Diptilomiopus* sp. occur on this host but infestation is never of serious nature.

51. PERIWINKLE (*Vinca rosea*)

Amblyseius largoensis (Muma) and *Paraphytoseius multidentatus* S. & S. have been recorded on this host but no plant feeding mite has been reported causing damage to this plant.

3.15 WEEDS/FODDER

Lantana

Phytoseius neocorniger : Gupta (1977: *Indian J. Acar.*, **1** : 11-18).

Eichhornia crassipes

This aquatic weed is infested by oribatid mites *Punctoribates insignis* Berl., *Galumna chujoi* Aoki., *Scheloribates praeincisus* Berl., *S. decarinatus* Aoki, *S. sicula* Berl.

Population density of *Punctoribates insignis* was highest. Analysis of gut content showed presence of leaf tissues suggesting their phytophagous habits. This host forms favourable diet due to high number of eggs and immature stages of this mite on this host. May be, this will form prominent bio-controlling agent. *G. chujoi, S. sicula* did not feed on leaves, their gut contents had fungal hyphae (Sheela and Haq, 1989, *Progress in Acarol.*, **2** : 207-210).

Singh *et al.* (1989: *Progress in Acarology*, **2** : 211-214) surveyed water hyacinth (*E. crassipes*) and reported the occurrence of *Monoschelobates* sp., *Brachychthonius* sp., *Lasioseius* sp., *Ololaelaps* sp.,*Eutetranychus orientalis*, *Cunaxa* sp., *Tyrophagus putrescentiae.* Most of them were found on decomposing root and shoot portions of plants. Density of *Brachychthonius* sp was highest followed by *Lasioseius* sp. and *Ololaelaps* sp.

Rather (1995) recorded *Tetranychus urticae* on weeds (*Forsythia japonica, Rosa macrophylla, Lathyrus sativa, Solanum nigrum, Datura stramonium*).

Sumangala and Haq (1995) reported *Eutetranychus orientalis* severely attacking *E. crassipes* causing bronzing of leaves and declining chlorophyll level to 47% over uninfested plant.

Cyperus rotundus

Steneotarsonemus sp. was recorded on this host. No economic importance is known.

Cynodon dactylon

Steneotarsonemus conoi was recorded on this host. No economic importance is known (Karmakar, 2010, p. 43).

Parthenium hysterophorus

Tetranyhcus neocaledonicus Andre : Gupta (1985) mentioned the occurrence of this species on this host. Kumar *et al.* (1979: *J. Ent. Res.*, **3** : 32-35) reported this mite doing natural control of this weed.

Tetranyhcus neocaledonicus Andre : Puttaswamy *et al.* (1973, *Curr. Sci.*, **45** : 118) reported this species on *Parthenium.*

Brevipalpus phoenicis : Dagar and Singh (1979: *Curr. Sci.*, **48** : 71-72) reported this mite as a new pest of this weed.

Physalis minima

Polyphagotarsonemus latus (Banks) : This mite was recorded on this weed (Das and Raychaudhuri, 1979: *Sci. and Cult.*, **45** : 169-170)

Eichhornia crassipes

This notorious weed is attacked by a number of mite species. Pal (1990: *Env. and Ecol.*, **8** : 1342-1343) reported the following mites on this host which may be of some economic importance.

Plant feeding	**Predatory**
1. *Acarus* sp.	1. *Pseudocunaxa* sp./*Euseius coccosocius* (Ghai & Meneon)
2. *Tyrophagus putrescentiae* (Schrank)	2. *Scirula* sp.
3. *Hydrozetes terrestris*	3. *Agistemus* sp.
4. *Acterozetes* sp.	4. Trombidiidae
5. *Scheloribates* sp.	5. Erythraeidae
6. *Galumna* sp.	**Unknown association**
7. *Punctoribates* sp.	1. *Platyseius subglaber*
8. *Eutetranychus orientalis* (Klein)	2. *Lasioseius* sp.
9. *Eotetranychus* sp.	3. *Holostaspulla* sp.
10. *Tarsonemus* sp.	4. *Ololaelaps sellinicki* Bregetova & Koroleva
	5. *Psedoparasitus* sp.

Jagannath & Visalakshy (1989) established *Orthogalumna terebrantis* Wallwork for control of water hyacinth at Bangalore. Mukherjee *et al.*, (1987: *Sci. & Cult.*, **53** : 180-181) reported the following mites on water hyacinth. Most of the mites were found in decomposed roots and shoots except *Tyrophagus putrescentiae* which was found on undersurface of leaves. The first two species were very high in number.

Hydrozetes terrestris

Trimalaconothrus herotrichus

Scheloribates sp.

Lasioseius sp.

Cunaxa sp.

Tyrophagus putrescentiae

Croton sparciflorus

1. ***Amblyseius largoensis*** **:** This predatory mite occasionally occurs on this weed.

Fodder Grass

Oligonychus indicus (Hirst)

Petrobia latens (Muller)

The mite species recorded on other weeds are :

9. *Urena lobata* : *Schizotetranychus* sp.

10. *Oxalis corniculata* : *Petrobia harti* (Muller)

11. *Euphorbia hirta* : *Amblyseius herbicolus* (Chant)

12. *Eleusine indica* : *Scapulaseius suknaensis* (Gupta)

13. *Cyperus rotundus* : *Schizotetranychus andropogoni* (Hirst)

14. *Chenopodium album* : *Tetranychus urticae* Koch

15. *Amaranthus viridis* : *Tetranychus neocaledonicus* Andre

16. *Acalypha indica* : *Tetranychus neocaledonicus* Andre

17. *Solanum nigrum* : *Tetranychus urticae* Koch and *Paraphytoseius multidentatus* S. & S. have been recorded on this host but no plant feeding mite is known doing any damage to this plant.

3.16 FOREST TREES

1. SISHAM (*Dalbergia sissoo*)

Tetra sissoo Mohanasundaram

Dhooria & Sidhu (1995) reported that this mite infested sisham tree severely on ventral surface of young leaves. Feeding causes downward rolling, followed by dirty red colouration on ventral surface. Population per leaf was 64–361 (leaf size 3.57–7.00 cm^2). Plants under shady condition had more infestation. Spraying of ethion or dicofol at recommended doses will control this mite.

Tetranychus neocaledonicus Andre

This mite was reported on sisham (Bindra & Singh, 1970)

Tetranychus urticae/T.ludeni : These mites are reported to attack forest trees in Rajasthan (Chouhan & Yousuf, 1996: *Bull. Pure & Appl. Sci./Zoology*, **15**(1) : 17–18).

2. BAMBOO (*Bambusa* spp.)

Gupta (1978: *Indian J. Acar.*, **2** : 60–77) : reported *Typhlodromus bambusicolus* on bamboo in Assam.

Gupta (1985) listed the following mites on bamboo but their economic importance is uncertain.

Aponychus corpuzae Rimando

A. sarjui Gupta

A. baghensis Prasad

A. lalii Prasad

Neopetrobia simlaensis Prasad

Euseius coccineae (Gupta)

A. kulini Gupta

A. largoensis (Muma)

Euseius bambusae (Ghai & Menon)

Cunaxa bambusae Gupta

Rather (1995) : reported *Tetranychus urticae* on forest trees like *Morus alba, Salyx babylionica.*

3. ROSE WOOD (*Dalbergia latifolia)*

Gupta (1985) listed *Typhlodromus rickeri* Chant, a predatory mite on this host

4. SHAL (*Shorea robusta)*

Gupta (1985) listed the following mite species on this plant but mentioned no economic importance :

Oligonychus biharensis (Hirst)

Euseius alstoniae (Gupta)

Tegonotus bengalensis Mondal & Chakrabarti

Amblyseius shoreae Gupta

Rhyncaphytoptus shoreacola Mondal, Ghosh & Chakrabarti

S. suknaensis (Gupta)

Phytoseuis kapuri Gupta

Phytoseius macropilis (Banks)

5. TEAK (*Tectona grandis)*

Gupta (1985) listed the following mites from this host. Nothing about their economic importance is known :

Tetranychus ludeni Zacher

Disella tectona Das & Chakrabarti

Tenuipalpus tectonae Mohanasundaram

Anthocoptes tectonae Mohanasundaram

Scapulaseius suknaensis (Gupta)

A. largoensis (Muma)

6. JHAU/CASUARINA (*Casuarina equisetifolia)*

Gupta (1985) listed the following species on this host. However, their economic importance is unknown :

Phytoptus casuarinae (ChannaBasavanna)

Typhlodromus neotransvaalensis (Gupta)

Typhlodromus garhwalicus (Gupta)

Tuckerella indica Prasad

7. ARJUN (*Terminalia tomentosa*)

Tuckerella delhiensis Ghai & Maninder

8. MAHOGINI (*Swietenia mahogini*)

Calacarus swietensis Chakrabarti & Mondal - Gupta (1985)

9. MAHUA (*Madhuca longifolia*)

Gupta (2005) listed the following mites on this plant :

Tegonotus birbhumensis Ghosh & Chakrabarti

Aceria bassiae Ghosh & Chakrabarti

10. PALAS (*Butea monosperma*)

Gupta 1985 listed the following mites on this plant :

Brevipalpus pulcher (C. & F.)

Euseius bambusae (Ghai & Menon)

11. *Lagestroemia thorellii / L. indica*

Gupta 1985 listed the following mites on this plant :

Oligonychus mangiferus (R. & S.)

Brevipalpus californicus (Banks)

Brevipalpus karachiensis Chaudhri *et al.*

12. BABLA (*Acacia arabica*):

Gupta (1985) listed the following mite species on this host plant :

Tenuipalpus acacia Maninder & Ghai

Tenuipalpus caudatus (Duges)

Typhlodromus divergentis Chaudhri *et al.*

Amblyseius largoensis (Muma)

Scapulaseius eucalypticus (Gupta)

Typhlodromus communis Gupta

Typhlodromus rickeri Chant

Rhombacus eucalypti Anon, 2003

13. PINE (*Pinus* sp.)

Tuckerella kumaonensis Gupta

Euseius bambusae (Ghai & Menon)

14. SILVER OAK

Oligonychus biharensis (Hirst) - Anon.

15. *Cesalpinia pulcherima*

Pronematus fleschneri Baker

16. EUCALYPTUS (*Eucalyptus globulus*)

Gupta 1985 listed the following mite species on this host but their economic importance is uncertain :

Oligonychus punicae (Hirst)

Euseius eucalypti (Ghai & Menon)

Scapulaseius eucalypticus (Gupta)

Amblyseius largoensis (Muma)

Typhlodromus communis Gupta

Typhlodromus rickeri Chant

Brevipalpus californicus (Banks)

Rhombacus eucalypti Ghosh & Chakraborti

17. BANYAN (*Ficus benghalensis*)

Gupta 1985 listed the following mite species on this host but their economic importance is uncertain:

Amblyseius largoensis (Muma)

Typhlodromus homalii Gupta

Neotegonotus indicus Mondal & Chakrabarti

Colopodacus bengalensis Mohanasundaram

Aceria infectoriae ChannaBasavanna

Neotegonotus fastigatus (Nalepa)

18. *Ficus religiosa*

Gupta 1985 listed the following mite species on this host but their economic importance is uncertain:

Eutetranychus orientalis (Klein)

Euseius bambusae (Ghai & Menon)

19. DEODAR (*Polyalthia longifolia*)

The following mites are known to occur on this plant. Nothing about their economic importance is known :

Eutetranychus orientalis (Klein)

Brevipalpus karachiensis Chaudhri *et al.*

Calacarus polyaltheae Mohanasundaram

None of the above species causes any serious damage.

20. SIRISH (*Albizzia procera/A. lebbeck*)

Brevipalpus karachiensis Chaudhri *et al.* - no economic damage is caused.

3.17 CASH CROPS (SUGARCANE & TAPIOCA)

1. SUGARCANE (*Saccharum officinarum*)

Aceria saccharini* Wang / *Aceria sacchari Channabasavanna

These mites are very common pests of sugarcane in many parts of India Muthukrishnan (1956: *Curr. Sci.*, **25** : 234-235) was the first to report this mite *A. sacchari* causing galls, pustules, erineum, etc. on sugarcane. Those are initialy light green and become rusty red at later stage. According to some authors, the erineum formation may be because of injection of some toxin during feeding and excretion of nitrogenous waste products. This causes disruption of epithelial tissues. Subsequently,this disease was reported from various parts of India. The contents of phosphorus, iron,potassium, were higher in infected regions while the increase of total sugar was insignificant. No change in sodium level was observed though changes took place in silica,calcium,magnesium which redused marginaly. The colonization of mites in differant sugarcane varities depended not only on physico-chemical differances of varities but also on anatomical characters of leaf sheath. The association of streak virus disease with this mite has been reported (Sithanantham & Velayutham, 1979: *First All India Symp. Acarology, Bangalore* : 22; Gupta, 1985)

Abacarus sacchari ChannaBasavanna

Patra *et al.*, (1994) (*Env. & Ecol.*, **12** : 174–177) reported this mite on sugarcane and studied its seasonal occurrence and chemical control.

Oligonychus indicus (Hirst)

This is a greyish green or whitish mite with black blotches scattered all over dorsum. They colonize on undersurface of leaves which remain covered with thin webs.

Damage : Feeding on sugarcane causes appearance of reddish spots which increase with increase of attack and later those turn into reddish patches. Gradually, those spread on entire leaf turning colour of the leaf to red and the crop looks as if burnt.

Seasonal occurrence : The population starts building from first week of September and reaches peak in first fortnight of October. During the non-cropping season, the mite remains on Johnson grass and reaches peak there during April. Later, it migrates to sugarcane crop where it starts increasing till July until monsoon rain washes away the mobile stages keeping the eggs intact. Those eggs serve as source of re-infestation of sugarcane. They start multiplication to re-build their colony from September to reach peak in October.

Biology : Gupta *et al.*, 1974 (*Acarologia*, **16** : 436–440) studied biology of this mite on different food (sugarcane, sorghum, maize) and at five temperatures (25, 27.5, 30, 32.5, 35°C) and the information on biology on sugarcane given below is based on that.

The minium time taken to complete the life cycle was on maize at 32.5°C (5.15± 0.31 days), maximum was 11.73± 0.63 days on sorghum at 25°C; highest fecundity (75.92 ± 35.75 eggs) was on maize at 30°C (unfertilized) and minimum was 11.00± 4.32 on maize at 35 °C (unfertilized). The corresponding figures for fertilized females were 73.20± 32.87 on sorghum at 30°C and 10.44 ± 4.34 on sugarcane at 27.5°C.

The authors concluded that in comparison to sugarcane and sorghum, maize was better food and 30°C was the better temperature for this mite because of minimum time taken to complete the life cycle and high fecundity of both fertilized and unfertilized females on this host and temperature. Sorghum was the second best food

Varietal Preference : The varieties with tough leaf texture and spinose undergrowth on the undersurface of leaves are less susceptible to this mite.

Dispersal : Through wind current.

Control : Clipping of infested leaves and destruction of wild host plants will reduce the mite incidence. Lime Sulphur treatment will also control this pest. Sidhu & Dhooria (1972) reported good ovicidal action of tetradifon and galecron. Sidhu *et al.* (1972) reported good performance of carbophenothion, dicofol, monocrotophos.

Natural enemies : *Euseius delhiensis* (Narayanan & Kaur), *Scymnus gracilis, Stethorus gilvifrons, S.pauperculus, Scolothrips indicus* are some of the important natural enemies (Gupta, 1985).

Oligonychus sacchari (McG.)

Gupta & Gupta, 1978 (*Indian J. Acar.*, **3** : 90) recorded this mite on sugarcane in M.P.

Schizotetranychus andropogoni (Hirst)

This is called the sugarcane web mite. It is pear shaped, pale with dusky spots on dorsal surface. Legs are short, the anterior two are directed forward and posterior two are directed backward.

Damage : Thousands of mites remain on under surface of leaves making small oval colonies covered with thin webs, arranged longitudinally on either sides of mid rib. As many as 1300–1500 colonies may be seen on each leaf. The feeding causes appearance of whitish patches. Infestation is more on ratoon crops than on newly planted crops.

Biology : Its life cycle is completed in 7–10 days depending upon temperature and humidity.

Seasonal occurrence : The population of this mite on sugarcane is more on premonsoon period but it occurs on paddy during August–September.

Control : Monocrotophos 0.075% or wettable sulphur 2g/L or dicofol (0.05%) will be quite effective. Prakash & Avasthy (1983) reported phosalone, dicofol, chlorfenvinphos which were effective against this mite. Cleaning of grasses in sugarcane field will reduce infestation of *S.andropogoni*. Tiwari (1983) reported phosalone (0.05%), ethion (0.02%) and dicofol (0.03%) as quite effective to check multiplication of web mite and the residual effect lasted for 12 days.

Steneotarsonemus bancrofti (Michael)

This is a tiny, transparent, yellowish brown mite. Leg IV femur in female is having flange-like expansion on inner margin.

Damage : The feeding causes formation of rusty patches. The internodes give a scabby corroded appearance. Mites live on cane tips on under surface of green leaf sheath. The feeding produces transparent depressions on young stalk. Later, those become rough, opaque and the whole streak of cane may be covered with roughened surface. The fungus, *Collectrotrichun* further infests the damaged tissues. This leads to develop red patches (Gupta, 1993).

Control : Dicofol or ethion at their recommended doses may be applied for its control :

Natural enemies : The following predatory mites have been recorded;

Euseius alstoniae (Gupta) - Punjab - Gupta, 1977: *Indian J. Acar.*, **1** : 28–37

E. sacchari (Ghai & Menon) - Gujarat - As above

N. dhooriai (Gupta) - Punjab - As above

Phytoseius kapuri Gupta - Gujarat - Gupta, 1977: *Indian J. Acar.*, **1** : 11–18.

2. TAPIOCA (*Manihot esculenta*) Cassava

Tetranychus urticae Koch

This mite regularly infests tapioca in India. Saradamma & Nair (1970) - studied its infestation on 10 varieties of tapioca and found Elavan, Kayyalchady, H-226, Mankozhunnan and Sundarivella harboured significantly lesser number of mites. Lal *et al.*, (1982: *Indian J. Acar.*, **7** : 5–10) reported this mite on cassava. Population was poor or absent during June - December, thereafter suddenly increased attaining peak during January - April. Increase of mite population was correlated with decrease in humidity and non significantly correlated with increase in maximum temperature (Anon, 2003) from Kerala.

Tetranychus neocaledonicus Andre

Lal (1982) recorded it on Cassava and made similar observations as mentioned for *T. urticae* above.

Eutetranychus orientalis (Klein)

Lal (1982) recorded this species on Cassava and made similar observations as mentioned for *T. urticae*. Lal & Pillai (1980: *Indian J. Acar.*, **4** : 68–77) tested 27 pesticides against *E.orientalis* infesting cassava in Kerala and on the basis of preliminary trial they reported that dicofol, dimethoate, methyl demeton, monocrotophos, phosalone, ethion and thiometon were most promising having both initial knock down and residual effects. Later, ethion (0.03%, 0.05%) and dimethoate (0.05%) were found most effective providing excellent control of mites upto 30 days. Phosalone, monocrotophos and dicofol all at 0.05% also proved effective.

Tetranychus ludeni Zacher

Puttaswamy & ChannaBasavanna (1982: *Indian J. Acar.*, **6** : 72–76) reported this on tapioca and studied its biology on this host. The study indicated that this mite feeding on this host completed life cycle in 10–11 days and laid least number of eggs (87/female) as compared to other hosts like castor, *Amaranthus*, mulberry.

Oligonychus biharensis (Hirst)

Due to its infestation on Cassava, the epidermal cells become irregular, distorted. Mesophyll layer of leaf was damaged. Palisade parenchyma showed reduction in number of cells and were punctured with large intercellular spaces in comparision to control leaves which had closely packed parenchyma cells. Spongy parenchyma cells also collapsed, punctured with intercellular spaces. Reduction in chloroplast and chloplast content was observed. The punctured cells do not take part in metabolic activities of cells. (Kaimal *et al.*, 2010 : 71–72).

3.18 MUSHROOM

The mushrooms are the microbes used as source of human food because of being rich source of nutrients. In India, three types of mushrooms are grown commercially, button mushroom (*Agaricus* spp.), oyster mushroom (*Pleurotus* spp.) and paddy straw mushroom (*Volvariella* spp.). The cultivation of milky mushroom (*Calocybe* sp.) has also been introduced. All these mushrooms differ in their shape, colour and biochemical composition and required different infrastructure facilities for cultivation. The major mushroom growing states in India are Tamil Nadu, Maharashtra, Punjab, Haryana,Uttar Pradesh. India has started exporting mushroom and already exported 6380.12 tonnes in countries like USA, Netherlands, Israel, Switzerland, Germany, Korea, Sweeden, Australia, Brazil, Denmark etc. (Hanbook: Horticulture ICAR, 2010)

The mushroom is attacked by a good number of mite species, often threatening mushroom cultivation. The different species are

Rhizoglyphus echinopus F. & R.

Das *et al.*, 1988 (*Env. Ecol.*, **6** : 669–671) reported this mite infesting *Pleurotus tricholoma, Volvariella* sp.

Damage : This mite initially makes small pin - head holes on mycelial mats. Later, it attacks base of the stalk during budding and fruit body stage. The basal area of infested mushroom becomes pointed. Lower half of stripe changes its white colour to yellowish or brownish. The gills are also affected in case of severe infestation and the colour changes to yellowish brown. A dense cover is formed all over the mushroom bed. This mite does damage to winter type of mushroom (*Pleurotus sajor - caju* and *P. ostreatus*). The yield loss due to infestation of this mite may be as high as 75–80% and EIL level was 50–100 mites/50 gms of compost (Das *et al.*, 1987). The circumferance of mushroom was reduced by 37% and weight was reduced by 36.30%.

Biology : The life cycle of this mite is influenced by RH as its population increases with higher humidity (90%) and at 30% RH, it fails to develop. The duration of different stages appears to be variable with temperature and RH and the optimal conditions of different stages were : egg (20°C x 90%RH), larva (30°C x 90% RH), protonymph (20°C X 90%RH), deutonymph (30°C X 90% RH) and adult (20°C X 90%RH). Max population was found upto 1.5 cm mushroom depth and decreased gradually with depth. The maximum fecundity was at 20°C and 90% RH.

Seasonal occurrence : This mite appears during January–March i.e. in mild climate. A temperature of 35°C was found unfavourable for this mite. A positive correlation existed between temperature and density of mite population and non significant relation was found with mite density and RH.

Control : Screening of doors/windows with 20 mesh net will prevent infestation of mushroom from outside. Sterilization of straw used for mushroom bed will give effective result in controlling this mite. 0.04% of dichlorvos/ethion/dicofol/ malathion provided 80% mortality. Dichlorvos and ethion gave total mortality after 4 days while dicofol and malathion took 5 and 7 days, respectively to give total mortality. The plant oils like citronella, clove, wintergreen also were good.

Diet preference : Somchoudhury *et al.* (1983) tested different types of artificial diets on population development of mushroom mites. For *R. echinopus,* a maximum increase on population of this mite was with agar + wheat + karnel + yeast extract + distilled water, followed by diet of agar + dextrose + distilled water), agar + dextrose + wheat kernel + mushroom powder + distilled water.

Tyrophagus dimidiatus Hermann

Das *et al.,* (1988: *Env. & Ecol.,* **6** : 669–671) recorded it from West Bengal.

Damage : This mite feeds on aerial and subterranean parts of mushroom and infests summer type mushroom i.e. *T. lobayense* and *Volvariella volvacea.* The infestation on mycelia produces similar type of symptoms as in case of *R. echinopus.* The damage becomes more severe during fruiting stage. The mite hollows out basal portion of stalk in course of time and through that entry point they reach to the cap. The cavities of various sizes are formed on the stalk and cap in large mushroom rendering them unfit for sale. The whitish fruit body turns brown and stalk colour changes to blackish brown. Dense cover of mite is seen all over mushroom body and mushroom bed. It normally attacks summer type mushroom like *T. lobayense* and *V. volvacea.* The extent of loss may be as much as 79.24%. The number of bud and fruit body reduces significantly and that caused significant reduction of mushroom. Reduction in bud size was 41.33%, the reduction in cap of mushroom was- 37% and weight loss was 80.10%. The gill portion was not infected by this mite. The yield loss was reported to be 75–80% (Das *et al.,* 1989).

Biology : It takes 17–24 days to complete the life cycle (egg - adult). The fecundity of female is 40–60 eggs (Jary & Stapley, 1937: *J.S. East. Agr. Coll.,* **41** : 67–74). The preferred artificial diet was mixture of agar + dextrose + wheat kernel + mushroom powder. It was followed by agar + wheat kernel + yeast extract + distilled water (Das *et al.,* 1987).

Seasonal occurrence : It occurs on mushroom during March–May and lasted till June. The population of mite was positively correlated with RH but no relation with temperature was found. Maximum mite population was when RH was high and was minimum when RH was at 56–60%. .

Control : Sterilization of straw components of mushroom bed is very effective LD_{50} temperature was found to be 60 ± 1°C - 62.5 ± 1°C while, temperature of 70 ± 1°C - 72.5 ± 1°C caused 100% mortality. Exposure to mite to 62.5°C for 30 minutes and 57.5°C for 45 minutes caused total destruction. Among the chemical pesticides dichlorvos, ethion, dicofol registered total mortality. The oils of citronella, clove, karanja, neem were good and had no detrimental effect on mushroom.

Tyrophagus berlesi Michael

This mite makes holes in caps of the mushroom like other tyroglyphid mites.

Tyrophagus putrescentiae (Schrank)

Mukherjee & Somchoudhury (1972) reported this mite from West Bengal infesting mushroom and feeding on mycelium and sporophores resulted in small irregular pits on stalks and caps.Under heavy infestation, buttons are completely damaged leaving hollow stalks.

Histiostoma heinemanni Hill & Diahl.

This mite is an important pest of mushroom.

Damage : This mite feeds both aerial and subterranean parts of mushroom. This mite attacks summer type of mushroom viz *T. lobayense* and *V. volvacea*. It infests mycelial stage and due to its infestation, the mushroom fails to reach to the fruit body stage. Subsequently,the entire aerial part is attacked resulting in arresting the vertical growth of mushroom and its growth takes place in crawling manner. The infested mushroom suffers from decomposition. Mites are seen inside and outside of stalk and cap. The yield loss is significant. The bud stage of mushroom is most preferred and inflicted 64.83% damage, circumference reduction - 70%, cap thickness reduction -75.43% and cap weight reduction - 91.17%. The total yield loss may be 75–80% and economic injury level was 50–100 mites/50 gm of compost (Das *et al.*, 1989).

Biology : The maximum fecundity was seen at 30°C. The rate of development increased with increase in temperature. The optimal condition of development was found to be egg - 20° x 90%, larva 30°C x 90% RH, protonymph, 20°C x 90% RH, deutonymph - 30°C x 90% RH and adult 20°C x 90%. The mite failed to develop at 60% RH irrespective of temperature. The preferred artificial food was agar + dextrose + wheat + kernel + mushroom powder + distilled water.

Seasonal occurrence : The mite population had shown positive correlation with temperature and RH. The infestation starts in June, continues till October and diminishes thereafter. The population attains at highest level during June–July.

Control : Sterilization of straw components of mushroom bed was found to be highly effective in controlling mushroom mites. The LD 50 temperature value was 60 ± 1°C - 62.5 ± 1°C while 70 ± 1°C - 72.5 ± 1°C caused 100% mortality. Ethion application will be effective. The plant extracts gave mortality as citronella (64.44%), clove (49.77%), wintergreen (43.59%), Chaulmoogra (40.65%), Karanja (7.78%) and neem (7.30%). The storage of compost manure and old manure should be kept 1–2 km away to prevent mite infestation. Burning of sulphur is also good.

Histiostoma gracilipes Banks

This mite voraciously feeds on the spawn as well as all stages of developing crops.

Hypoaspis miles Berlese

This was recorded in mushroom *Tricholoma, Volvariella* (Das *et al.*, 1988).

Damage : Das *et al.* (1989) reported yield loss to the extent of 75–80%, ETL was 50–100 mites/50 gms of compost. As regards artificial diet, this mite preferred mushroom extract as food and no progeny was produced without it.

Seasonal occurrence : This infestation starts in October, continues till November and disappears thereafter. Both temperature and RH had good influence on the mite population. At 70% RH level,the population of mite was maximum and further decrease of RH below 60% drastically reduced mite population. In general, this mite shows similar relationship with abiotic factors as is shown by *H. heinemanni.* As regards tempearature, this mite appears to be tolerant.

Control : Dichlorvos/ethion provides total mortality after 4 days, dicofol and malathion took 5 and 7 days, respectively. Citronella oil registered 64.44% mortality and total mortality was achieved after 7 days. Clove oil, wintergreen oil, Karanja oil, Chaulmoogra also were good giving mortality ranging from 49.77% to 70.30%. No phytotoxicity was recorded on mushroom due to application of oils.

Some tyroglyphid mites are carried to mushroom through dipteran flies and staphylinid beetles.

Tyrophagus longior Gervais

These mites are carried to mushroom beds through manure in compost preparation.

Tarsonemus tarsalis

This infests mushroom through straw. They occur in cracks and crevices of mushroom house.

Tarsonemus myceleiphagus Austin & Jary, *T. confusus* Ewing

These mites grow in thousands on mushroom body and damage mycelium, stem, caps and sporophores. Affected tissues become reddish. The bases and stipes of affected mushroom become brown. For control of tarsonemid mites, TEPP@ 1lb/ 100 sq ft. application before and after casing and again during cropping is good.

Caloglyphus mycophagus Megnin, *T. berlesei* Michael

These mites make holes on caps of mushroom. They take about 8-15 days to complete the life cycle at 20°–21°C. These mites make hollows and tunnels on stalks and caps of mushroom. The maximum number of eggs laid/female may be as high as 325.

Pygmephorid mites (*Pygmephorus* spp.)

These mites damage more qualitatively than quantitatively as these mites feed on mycelium body beneath the casing layer as well as on fruit body. It is known to cause allergic reaction in USA.

Linopod mites (*Linopodes* spp.)

These mites damage root system causing constriction at the base of the stalk and stipe and discolour it to pinkish brown. In case of severe damage the mushroom turns into withered filaments and may cause about 40% damage. They do not feed on mycelium.

Parasitus consanguineus Oudemans & Voigts

Trivedi (1988) reported this mite in beds of cultivated mushroom, *Agaricus bisporus* (buttom mushroom) in Karnataka.

Tyrophagus perniciosus Zachvatkin

Mukherjee & Somchoudhury (1972) reported it from West Bengal.

Undet mite species : Kotwal & Boni (1999) reported an undermined species attacking buttom mushroom (*A. bisporus*) as pest with population varying from 15-60/30 gm sample of casing soil from 3rd week till last picking ending March, 1996. Chlorpyriphos (50 ppm) in compost + 25 ppm in casing and neem cake powder (1%) in compost effectively helped in management of mites.

Effect of artificial diet on population development of mushroom mites : Das *et al.* (1983) investigated the effect of artificial diets on development of mushroom mites and observed significant difference among 4 species of mushroom mites as well as 8 kinds of mushroom diets. For *R.echinopus*, the favoured artificial diet was 0.5g agar + 1gm wheat kernel + 0.1 g yeast extract + 10 cc distilled water, followed by 0.5 g agar + 2 g dextrose + 10 cc distilled water heated for 10 min at 60± 1°C. For *T. dimidiatus*, the best result was obtained with 0.5g agar + 1 g dextrose + 1 g wheat kernel + 2 g mushroom power + 10 cc distilled water heated for 10 min at 60± 1°C, followed by 0.5g agar + 1g wheat kernel + 0.1g yeast extract + 10 cc distilled water heated for 10 min at 60± 1°C. For *H.miles*, the preferred one was 0.5 g agar +2 g dextrose + 1 g wheat kernel + 10 cc straw juice made by heating 5gm straw+ 15gm distilled water heated for 10 min at 60± 1°C. This indicated that different nutritional requirements are needed for different species of mushroom mites.

Feeding behaviour of mushroom mites : Das *et al.*, (1993) studied feeding behaviour of different mushroom mites. It was reported that the number of *R. echinopus* increased from 20.00 to 53.33 after 15 days of mite inoculation in compost bed. The mushroom inoculated beds, its number increased to 203.33 and 176.62 in *sajor - caju* and *ostreatus* species of mushroom, respectively. Significant increase in mite population took place when compost bed was inoculated with mushroom spawn. Similar increase took place in other three species of mushroom mites when they were allowed to grow in spawned and unspawned compost beds. Rate of increase was maximum in *H. heinemanni* followed by *H.miles* and *T. dimidiatus*. Rate of increase in spawned and unspawned beds in all three species was statistically significant. Population of *R. echinopus* increased from 20 to 490 on 25th day after spawning but declined to 100 on 45th day after spawning. The other two species, *H. miles* and *H. heinemanni* followed more or less similar pattern in their population growth as was seen in *R. echinopus*.

Sources of mite infestation in mushroom : *Tyrophagus dimidiatus* which is one of the major pests of mushroom is present in hey, straw, etc. which are used for making mushroom beds. This mite feeds on fungi which develop on beds. The other species of *Tyrophagus* which also occurs in mushroom is present in material used for making beds. The tarsonemids which infest mushroom also get entry there through straw. Some of the *Tyrophagus* mites like *T. longior* get entry through old manure and compost or through dipteran flies. The staphilinid beetles are carriers of hypopial stages of mites. *Histiostoma* mites are carried to mushroom bed by flies. The straw is the source of infestation of many *Linopodes* mites. The source of pygmephorid mites in mushroom beds is through compost.

Rather & Haq (2010: *Abst. Int. Symp-Cum-Workshop, Acarology, Kalyani* : 142-143) tested some plant products against mite infesting mushroom, *Agaricus bisporus* in Kashmir and reported that *Artemesia* and *Juglans regia* extracts @ 6% can be utilized for controlling of mites with no phytotoxic effect in mushroom houses as they provide complete control.

3.19 STORED PRODUCT MITES

The grains, dried fish, honey, various food and food products are often attacked by a number of pests which include insects, mites, rodents, birds and microbes. They not only cause serious damage to the food articles but also make them unsuitable for human consumption as well as make those useless for germination. Sometimes the damage is so severe that those become unsuitable even for cattle feeding. Apart from causing damage due to direct feeding, they often increase the humidity of the granary which invite fungi and those cause further damage. The feeding of mites on grains, apart from causing damage mentioned above, they also cause depletion of carbohydrate, protein, fat of the grains and consequently those loose food values. There are mites occurring in store house which are known to cause severe itching, irritation on body parts and cause dermatitis to those who handle the grains. Apart from the harmful mites, there are some beneficial mites. which act as predators of damage causing mites and insects. Due to these manifold importance, the stored product mites have received global attention including India and fairly a good amount of work has been done.The mite species reported out of those investigations from India are briefly mentioned hereunder :

Family : **ACARIDAE**

Acarus siro Linn.

This is one of the commonest mites infesting stored products throughout the world. Female is 350–600 microns long and male is 320–450 microns long, whitish and sometimes occur in astronomical numbers.

Damage : It is found in storage, processed serial products and whole grain causing damage. It is of high economic value as not only they damage grains by feeding but also by changing the moisture content of the storage, they invite development of mould. They also carry viable spores both internally and externally and thereby contaminate the food making their consumption unsuitable by humans. Normally, when the seed coat is intact, they do not attack the grains but while thrashing and storage, the grains are damaged, the mites make entry into the grains. This has been reported from Bihar on stored wheat (Nahar & Gupta, 1980) on rice in Orissa (Prakash & Rao, 1988), West Bengal on stored wheat, rice (Gupta *et al.*, 1991), Kolkata (Gupta & Chatterjee 2004), and Karnataka (Nangia, 1986). The grains having .moisture content of 14% are more seriously attacked while those with less than 13% moisture content remained unaffected.

Biology : This mite prefers 25–31°C and 62% RH and higher RH above 80–85% was reported unfavourable (Solomon, 1962).

Acarus grifithsi Ranganath & ChannaBasavanna

This mite has been reported on stored products in Karnataka (Nangia & ChannaBasavanna (1989: *Progress in Acarology*, **2** : 243).

Acarus farris (Oudemans)

Gupta & Chatterjee (2004) recorded it from stored products in West Bengal.

Tyrophagus putrescentiae (Schrank)

This is a colourless mite but colour changes with the type of food they consume. Apart from stored products, they also occur in different other habitats like bird nests, house dust, plants. This is a widely distributed species and from India it is known from most of the states (Nahar & Gupta, 1980 on stored rice), Gupta *et al.*, 1991 on stored wheat and rice). Nangia (1986) reported that over 60% of the samples taken from stored products had this mite.

Damage : Apart from damaging stored products, it is a pest of fungal culture. It is found in stored food with high protein and fat contents, dried eggs, ham, etc (Hughes, 1976). Groundnuts, safflower, rapeseeds are preferred over linseed, palm kernel, poppy seed and cotton seed. The Fat Acidity Value (FAV) for wheat samples infested with this mite was higher than that infested with *Suidasia nesbitti*. Mite infested grains had shown 0.2–46.3% reduction in germination power. The moisture content of wheat remained 15±2% during entire period of investigation and differences were not significant between infested and uninfested wheat samples (Nangia & ChannaBasavanna, 1995).

Biology : The lower temperature limit for development was 7–10°C and the highest was 35 - 37°C. Life cycle took 8–46 days at 32°C and 90% RH, when wheat grain was used as food (Cunnington, 1965). The life cycle took 21 days at 32.2°C and 98–100% RH using brewer's yeast as substrate (Baker, 1967). Silkworm cocoon provided ideal atmosphere for development of acarine. *T. putrescentiae* stuffed cocoon when put into Berlese's funnel, a large number of this mite could be collected in the receiver. Silk protein, fibroin, serecin provided nutrition to mites. The fungal growth on cocoon was also found infested by this mite (Nangia *et al.*, 1999). The egg - adult period in case of different exposures were 12.89 ± 0.68, 10.86 ± 0.57, 10.02 ± 0.58, 9.12 ± 0.53 and 8.6 ±0.52 at 5, 10, 15, 20 and 25 hours of exposures, respectively. The corresponding figures for oviposition were 11.25 ± 4.05, 14.00 ± 2.78, 9.75 ± 3.62, 7.86 ± 2.03 and 7.02 ± 4.24, respectively. The respective figures for number of eggs laid per female were 80.55 ± 20.14, 93.86 ± 18.76; 56.52 ± 20.13, 40.73 ± 10.14 and 39.58 ± 9.12. The percentage of hatchability was 80.70, 65.80, 48.78, 45.00 and 42.65, respectively. There was higher mortality of eggs when exposed to direct UV rays as compared to other developmental stages. Survival percentage was negligible after 30 hrs of exposure (Kumud & Mathur, 1989). At 27±1°C and 80 -85% RH with food of wheat flour + yeast (4 : 1), the life cycle of *T. putrescentiae* was completed in 12–15 days. Total survival percentage (egg – adult) and hatchability were respectively 73 and 93% (Kumud *et al.*, 1987, III Acarology Congress : 21). This mite had higher metabolic rate than that of *S. nesbitti* and therefore the extent of deterioration of seeds also varied (Abrol *et al.*, 1989: *Progress in Acarology*, **2** : 271–273).

Control : Some plant products like powdered rhizome of turmeric, leaves of neem and fenugreek (1–2% conc) and their extracts with acetone, ethanol, petroleum @650 mg/cm were tested and it was found that neem treated seeds had minimum number of *T.putrescentiae* (Nangia & ChannaBasavanna, 1995).

Tyrophagus sp.

An undetermined species of *Tyrophagus* was recorded on stored wheat and rice from Bihar, West Bengal. Nahar & Gupta (1980: *Bull. grain Tech.*, **18** : 130–134; Gupta *et al.*, 1991: *Bull Grain Tech.*, **29** : 47–49).

Tyrolichus casei Oudemans

This mite was recorded from stored products in Karnataka mainly from floor debris, wood work, cracks - crevices of stored godowns. Wheat was the most preferred food, followed by wheat flour. It has also been recorded from soil, hey, debris of thrash yards, poultry feed (Nangia & ChannaBasavanna, 1989; 1997).

This mite is available throughout the year but its availability is more when crops were harvested and heaped at the yards (Nangia & ChannaBasavanna, 1991).

Biology : Its total life cycle takes 12–15 days at room temperature of 26.5°C and 70% RH and no hypopial stage could be seen. The temperature of 30 ± 1°C and

80% RH were most suitable for rapid growth and lower mortality. This mite took 6–7 days in completing life cycle. Oviposition was maximum (187.00) at 30 ± 1°C and 100% RH. The intrinsic rate of increase was highest at 30 ± 1°C and 100% RH, while rm was directly proportional to rise in temperate except at 40±1°C. The mean generation time (T) was shorter at 10 ± 1°C at all the RH levels and longest at 30 ± 1°C in combination with tested humidities. This mite can not tolerate low temperature (Nangia & ChannaBasavanna, 1989).

Control : Turmeric treated wheat showed least number of *C. casei* and was most effective repellent. Neem extract was equally good (Nangia & ChannaBasavanna 1995: *V Acar. Symp., Bangalore* : 74).

Aleuroglyphus ovatus Troupeau

This has been reported on stored wheat, wheat flour, red chilli (Putatunda *et al.*, 1999: *VI Acar Congr.*, : 63), Kerala (Vijayambika & John, 1977: *Indian J. Acar.*, **2** : 24–29), Karnataka (Nangia & ChannaBasavanna, 1989: *Progress in Acarology*, **2** : 141–147).

Damage : The FAV (Fat Acidity Value) for wheat samples due to infestation of this mite was highest than those infested by *S. nesbitti* for the first 30 days of storage. The infested wheat samples showed 0.2–46.3% reduction in germination. The microbial infection included *Aspergillus* and *Alternaria* sp, (Nangia & ChannaBasavanna, 1995).

Control : Turmeric treated wheat had shown least number of *A. ovatus* and was found to be most effective repellent (Nangia & ChannaBasavanna, 1995).

Caloglyphus berlesei (Michael)

It was reported on wheat flour in Haryana (Putatunda *et al.*, 1999), storage floor and godown (Nangia & ChannaBasavanna in Karnataka, Nangia & ChannaBasavanna, 1989), thrashing yard (Nangia & ChannaBasavanna, 1991), stored products in West Bengal (Gupta & Chatterjee, 2004).

Damage : Not much is known about the damage caused by this mite on stored grain.

Caloglyphus mycophagus Megnin

Putatunda *et al.*, (1999) recorded it from wheat flour in Haryana.

Caloglyphus rhizoglyphoides Zachvatkin

Its record was made from Haryana on wheat flour (Putatunda *et al.*, 1999).

Tyroglyphus entomophagus (Laboulbene)

Putatunda *et al.*, (1999) recorded it from wheat flour in Haryana.

Caloglyphus oudemansi (Zachvatkin)

Its record was made from Kerala as a pest of stored grain like *Cajanas cajan* and *Cisar arietinum* (Bengal gram) (Mubarak & Haq, 1989: *Progress in Acarology*, **2** : 265-269).

Biology : The duration of different developmental stages was incubation - 3 - 4 days, larva - 1 day, quiescent larva 0.25-0.35 days (Av. 0.33 days), protonymph - 1-2 days (av. 1.5 days), quiescent protonymph - 1 day, Tritonymph 2-3 days (av. 1.5 days), quiescent tritonymph - 1 day. Total development period 9-25 days (Av. 10.63 days). Mating lasted for 30-45 seconds. Fecundity - 188-230 eggs per female, oviposition period - 2-3 weeks. Mated female laid more eggs than unmated counterparts. No hypopial stage was noticed (Mubark & Haq, 1989). Life cycle is influenced with the type of food provided.

Lardoglyphus konoi (Sasa & Asanuma)

This is an important pest of dried and salted fish in fish processing areas.

Damage : This is a serious pest of dried fish. John (1979: *I Acar, Congress, Abst.*, 49) studied factors influencing infestation of cured fishery products and reported that this mite preferred host like *Equula blochii, Anchoviella cammersoni, Caranx carangus*. The infestation can be kept at a minimum level if the product can be kept in sufficient quantities of salt before curing. It was suggested that the transport facility should be better so that the stored fishes reach to the consumers quickly. Vijayambika *et al.*, (1979: *I Acar Congr. Abst.*, 45) studied host preference of adult *L. konoi* and evaluated intensity of infestation on cultured experimental samples. Its population fluctuation and correlation with temperature and humidity were studied by Vijayambika *et al.*, (1979: *I Acar Congr. Abst., 45*) and its host range on cured fish and molasses was studied by Vijayambika *et al.*, 1979). The studies pertaining to histochemistry, internal anatomy, functional histology of digestive system, etc. were made through a series of works by Vijayambika & John (1974, 1975, 1975a, 1975b). Vijayambika *et al.* (1980) stressed upon better hygienic condition to minimize this mite infestation. Nangia & ChannaBasavanna (1989) collected it from floor debris and dust accumulated in godowns and warehouses.

Tyroborus lini Oudemans

This mite is known infesting Bengal gram in Haryana (Mathur 1979: *Acar. Newsl.*, **9** : 3), Karnataka (Nangia & Channavasanna, 1989) and as grain feeders (Gupta *et al.*, 1991), stored grain in West Bengal (Gupta & Chatterjee, 2004). It appeared during March, 1979 (average temperature 10.3-23.4°C, Av. RH 55.5-89.7%). The population started developing from 3rd week of March (Av.temperature 12.2°C-30.5°C, Av. RH 30.8-78%) and disappeared finally in 2nd week of April, 1979 (Av temp 18.7-36.5°C, Av. RH. 29.8-77.55%). Mites apart from feeding of grains, also fed on grain debris which it preferred more than the grain itself.

Rhizoglyphus echinopus Fumouze & Robin

It is an important pest of stored grain and especially infests bulb of potato and can feed on any decaying plant. Mohanasundaram (1990: *Acar. Newsl.*, 17-18 : 14) reported this species in Tamil Nadu on a number of bulbs of stored products like onion, garlic, tuber rose, banana, sweet potato, turmeric, zinger, coconut, sugarcane. Its occurrence is more on rotting tissue than on healthy ones. The association of fungus *Fusarium oxysporum* infestation was also seen. Its culture could be easily developed on rotting tissues with fungus on agar plate. Wadhi *et al.*, (1971, *Indian J. Ent.*, **33** : 107-108) reported this species on potato from West Bengal. Mohanasundaram & Parameswaram (1991) also recorded it on rotting agricultural crops.

Biology : Its biology excluding hypopial stage takes 7-27 days at 13-23°C. It is known to have hypopial stage which is carried by insects.

Rhizoglyphus singularis

Mohanasundaram & Parameswaram (1991) recorded it associated with rotting and decaying agricultural products in Tamil Nadu.

Rhizoglyphus robini Claparede

Nangia & ChannaBasavanna (1989) reported it from floor debris of godowns and warehouses in Karnataka. It was common in wheat storage followed by wheat bran and poultry feed.

Rhizoglyphus sp.

Gupta *et al.* (1991) reported an undetermined species from stored wheat and rice as grain feeder in West Bengal.

Tyrophagus longior Gervais

Nangia & ChannaBasavanna (1989) recorded this mite from Karnataka collected on floor debris and dust accumulated on storage and warehouses in Karnataka. Wheat, wheat flour and poultry feed are the other habitats wherefrom this mite was collected. Gupta & Chatterjee (2004) recorded it from West Bengal collected on stored product. Its collection records are also from decaying and rotting agricultural crops in Tamil Nadu (Mohanasundaram & Parameswaram, 1991) bee hives in Haryana (Abrol *et al.*, 1994: *Curr. Sci.*, **66** : 105).

Carpoglyphus lactis Linn.

Nangia & ChannaBasavanna (1989) recorded this species from floor dust of storage house and warehouse in Karnataka. It is common in food substances rich with sugar from which bacterial activity gives rise to lower fatty acids such as lactic acid, acetic acid. It also infests cheese, old cocoa, beans, groundnuts, stored Christmas pudding (Hughes, 1976).

Biology : A female can lay 25–72 eggs in a week, longevity - 40–50 days.

Carpoglyphus sp.

This occurs in stored grain more as saprophagous or fungivorus rather than as grain feeders causing damage by contamination of grains. Mathur & Mathur (1983) collected this from wheat, lentil, millets from farmer's, houses in Hisar. Floor dust collected from grinding mill also yielded a large number of this species in Haryana.

Suidasia medanensis Oudemans

This has been reported from different stored products like cured fish, prawn, molasses in Kerala (Cicilykutty & John, 1979: *Abst. I Acarology Congress* : 46). The study was conducted on different levels of preference of this species on different hosts using different methods like frequency of occurrence of infested samples of a species in the filed, by making actual count of mite in the field samples of different hosts and by estimating the actual count of mites on experimental samples of different species of hosts, cured and exposed to infestation under known condition. Correlation coefficient of adult population and RH was highly significant and the same with population and temperature was non significant (Cicilykutty & John, 1979). This species was also recorded from floor dust of store house and warehouse in Karnataka (Nangia & ChannaBasavanna, 1989). The influence of physiological condition (moisture content) of flesh of fish on the intensity of infestation of this mite was studied (Cicilykutty *et al.*, 1981) and similar study on salt was also done (Cicilykutty *et al.*, 1981). Its report on stored wheat and rice was also made from West Bengal as grain feeder (Gupta *et al.*, 1991).

Suidasia nesbitti Hughes

This is another one of the most common mite species known to occur on stored samples in different parts of India. This mite could be collected from stored wheat, rice, bran, pearl millet, Bengal gram, lentil, dried peas from Haryana (Mathur & Mathur, 1983). Kalaeman *et al.* (1987) reported it from dried fish products. Its records are also available from thrashing yard in Karnataka (Nangia & Channabasavanna, 1991), debris of store house (Nangia & Channabasavanna, 1989), on stored rice in Bihar (Nahar & Gupta, 1980).

Damage : The effect of infestation on germination of grains like wheat, pearl millet, chickpea under laboratory condition revealed that the germination percentage was 85.1% in uninfested seed and in infested seeds it was 85.1, 83, 79.3, 70.6, 69.8, and 67,2% after 4th, 8th, 12th, 16th, 20th, 24th, weeks, respectively. Pearl millet suffered the maximum loss in germination (24.35%), followed by wheat (20.61%) and chickpea (12.11%) (Singh & Mathur, 1995, *Abst. V Nat. Symp. Acarology*, 71). The infested wheat grain by this mite had lower FAV as compared to uninfested samples. Mite infested samples showed 0.2–46.3% reduction in germination (Nangia

& ChannaBasavanna, 1995). The protein contents of grains were decreased when grains were exposed upto 1500 mites, feeding after 15 days. However, at higher level there was no reduction and rather it increased because of production of uric acid in mite excreta as well as contamination of dead mite bodies. Though nitrogen content was high at higher level of infestation but that food was unhygienic and unsuitable for human consumption. The increase in nitrogen content in wheat can be treated as index of population density to detect mite and insect population in cereals. Chemical analysis of infested products showed no decrease in nitrogen content even at higher level of infestation which indicated that some external energy compensated the loss. May be the body fragments, cast skins, excreta, nitrogenous waste products added to nitrogen content of flour (Singh, 1999: *Abst. ASI Silver Jubilee Symp. Bangalore*, 30).

Biology : The life cycle is completed in shorter duration on bajra with egg, larva, proto, and trionymph taking 2.71, 2.61, 2.42 and 2.31 days, respectively. Life span of adult mite was longest (av. 15.10 days) on bajra and shorter on Bengal gram (Av. 13.03 days). Larval, protonymphal and tritonymphal mortality on bajra was 3.9, 4.1 and 3.7%, respectively as compared to 6.07, 5.2 and 4.9% on wheat and 7.8, 6.8 and 6.2% on Bengal gram, respectively. Bajra was most susceptible to mite attack (Singh & Mathur, 1990). Among different temperatures like 25, 27.5, 32.5°C on which life cycle of this mite was studied, 27.5 °C was found to be most suitable because the life span of adult female was longest, mortality of different stages was minimum and fecundity was maximum. (Singh & Mathur 1987, *Abst. III Acar Congr.*, p.22). Its life cycle was also studied in West Bengal (Saha & Modak, 1989: *J. Beng. Nat Hist. Soc.*, **11** : 63–66). Das (1988) studied effect of temperature on biology of *S. nesbitti* occurring on silk worm cocoons in West Bengal.

Control : Neem treated wheat had lowest population of *S. nesbitti* and so also was with neem leaf powder (Nangia & ChannaBasavanna, 1995). Mustard oil, groundnut oil, neem oil, sesamum oil and castor oil, all were effective in protecting redgram seeds against the infestation of *S. nesbitti* at 0.25 ml/kg, 0.50 ml/kg and 0.75 ml/kg as compared to control. Neem oil was superior to others in preventing adult emergence. In all the treatments the longevity was less as compared to control. Duration of adult survival was less in neem oil. Progeny in all the treatments was less as compared to control. Difference in longevity and adult emergence due to different levels of treatments were also statistically significant. Neem oil was superior to all other treatments. The duration of adult survival was shortest in neem oil followed by castor, ground nut, mustard and sesamum oil. The concentrations of 0.25 ml/kg, 0.50 ml/kg and 0.75 ml/kg of oil successfully controlled the mites infesting pigeon pea seeds (Singh, 1999: *J. Acarol.*, **15** : 77–79).

Neosuidasia faini Ranganath & ChannaBasavanna

Nangia & ChannaBasavanna (1989) recorded this species from floor dust of godown and warehouses in Karnataka.

Family **GLYCYPHAGIDAE**

Lepidoglyphus sp.

Ghai (1964) recorded this mite as saprophagous and fungivorus from storage but not as grain feeders. It causes contamination of viable spores.

Blomia freemani Hughes

Its occurrence has been reported from pearl millet flour in Hisar (Putatunda *et al.*, 1999: *J. Acarol.*, **15** : 64-67).

Glycyphagus domesticus (De Geer)

This is a cosmopolitan species and apart from stored product it also occurs in house dust, human habitation, bird nests and animals. It has also been reported from stored silk worm, *Bombyx mori*, cocoon of PM, PMx, NB $4D_2$ and bivoltine ($NB4D_2$, Nb_{18} and KA). The other mites associated with this was *Lepidoglyphus destructor, T. putrescentiae, Glycyphagus domesticus,Kleemania plumigera,Blattisocius tarsalis* and *B. keegani.* The silk protein, fibroin, serecin provided nutrients to *T. putrescentiae.* The infested cocoons appeared dull and faded (Nangia *et al.*, 1999: *Abst. ASI Silver Jubilee Symp.*, 83). Increase of moisture content tended the increase of fungal growth (*Penicillium, Aspergillus*).

Its other reports include stored wheat and rice in West Bengal as fungivorous (Gupta *et al.*, 1991) and floor debris of store house and warehouse (Nangia & ChannaBasavanna, 1989).

Glycyphagus sp.

Mathur & Mathur (1983) collected this from rice, pearl millet, barley, dried pear, floor dust, pulses like lentils, black gram, causing grocers itch.

Lepidoglyphus destructor (Schrank)

Nangia & ChannaBasavanna (1989) collected it from floor of warehouse and Nangia *et al.*, (1999) from silk cocoons from Karnataka. Its population on infested cocoons was less as compared to *T. putrescentiae.*

Glycyphagus hughesi Pillai

Pillai (1955) recorded it from stored wheat (Prasad, 1974).

Glycyphagus ornatus Kramer

Its record is from floor debris of storage and warehouses in Karnataka (Nangia & ChannaBasavanna, 1989).

Austroglycyphagus geniculatus Vitzthum

This was collected from floor debris of storage and warehouses in Karnataka. The storage had wheat, wheat flour, bran, etc (Nangia & ChannaBasavanna, 1989: *Progr. in Acar.*, **2** : 241–248).

Austroglycyphagus sp.

It was extracted from insect free red gram from farmers' house in Karnataka. No damage was caused by this mite. It might be feeding on fungal spores.

Blomia tropicalis Bronswijk *et al.*

This was collected from samples of storage and warehouses in Karnataka (Nangia & ChannaBasavanna, 1989). It was also recorded from thrashing yard in Karnataka. The peak population attained when the crop after harvesting was heaped in thrashing yard.

Family **ANOETIDAE**

Histiostoma humidiatus

Mohanasundaram & Parameswaram (1991) recorded this mite associated with decaying and rotting agricultural crops in Tamil Nadu.

Family **PYROGLYPHIDAE**

Dermatophagoides farinae Hughes

Putatunda *et al.*, (1999) recorded this mite from pearl millet (*Pennisetum typhoideum*) in Hisar. It has also been recorded from thrashing yard and floor debris of storage (Nangia & ChannaBasavanna, 1989, 1991) while Gupta *et al.* (1991) collected it in association with stored wheat and rice in West Bengal. It was also collected from floor dust of FCI godown in Bihar (Nahar & Gupta, 1980), West Bengal (Gupta & Chatterjee, 2004). This mite causes house dust allergy.

Dermatophagoides pteronyssinus Trouessart

Its records are from thrashing yard and storage debris in Karnataka (Nangia & ChannaBasavanna, 1989, 1991). It was also collected from dust of granaries in Bihar (Nahar & Gupta, 1980), West Bengal (Gupta & Chatterjee, 2004).

Euroglyphus maynei Cooreman

Its records are from thrashing yard and from storage debris in Karnataka.

Euroglyphus longior Trouessart

Nangia & ChannaBasavanna (1989) recorded it from storage debris in Karnataka.

Family **PYEMOTIDAE**

Acarophenax nidicolus

Putatunda *et al.* (1999) reported this mite from Hisar infesting stored wheat.

Acarophenax triboli Newstead & Duvall

Nangia & ChannaBasavanna (1989) and Putaṭunda *et al.* (1999) recorded this species from store house debris and stored wheat, respectively.

Acarophenax sp.

This was found feeding on stored grain insect *Tribolium castaneum* infesting wheat in Hisar. It was found in the region between head and thorax. This is a predatory species.

Pyemotes herfsi Oudemans

Its record was from Karnataka from storage, floor debris (Nangia & ChannaBasavanna, 1989). The stored products were heavily infested with *Tribolium* sp on which it was seen feeding by sucking tissue fluid.

Pyemotes ventricosus (Newport)

Its records are from storage floor debris and thrashing yard in Karnataka (Nangia & ChannaBasavanna, 1989, 1991).

Pyemotes sp.

Mathur & Mathur (1983) record it from Hisar collected from storage having insect pest and reported this mite as its predator.

Family CHORTOGLYPHIDAE

Chortoglyphus arcuatus Troupeau

Its record is from storage, floor debris in Karnataka (Nangia & ChannaBasavanna, 1989).

Family CHEYLETIDAE

Cheyletus eruditus (Schrank)

This is a most dominating predatory species in storage feeding upon *Acarus siro* (Ghai, 1976). Its records are from papad in grocers' shop from Haryana (Mathur & Mathur, 1983), feeding upon *Trogoderma granarium* (Somchoudhury & Mukherjee, 1971), thrashing yard in Karnataka (Nangia & ChannaBasavanna, 1991), stored wheat and rice in West Bengal (Gupta *et al.*, 1991), stored wheat and rice in Bihar (Nahar & Gupta, 1980). All the reports indicate this species as predators of stored gain insects and mites.

Cheyletus malaccensis Oudemans

The records of this species are from many habitats and some of those are from stored grain from West Bengal (Gupta *et al.*, 1991), stored wheat from Bihar (Nahar & Gupta, 1980), stored pulses from Hisar (Putatunda *et al.*, 1999; Mathur & Mathur, 1983), floor debris of store houses in Karnataka (Nangia & ChannaBasavanna, 1989).

Biology : Nangia & ChannaBasavanna (1990) studied biology of this species at 24 ± 1°C and 80% RH under laboratory condition. It passed through egg, larva, protonymph, deutonymph and adult stages. Duration of different stages is as; incubation - 2.6 ± 1°C days, % hatching - 88.6%, larva - 3 ± 0.5 days, I quiescent stage 1 ± 0.5 days, protonymph - 4 ± 0.5 days, II quiescent stage - brief, deuto nymph - 4 ± 0.5 days, longevity of male 42 ± 5.0 days, female 37 ± 5.60 days, average fecundity 37 ± 7.22 eggs, cannibalism often occurs. At 27 ± 1°C, it completed life cycle in 19 days (Kumar & Mathur, 1995: *Abst.V Nat. Symp. in Acarology* : 73). Its population attained peak in March and the prevailing temperature of that month was most preferred and population declined thereafter.

Cheyletus fortis Oudemans

Its record is from stored wheat from Bihar (Nahar & Gupta, 1980).

Cheyletus malayensis **Cunliffe**

Its record is from stored wheat and rice in West Bengal (Gupta *et al.*, 1991).

Cheyletus strenuus

Putatunda *et al.* (1999) recorded this predatory mite from stored black gram (*Phaseolus mungo*) in Hisar.

Cheyletus aversor Rohdendorf

Nangia & ChannaBasavanna (1989) collected it from store house debris in Karnataka.

Cheyletus trouessarti Oudemans

Its record is from storage floor debris in Karnataka (Nangia & ChannaBasavanna, 1989).

Acaropsis sollers Kuzin/*Acaropsis docta* Berlese

These are important predatory mites in storage and feed on insect pests of stored grain, *viz. Rhizopertha dominica*. Its other records are stored wheat in Hisar (Putatunda *et al.*, 1999), stored grain from West Bengal (Gupta *et al.*, 1991; 2004), stored wheat & rice from Haryana (Mathur & Minocha, 1981), Bengal gram, green gram, lentil, dried pea in farmers' house in Hisar (Mathur & Mathur, 1983), debris of storage floor (Nangia & ChannaBasavanna, 1989), in storage feeding upon *Trogoderma granarium* (Kapil & Bhanot, 1973).

Biology : Its biology feeding upon eggs of *Rhizopertha dominica* infesting stored wheat grain revealed different developmental periods as larva - 2.86 days, protonymph - 3.63 days, deutonymph - 2.5 days, average female longevity - 15.16 days, average oviposition - 1.03 eggs/day, male longevity - 9.63 days, average consumption of *R. dominica* eggs - 1.19 eggs/day/larva, 1.30 eggs of *R. dominica* per protonymph/day and 1.46 eggs per deutonymph per day. Female mite consumed 1.62 eggs per day and male consumed 0.52 eggs per day in *A. docta*. This predatory mite can be a good biocontrolling agent (Singh, 1984: *Abst. Nat. Symp Non-insect pests* : 9). The consumption of eggs of *Trogoderma granarium* was 1.54, 1.33 and 0.66

per day by female and that of male was 1.08, 0.95 and 0.5 eggs/day in case of 1, 2, 3 days old eggs, respectively (Mathur & Minocha, 1989: *Progress in Acarology*, 2 : 255–258). According to Kapil & Bhanot (1972) an average of 1.77 eggs of *T. granarium* were consumed per female per day. It also fed upon eggs of other insect pests of stored products (Singh, 1972). This mite could also develop on dead remains of insects as well as fungal spores. This mite showed cannibalism even in presence of natural food. The eggs of *T. granarium* were the most preferred food and did not feed on larval and nymphal stages of the insect. The rate of consumption increased with the increase in number of eggs of *A. sollers* as well as increased feeding was evident with increase in number of eggs of *T. granarium*. Howeve, this mite failed to get full nourishment feeding upon its own eggs and required eggs of *T.granarium* (Mathur & Minocha, 1981: *Contrib. Acar.*, : 123–128).

This predator occurred throughout the year and could tolerate extreme climate condition of Haryana. Its population reached peak in August during which the favourable temperature prevailed and at temperature below that level, the population declined and disappeared. High humidity helped in building up population (Mathur & Mathur, 1987: *Abst. III Acarology. Symp.*, : 27).

Cheletonota sp.

Its record was made from stored wheat in Hisar (Putatunda *et al.*, 1991).

Cheletonella rugosa

Putatunda *et al.* (1999) recorded it from stored wheat in Hisar.

Eucheletopsis sp.

Putatunda *et al.* (1999) recorded it from stored wheat in Hisar.

Chelenotus sp.

Its record was made from stored wheat in Hisar (Putatunda *et al.*, 1999).

Neoacaropsis granulatus Volgin

Putatunda *et al.* (1999) collected it from stored wheat in Hisar.

Cheletopsis major

Putatunda *et al.* (1999) recorded this species from stored grain (Dal) in Hisar.

Cheletomorpha lepidopterorum (Shaw)

Nangia & ChannaBasavanna (1989) reported this from floor debris of storage and warehouse in Karnataka.

Eucheyletia sp.

Nangia & ChannaBasavanna (1989) collected it from debris of storage floor in Karnataka.

Hemicheyletia hisariensis Mathur & Mathur

Mathur & Mathur (1983) described this as new from wheat and straw debris associated with cunaxoid and *Kleemania* sp. in Hisar.

Hemicheyletia sp.

Nangia & ChannaBasavanna (1983) collected it from floor debris of store house in Karnataka.

Family **TETRANYCHIDAE**

Tetranychus neocaledonicus Andre

Nangia & ChannaBasavanna (1989) recorded this mite in storage and warehouse floor dust in Karnataka. It may be an accidental occurrence.

Family **RAPHIGNATHIDAE**

Gupta *et al.* (1991) recorded some undetermined species of this family from stored wheat and rice in West Bengal as predator.

Family **CUNAXIDAE**

Cunaxa capreolus (Berlese)

Gupta *et al.* (1991) collected it from West Bengal occurring on stored wheat and rice as predator.

Cunaxa setirostris (Hermann)

Its record was made from stored products (Gupta & Chatterjee, 2004). It is an efficient predatory mite known to feed upon phytophagous mites (Gupta, 2002) but its predatory habit in stored products was not ascertained

Cunaxa sp.

Nangia & ChannaBasavanna (1989) recorded it from Karnataka in floor dust of storage and warehouses.

Cunaxoides sp.

This was collected from wheat bran and straw debris from railway godown in Hisar.

Family **BDELLIDAE**

Spinibdella sp.

Nangia & ChannaBasavanna (1989) recorded it from floor dust of storage and thrashing yard.

Family **TARSONEMIDAE**

Acarophenax tribolii Newstead & Duvall

Nahar & Gupta (1980) collected it on stored wheat and wheat flour. These stored products were heavily infested with *Tribolium* sp. on which this mite was seen as parasite sucking tissue fluid from its host.

Tarsonemus granarius Lindquist

Nahar & Gupta (1980) recorded it from Patna on stored wheat flour. These stored products were heavily infested with *Tribolium* sp. on which this mite was seen as parasite sucking tissue fluid from its host.

Tarsonemus fusari Cooreman

Nangia & ChannaBasavanna (1989, 1991) reported its occurrence from Karnataka from floor dust of storage and warehouses as well as from thrashing yard.

Tarsonemus sp.

Rao & Prakash (1984) reported it from stored rice in Orissa and its record from West Bengal was on stored wheat as fungivorus (Gupta *et al.*, 1991).

Family **SCUTACARIDAE**

Scutacarus sp.

Nahar & Gupta (1980) recorded it from Bihar on stored wheat. Normally, the members of the group are found on moss and as parasites of insects.

Family **TYDEIDAE**

Pronematus fleschneri Baker

Gupta *et al.* (1991) reported it from stored wheat in West Bengal as fungivorous species.

Family **PACHYLAELAPTIDAE**

Pachylaelaps femoralis Bhattacharyya

Nangia & ChannaBasavanna recorded this species from thrashing yard in Karnataka. Peak population was seen when the crop was harvested and heaped at the yard.

Family **AMEROSEIIDAE**

Kleemania plumigera (Oudemans)

Its record was made from staffed stored silk worm cocoons in Karnataka. Staffed cocoons of PM, NB4 D2 and bivoltine (NB4 D2, NB 18 and Ka) when put into

Berlese funnel, this mite could be recorded in receiving vessel fitted with the stem of the funnel. Silk protein, fibroin and serecin provided nutrition to this mite. Increase of moisture content also increased the fungal growth. It was also recorded from storage debris in Karnataka (Nangia & ChannaBasavanna, 1989).

Kleemania plumosus (Oudemans)

Its record was made from floor debris of storage house in Karnataka. Its record was also made from stored rice and wheat from West Bengal (Gupta *et al.*, 1991) and stored wheat from Bihar (Gupta & Nahar, 1980).

Kleemania sp.

This was collected from grains infested with *Austroglycyphagus* sp. on wheat, straw debris containing *Hemicheyletia hisariensis* and cunaxid species. Nahar & Gupta (1980) also reported an undetermined species of this genus infesting stored wheat in Bihar.

Kleemania bengalensis Bhattacharyya

Gupta *et al.* (1991) recorded it from stored wheat and rice in West Bengal as fungivorous or of uncertain association. This may be a mycophagous species and easily develops on moulds.

Arctoseius butleri (Hughes)

Nangia & ChannaBasavanna (1989) collected this from floor debris of a warehouse in Karnataka. Nangia *et al.* (1991) recorded it from thrashing yard in Karnataka. This is a predatory mite on acarids.

Lasioseius sp.

Gupta & Chatterjee (2004) recorded it from stored products in West Bengal.

Blattisocius tarsalis (Berlese)

Gupta *et al.* (1991) reported it from stored wheat and rice in West Bengal as predator. Nangia *et al.*, (1999) recorded this from silk cocoons. Affected cocoons looked dull and silk thread revealed ridges and furrows. Nangia & ChannaBasavanna (1989) recorded it from floor debris of warehouse in Karnataka. This appears to be a predatory species but also is known to occur on moth which they use as carrier for dispersal (Hughes, 1976).

Blattisocius dentriticus (Berlese)

Gupta *et al.* (1991) reported it from stored wheat and rice in West Bengal as predator. Nangia *et al.*, (1991) reported it from stored wheat and rice in West Bengal. Affected cocoons looked dull and silk thread revealed ridges and furrows. Nangia & ChannaBasavanna (1989) recorded it from floor debris of warehouse in Karnataka. This appears to be a predatory species feeding on *Tyrophagus putrescentiae.* It has also been recorded on insect body, mould on coconuts, etc. (Hughes, 1976).

Blattisocius keegani Fox

Nangia & ChannaBasavanna (1989) reported this species from Karnataka from debris of warehouse. This is a predatory species and is known to feed upon eggs of grain beetles.

Blattisocius mali (Oudemans)

This was collected from floor dust of storage and warehouse in Karnataka (Nangia & ChannaBasavanna, 1989). This species fed on acarid mites.

Melichares sp.

This mite was collected from floor dust of storage and warehouse debries in Karnataka. This is a predatory species and is known to feed upon eggs of grain beetles.

Proctolaelaps sp.

This predatory mite was recorded from Karnataka on storage (Nangia & ChannaBasavanna, 1989). This appears to be a predatory species feeding on acarid mites.

Family **LAELAPIDAE**

Androlaelaps casalis casalis Berlese

This mite was collected from stored wheat and rice in West Bengal, floor debris of storage in Karnataka (Nangia & ChannaBasavanna, 1989), from stored grains in Lucknow. Its seasonal occurrence was also studied. This is a predatory species feeds mostly on acarid mites, However, it occurs in other diverse habitats like bird and bat nests, in dust, in poultry house as well as in soil.

Hypoaspis aculeifer (Canestrini)

Its records are from floor debris of storage and warehouse in Karnataka (Nangia & ChannaBasavanna, 1989, Nangia *et al.*, 1991). This mite is a predatory one and is also known from rodent nests.

Hypoaspis calcuttaensis Bhattacharyya

Nangia *et al.* (1981) could collect it from thrashing yards in Karnataka where the harvested crops were heaped. Its association with stored products is uncertain.

Family **MACROCHELIDAE**

Macrocheles muscaedomesticae (Scopoli)

Its record was from Karnataka from store debris (Nangia & ChannaBasavanna, 1989). This is an insect associated mite and might have entered storage through its host insects. It feeds on eggs of house fly, dung beetle, etc. (Hughes, 1976).

Family **PARASITIDAE**

Parasitus bengalensis Pramanik

It was recorded from thrashing yards in Karnataka having heap of harvested crops (Nangia *et al.*, 1991). Nothing is known about its association.

Parasitus primitivus Oudemans

Nangia *et al.*, (1991) recorded it from thrashing yards in Karnataka. In what way it is associated with storage is not known.

Family **EVIPHIDIDAE**

Eviphis cultratellus Berlese

Its record is from thrashing yards in Karnataka. In what way its association is with store house is not known.

Eviphis indicus Bhattacharyya

Its record is from thrashing yards in Karnataka (Nangia *et al.*, 1991). Its nature of association with stored products is doubtful.

Family **UROPODIDAE**

Trematura sp.

Nangia *et al.* (1991) got it from thrashing yards in Karnataka. It's nature of association with stored grain is uncertain.

Fuscuropoda marginata Koch

It is one of the commenest mite species occurring on mouldy grains. It was recorded from heavily infested and mouldy stored wheat and rice in West Bengal. This is a fungivorous species (Gupta *et al.*, 1991). However, it is known to attack immature stages of mites and also acts as scavenger (Hughes, 1976).

Uroseius sp.

Its record was from stored wheat and rice from Bihar (Nahar & Gupta, 1980). It is a fungivorous mite.

Leiodinychus sp.

Gupta *et al.* (1991) collected it from stored wheat and rice in West Bengal. It is a fungivorous mite.

Leiodinychus krameri (Berlese)

Nahar & Gupta (1980) reported it from stored rice in Bihar. It was found to be one of the commonest mites in stored grain. This mite prefers dampy and mouldy grains. It was also recorded from West Bengal infesting stored wheat and rice where it was abundantly available. It is a fungivorous mite. It prefers mould and occurs in large number in such habitat.

Family **GALUMNIDAE**

Gulumna flabellifera Hammer

This mite of uncertain association with stored grain was collected from thrashing yards from Karnataka (Nangia *et al.*, 1991). This appears to be fungivorous.

Family **OPPIIDAE**

Oppia nodosa Hammer

Its record was from thrashing yards in Karnataka (Nangia *et al.*, 1991). This appears to be fungivorous.

Family **ORIBATULIDAE**

Scheloribates rufafulvus Kramer

Nangia *et al.* (1991) recorded it from thrashing yards from Karnataka. Its association with stored products is uncertain.

Scheloribates laevigatus Koch

Nangia *et al.* (1991) got it from thrashing yards in Karnataka. Its association with stored products is of uncertain nature.

3.20. APICULTURE MITES

INTRODUCTION

It is estimated that 35% of all crops which human beings cultivate and use as food are pollinated by bees. Therefore, sustenance of bee population in nature is most important both for crops as well as for human beings. The decline in bee population will affect the pollination and seed development and these, in turn, will bring disastrous effect in agricultural economy.

Unfortunately the honey bees are often attacked by predators, parasites and diseases affecting their performance and pollination efficiency. Among these, mites are most important enemies. Even there are some mites which are interested to feed on the stored food deposited in the bee combs and thus deprive the bees of their food though that may not cause any direct damage to the bees. The parasitic mites which include both external and internal parasites severely affect the apiculture as because these affect the flying capacity and dispersal of the honey bees. More than 100 species of mites are known to be associated with honey bees (Putatunda, 2001), some of which are predators, some are parasites, some are phoretic, while others are scavengers. The last two types are not bee hive damaging while the first two are of great concern as they feed and reproduce on the brood and adult bees and cause threat to apiculture.

Because of the economic importance of honey bee associated mites, a good number of workers from different parts of India and abroad made valuable contributions towards exploration of mites on honey bees and their management. Some of the important references are: Delfinado & Baker (1959, 1962), Delfinado-Baker *et al.* (1985), Erickson *et al.* (1988), Bhaskar & Putatunda (1989), Abrol & Putatunda (1995), Abrol (1995), Mazumder (1995), Bobhorr (1998), Koushik (2003), Ombir (2003), Chillar *et al.* (2007), etc.

GENERAL NATURE OF INJURY

Mites suck the haemolymph from the skin of adults and immatures of bees causing intense pain, irritation, restlessness.

Often, in case of heavy infestation, they cause weakening of bee colonies, exhaustion of bees and drastic death of immatures. The bees become absolutely helpless to climb the mite infested colonies and finally they desert the colonies.

HONEY BEES AND THEIR MITE ASSOCIATES

Nature of association	Mite	Hosts (*Apis*)
Endoparasite	*Acarapis woodi*	*A. mellifera, A. cerana, A. florea*
Endoparasite	*A. dorsalis*	*A. mellifera*
Endoparasite	*A. externus*	*A. mellifera*
Predator	*Acaropsis sollers*	*A. mellifera, A. dorsata*
Ectoparasite	*Varroa jacobsoni*	*A. mellifera, A. cerana*
Ectoparasite	*Varroa underwoodi*	*A. cerana*
Ectoparasite	*Euvarroa sinhai*	*A. mellifera, A. florea*
Ectoparasite	*E. wongsirii*	*A. andreniformis*
Ectoparasite	*Tropilaelaps clareae*	*A. mellifera, A. cerana, A. florea, A. dorsata*
Ectoparasite	*T. stimulis*	*A. dorsata*
Ectoparasite	*T. koenigerum*	*A. mellifera, A. dorsata, A. florea, A. laboriosa*
Ectoparasite	*Pyemotes herfsi*	*A. cerana*
Phoretic	*Neocypholaelaps indica*	*A. cerana*
Phoretic	*N. apicola*	*A. mellifera*
Predator	*Allodinychus flagellifer*	*A. dorsata*

ECTOPARASITIC MITES

These mites attach themselves on the body surface of bee (larva, pupa and adult) and threaten the bee colony. Some of the external parasites of bees are discussed below :

Varroa jacobsoni Oudemans/*Varroa underwoodi*

This is an obligate parasite of bees and has no free living stage. *Varroa* mites attack both brood and adult bees.

1. Distribution and nature of damage : This is the most dangerous pest of bees and are distributed in tropical and temperate regions of the world infesting bee colonies. Their number may be 2-3 million / colony, suck the haemolymph from bees and make them weak. Larvae, pupae and adults become malformed, showing reduced pollinating capacity. Ultimately they cause death of honey bees collapsing the colonies.

This is a large reddish-brown mite, dorsoventrally flattened and occur between first two abdominal segments, or head and thorax or thorax and abdomen. They infest drone and worker cells. Mite population is more during spring and becomes maximum in autumn. Due to infestations, the larvae, pupae become malformed, workers and drones become crippled and legs and wings become deformed. The dried larvae become characteristically with raised head. Ultimately, the colony declines and collapses. In temperate climate, the untreated colonies may collapse due to varooasis three to four years after initial infestation. The population growth is lower in tropical and sub-tropical climates.

Some of the viruses associated with honey bees are Acute Paralysis Virus, Deformed Wing Virus, Acute Bee Virus and these are vectored by *Varroa*. They cause weakening of immune system of bees. The symptoms include malformed larvae, pupae and adult, irregular and spotty brood, depressed sunken cappings of brood, etc. (Chillar *et al.,* 2007).

They also transmit diseases like, Haffnosis and septicaeamia in bees.

The affected bees are *Apis mellifera* and *Apis cerana.*

Biology : The reproductive phase of the mother mite and ontogenesis take place exclusively in the sealed brood cells of the bee. Eggs are laid one by one in the pupa's cuticle. The mite and her offsprings feed on haemolymph 2-3 times a day for 3-9 minutes. Male mates as soon as first female comes out and male mates with more than one female and dies thereafter. The mother mite along with her inseminated daughters leave the cell for starting a phoretic life cycle. The juvenile mortality is most important factor that moderates reproduction success of *Varroa.* Under normal natural condition, the average reproduction rate is 1.3-1.45 in single infested worker brood and due to longer capping period 2.2-2.6 in drone brood.

Management :

Biological Methods : This method relies on peculiarities of mite biology by controlling its population at points of its life cycle where the mite is most vulnerable. A biotechnological method called "Trapping Comb Technique" has been suggested. The queen is restricted to a single brood comb which attracts majority of the reproductive mites in the colony. After three brood cycles more than 90% of mite population can be trapped and will be removed from the colony.

Chemical Control : Application of coumaphos, fluvalinate, foramamidine, amitraz, etc. may be used. However, care is to be taken so that the bees are not harmed, no resistance is developed to mites and no environmental hazard develops. There are several other methods for control and for those Chillar *et al.* (2007) may be referred to.

Tropilaelaps clareae Delfinado & Baker

Distribution and nature of damage : Its distribution is mostly in Asia and infests mainly *A. mellifera, A. cerana, A. florea, A. dorsata.* This is elliptical mite and reddish brown in colour. The life cycle is completed through egss

(1-1.2 days), larva (0.67-0.83 days), protonymph (2.5-2.8 days) and deutonymph (2.9-3.1 days) (Garg and Sharma, 1994).

Ø This mite infests heavily on honey bee causing mutilated wings, stunted abdomen and affecting egg laying. The affected honey bees show significantly reduced haemocyte counts in *Apis mellifera* (Abrol, 1995).

Management :

- Treatmenst with Fluvalinate and formic acid are effective.
- Thymol crystals are also effective.
- Farmers also often use sulphur powdering in very small amount on top wooden frame in the form of a single line by using handmade paper cones. Mites are killed due to sulphur powder which they face while walking on sulphur powder.

Euvarroa sinhai Delfinado

Distribution and nature of damage : This is a large brown mite, broadly pear shaped. It attacks only drone brood cells as well as attacks worker bees (Kapil & Agarwal, 1989).

- It is also an Asiatic species and attacks *A. florea* and *A. andreniformis.*
- The mite causes hindrance in the construction of queen cell.
- The peak population is attained during March-September.

Management : Chemical control mentioned above may be applied.

ENDOPARASITIC MITES

Acarapis woodi, (Rennie)/ ***A. Dorsalis*** Morgenthaler / ***A. Externus*** Morgenthaler

Distribution and nature of damage : These are a small mites, occur in trachea and air sacs of adult honey bees of *A. mellifera, A. cerana, A. florea.*

Almost 90% of bees get infested by these mites in USA and this causes a disease called "Isle of Wight".

The trachea of severely infested bees has brown blotches, with brown scabs or crust-like lesions. Due to attack, the bee life is shortened; affect flying efficiency due to atrophied flight muscles. Bees crawl spreading the wing in the form of 'K", due to separation of fore and hind wings. Bees become sluggish, produce yellow droppings and affect building of colonies.

Management : Use of menthol crystals for 2-4 weeks, formic acid and use of Folbex strips impregnated with Potassium Nitrate and 500mg Chlorobenzilate at weekly interval is recommended.

Phoretic mites : These mites use bees as carriers for movement from one place to another. However, when these mites are in large number, they affect the foraging ability of bees.

Neocypholaelaps indica Evans/***N. apicola***

Distribution and nature of damage : These two species occur in India, as well as other parts of Asia on *A. mellifera, A. cerana* which they use as carriers for dispersal from one point to another and probably do no damage to the bees.

Sometimes they may be feeding the stored pollen kept stored in the bee colonies.

Predatory mites

Apart from damage causing mites, there are also some mites associated with bees which are predatory in nature and predate on parasitic, phoretic or scavenger mites and thus, they also help in reducing the population of harmful mites. Some such mites belong to Cheyletidae, Pyemotidae, Bdellidae, Cunaxidae and Phytoseiidae.

Acaropsis sollers Kuzin/***Cheyletus malaccensis*** Oudemans/***Allodinychus flagellifer***

Distribution and nature of damage : These predatory mites are known to feed on the harmful ectoparasitic mites and thereby help in biological control.

***Pyemotes herfsi* Oudemans**

This mite also feeds on the immatures of the ectoparasitic mites.

SCAVENGER MITES

These include mites belonging to *Tyrophagus longior* Gervais, *Acarus siro,* Linn. *Austroglycyphagus geniculatus* (Vitzthum), *Rhizoglyphus* sp., *Kuzinia* sp., *Sennertia* sp. etc. and are often known to infest bee colonies but they mostly feed on stored pollen and other decomposed matters and by that they clean the bee hive. However, if their population becomes too heavy, they may cause nuisance to the bees.

CONCLUSION

- The major works have been done from North India and practically nothing has been done from rest of India indicating a huge gap in knowledge in this aspect.
- Safe management of honey bee mites is still unknown. The control method presently used often contaminates the stored honey in the hive. Therefore, safe management practice is yet to be developed.
- The dispersion and method of infestation need to be studied more thoroughly and suitable management technique needs to be developed.
- More extensive study in exploration of mites of honey bees is needed which will reveal many more unknown species and will throw light on their nature of damage.

4. LIST OF MITES OF AGRI-HORTICULTURAL IMPORTANCE, STORED PRODUCTS, MUSHROOMS IN INDIA

PHYTOPHAGOUS MITES

Order **PROSTIGMATA**

Family **TETRANYCHIDAE**

Genus ***Aplonobia***

sphaeralceae

Genus ***Aponychus***

bambusae, corpuzae, kodaikanalensis, sarjui, sulcatus

Genus ***Bakerina***

aculus, orissaensis

Genus ***Bryobia***

eharai,praetiosa, rubrioculus

Genus ***Bryobiella***

punjabensis

Genus ***Eotetranychus***

asiaticus, broodryki, communis, fremonti, frosti, guajavae, hicoriae, hirsti, indicus, irregularis, kankitus, ladakhensis, mandensis, neoperplexus, pamelae, populi, pruni, rajouriensis, ranikhetensis, rohilae, sexmaculatus, strichonsy, suginamensis, syzygii, truncatus, uncatus, weldoni.

Genus ***Eutetranychus***

africanus, bilobatus, caricae, citri, maximae, nagai, orientalis, pantopus, phaseoli

Genus ***Mesobryobia***

jobneri

Genus ***Monoceronychus***

terpoghossiani

Genus ***Neopetrobia***

simlaensis

Genus ***Oligonychus***

biharensis, coffeae, indicus, iseilemae, mangiferus, manishi, oryzae, plegas, ponmanaiensis, pratensis, punicae, sacchari, saccharinus, sapienticolus, thelytokus, tylus, vitis, yothersi.

Genus ***Petrobia***

latens, harti

Genus ***Porcupinychus***

abutiloni

Genus ***Schizotetranychus***

andropogoni, baltazari, cajani, fluvialis, hindustanicus, indicus, lechrius, mansoni, meghalayensis, tephroseae, undulatus.

Genus ***Stylophoronicus***

baghensis,lalii

Genus ***Tenuipalponychus***

citri

Genus ***Tetranychus***

afrindicus, angloensis, fijiensis, hydrangeae, hypogeae, lombardinii, ludeni, macfarlanei, neocaledonicus, papayae, puschelii, sayedi, tumidus, turkestani, udaipurensis, urticae, zaheri.

Family **TUCKERELLIDAE**

Genus ***Tuckerella***

delhiensis, indica, kumaonensis

Family **TENUIPALPIDAE**

Genus ***Aegyptobia***

mumulus

Genus ***Brevipalpus***

assamensis, californicus, chilensis, cucurbitae, deleoni, essigi, euphorbiae, karachiensis, lewisi, nangalensis, obovatus, phoenicis, pulcher, pruni, rugulosus.

Genus ***Cenopalpus***

sp.

Genus ***Dolichotetranychus***

cocos, floridanus, ramaniae, vandergooti

Genus ***Larvacarus***

transitans

Genus ***Neoraoiella***

eugeniae

Genus ***Obuloides***

rajamohani

Genus ***Pentamerismus***

oregonensis

Genus ***Phytoptipalpus***

albizziae

Genus ***Priscapalpus***

piarai

Genus ***Raoiella***

indica,macfarlanei,pandanae

Genus ***Swarnanychus***

bandipurensis

Genus ***Tenuipalpus***

aboharensis, acacii, amygdalusae, caudatus, cissampelosa, coimbatorensis, crassus, decus, dimensus, erythrinae, faresianus, fici, ghaii, granati, guptai, hastaligni, indicus, ixorae, jagatkhanensis, kesari, lalbaghensis, laminasetae, leguminae, leptadeniae, ludhianaensis, malligai, micheli, mustus, pernicis, pruni, punicae, punjabensis, pyrusae, quadrisetosus, solanensis, tectonae, tetragyzae, yousefi, zizyphae.

Genus ***Terminalichus***

delhiensis, karachiensis, panajiensis, psidi, serratus

Family **TARSONEMIDAE**

Genus ***Dendotarsonemus***

sp.

Genus ***Daidalotarsonemus***

sp.

Genus ***Fungitarsonemus***

sp.

Genus ***Hemitarsonemus***

dorsalis, piperai, sp.

Genus ***Lupotarsonemus***

randsi

Genus *Phytonemus*

sp.

Genus *Polyphagotarsonemus*

latus

Genus *Steneotarsonemus*

bancrofti, conoi, furcatus, pallidus, spinki

Genus *Tarsonemus*

ananus, berlese, fusari, granarium, krichneri, myceleiphagus, tarsalis

Genus *Xenotarsonemus*

sp.

Subfamily **SCUTACARIDAE**

Genus *Scutacarus*

sp.

Super family **ERIOPHYOIDEA**

Genus *Acalitus*

epiphytivagrans, gossypii, hibisci, latifoliae, meliosomae, reticulatae, schefferae

Genus *Acaricalus*

darjeelingensis

Genus *Aceria*

alangiae, asperae, abutiloni, acalyphae, acanthae, achyranthi, acervae, agallochae, ailanthae, alangae, anisomelae, antidotalae, asperae, asystasiae, balanites, bambusae, barleriae, boraginae, banyani, bassiae, berberae, borreriae, bucitneriae, commiphorae, corchorae, cajani, clerodendronis, cordiae, crotalariae, commelinae, dalbergiae, dactylonae, dasi, dendrocalamae, dhanikhariensis, donacis, delhiensis, dichrostachyia, dichotomae, docleri, donacis, erythrensis, eragrastae, erythrinae, feroniae, ficus, fistulae, gastrotrichus, granati, guerreronis, holoptelae, hopeae, infectoriae, jasmini, justiciae, kigeliae, kirganeliae, leucopyrae, linnae, longisetae, litsea, litchii, lycopersici, mangiferae, madukkaraiensis, malloticola, murudamalaiensis, meliosomae, medicaginis, mitragynae, mori, nandiensis, nerii, nothopegidae, nothopegiae, nimusopae, obliquae, phyllanthae, poae, pustulatus, polygalae, pongamiae, puttarudriahi, ruelliae, randi, reticulatae, saccharini, sapindi, securinegae, setaceus, seradanurensis, sheldoni,siruvaniensis, sinuatae, sorghi, spondiasiphagus, subramani, trichocnemum, tulipae, trianthemae, viddhagiriensis, vitifoliae, waltheriae, xeromphisi, ziziphi.

Genus *Abacarus*

anacardiae, asiaticae, arjunalis, delhiensis, foliavagrans, goaensis, gossypii, oryzae, pseudotriae, sacchari.

Genus ***Avacarus***

anacardiae

Genus ***Amalthacarus***

arnottinae

Genus ***Anthopoda***

fici, deviarensis, wightianae

Genus ***Acaphylla***

indiae, steinwedeni, syzygii, theae

Genus ***Acaphyllisa***

indiae, parindiae, pipera

Genus ***Acarhyncus***

bamboovagrans, dendrocalami

Genus ***Aculops***

acanthae, abutiloni, betonicae, boerhaeviae, dilemiae, excoecaria, extensae, ichnocarpi, kumari, leguminae, lycopersici, morindae, niphocladae, pelekassi, pittosporae, privae, xanthocarpi.

Genus ***Aculus***

asperus, atturensis, acutangulae, bangalorensis, colei, cassiae, ficivagrans, indicus, kolengii, leptadeniae, mckenziei, menoni, moringeae, montanae, pinnatasi, pterygospermae, sarcoceae, yelagiriensis.

Genus ***Anchiphytoptus***

giganticus

Genus ***Anthocoptes***

adhatodae, ayyanari, bamboovagrans, glycosmis, pavoniae, rutacevagrans, tectoniae, vitexae, walayarensis.

Genus ***Anthopoda***

deviarensis, fici, wightianae

Genus ***Artacris***

termanifagus, vagrans, vadalurensis

Genus ***Ashieldophyes***

fennadamensis

Genus ***Baileyna***

indica

Genus *Bakeriella*

ocimis

Genus *Brachendus*

grewae

Genus *Brionesa*

semecarpae

Genus *Catarhinus*

munnarensis, spontaneae

Genus *Calacarus*

araliae, brionesae, capsica, carinatus, channabasavannae, citrifolii, jasmini, keiferi, malvae, malvagrans, microrostrus, millingtoniae, palmae, polyalthiae, quisqualis, swietensis.

Genus *Calepitrimerus*

adinus, antedesmae, asperrimae, azadirachtae, cordiae, hispidus, leucadis, massanjoris, mysorensis, sagarensis, tabernaemontanis, woodfordis.

Genus *Cheiracus*

sulcatus

Genus *Ciraces*

chakrabarti, icacinae

Genus *Cisaberoptus*

kenyae

Genus *Cosetacus*

citrifolis

Genus *Colomerus*

alangii, neopiperis, palmae, vitis, woodfordis

Genus *Colopodacus*

bengalensis, cinnamomae, combretus, eugeniae, gynalaxtae, walayarensis

Genus *Cosella*

fleschneri, ichnocarpasia

Genus *Clypopatycus*

indicus

Genus *Cymoptus*

bengalensis

Genus ***Dendroptus***

sp.

Genus ***Dependaculus***

nothopegii

Genus ***Diptilorhynacus***

sinusetus

Genus ***Diptilomiopus***

alangii, atrocarpae, assamica, alagarmalaiensis, asperis, bengalensis, cumanis, camerae, cocculae, fevremovici, ficusis, holoptelus, indicus, integrifoliae, jevremoviei, knorri, lecasis, maduraiensis, thangaveli, trewier, ulmivagrans

Genus ***Disella***

granulacoxae, oblongifoliaevagrans, tectona, vagrans

Genus ***Ditrymacus***

integrifoliae, keiferi

Genus ***Diptacus***

cephalanthi, duabangipgagus

Genus ***Ectomerus***

chebulae

Genus ***Epicecidophyes***

clerodendris, indica

Genus ***Epitrimerus***

arimae, chandramohani, morindae, parasakthi

Genus ***Epiphytimerus***

palampurensis

Genus ***Eriophyes***

acaciae, alangii, anacardi, casuarinae, cernuus, coimbatorensis, cheriani, cymbopogonis, erineus, dichrostachia, ensifoliae, euphorbiae, ladakhensis, prosopidis, plectroniae, rotandae, terminaliac, tristiatus

Genus ***Floracarus***

beharensis, eugenifoliae, pollachiensis, salvifoliae, siruvaniensis, sivakumarii.

Genus ***Gammaphytoptus***

bangalensis, litseasis

Genus *Hemiscolocenus*

rares

Genus *Hornophyes*

andamanensis

Genus *Hyboderus*

globulus

Genus *Hyborhinus*

kallarensis

Genus *Indonotalox*

sudarsani

Genus *Indosetacus*

rhinacanthi

Genus *Indotegolophus*

darjeelingensis

Genus *Keiferophyes*

avicenniae, guamensis

Genus *Keiferana*

neolitseae

Genus *Mackiella*

borasis

Genus *Metaculus*

foveolatae, londaensis, mangiferae, sapindiphagus

Genus *Microruberculabus*

mudigerensis

Genus *Monotrimacus*

ocellatus, quadrangulari

Genus *Neocalacarus*

mangiferae

Genus *Neomesalox*

kallarensis

Genus *Neometaculus*

bauhiniae

Genus ***Neotegonotus***

indicus, fastigatus

Genus ***Neophytoptus***

ocimae

Genus ***Neocatarhinus***

ficusis

Genus ***Neocecidophyes***

mallotivagrans

Genus ***Neocosella***

ichnocarpae

Genus ***Neocolopodacus***

mitragynae, muruganii

Genus ***Neocupacarus***

flabelliferus

Genus ***Neodiptilomiopus***

vishakantai

Genus ***Neodirothrix***

tiliacorae

Genus ***Neodyherothrix***

piprae

Genus ***Neodactylus***

mohanasundarami

Genus ***Neodialox***

palmyrae

Genus ***Neodychrothrix***

celloshieldae, rutacevagrans

Genus ***Ncorhynacus***

combretis, rajendrani

Genus ***Neophantacrus***

mallotus

Genus ***Neoshevtchenkella***

rhusae

Genus *Nothopoda*

kallarensis

Genus *Notostrix*

flabelliferae

Genus *Notocaphylla*

chinensiae

Genus *Notodicrothrix*

anacardiae

Genus *Obesophyes*

linocierae

Genus *Paracaphylla*

streblae

Genus *Parachendus*

grewiae

Genus *Paratetra*

albizziae, elephantae, himalayana, integrifoliavagrans, murrayae

Genus *Paraciota*

tetracanthae

Genus *Paraphytoptus*

chrysanthemi, champacae, cristatae, elaeocarpae,jujubae

Genus *Phytoptus*

alangii, breyniae, canthii, carissae, casuarinae, cyperi, eletariae, ficivorus, glycosmisae, karnatakaensis, lantanae, laurae, morindae, pyri, rosae, rubifoliae, subbraoi, terminaliae

Genus *Phyllocoptes*

aliyamagarensis, asperaevagrans, ficivagrans, immigrans, indicae, salmaliae, shoreum, simplicifoliae, tomentosa

Genus *Phyllocoptruta*

adayarae, lanneae, malligai, musae, odinae, oleivora

Genus *Phyllocoptacus*

barringtonae

Genus *Porcupinotus*

humpae

Genus ***Procalacarus***

alyarensis

Genus ***Proartacris***

pinivagrans

Genus ***Prophyllocoptes***

riveae

Genus ***Proneotegonotus***

antiquorae

Genus ***Pseudodiptacus***

cassariasis

Genus ***Pseudocalepitrimerus***

dharamapuriensis

Genus ***Quadriporea***

mangiferae

Genus ***Rhombacus***

eucalypti

Genus ***Ramaculus***

karnatakaensis

Genus ***Rhyncaphytoptus***

ficifoliae, shoreacola

Genus ***Scolocenus***

spiniferus

Genus ***Stenarhynchus***

aristidus

Genus ***Spinacus***

lengenquus, pagonis

Genus ***Spinasetacus***

beddomeivagrans

Genus ***Thamnacus***

acanthae, elaegnae, elaegnae, euphorbiae

Genus ***Tegolophus***

artocarpi, bambusae, birbhumensis, calotropi, cordis, coimbatorensis, ficusi,gelonis, gmelinae, gmelinus, indica, kalyanii, kanadaliensis, monospermasis, nerii, spondiallus, vitexis.

Genus ***Tetra***

aegleis, anisomelae, ardiseae, asperae, bauhinae, bruhinae, coimbatorensis, cassiae, lanneansis, limonis, petuniae, shoreacola, sissoae, tephrosiae, trifoliae.

Genus ***Tegonotus***

bassius, bengalensis, birbhumensis, brideliae, cardiavagrans, coimbatorensis, convolvuli, dubrakani, ferrugineae, holigarnae, jambolensis, litseae, mangiferae, paraviflorae, schleicherae, semicarpae.

Genus ***Vasates***

cassiae, dhodabettaensis, pavetis

Genus ***Vilaia***

panithus, buchananiae

PREDATORY MITES

Order PROSTIGMATA

Family ANYSTIDAE

Genus ***Anystis***

baccarum, indica, nagalandensis, sp.

Genus ***Tencateia***

Kanthiensis, sp.

Genus ***Walzia***

darjeelingensis, indica, sp.

Family BDELLIDAE

Genus ***Bdella***

khasyana, maldahensis, sp.

Genus ***Bdellodes***

affinis, angustifolius, atro, augusta, grandiflora, manipurensis, procincta, sp.

Genus ***Biscirus***

sp.

Genus *Cyta*

sp.

Genus *Spinibdella*

sp.

Genus *Octobdellodes*

guajavae

Family CALIGONELLIDAE

Genus *Molothrognathus*

leptostylus

Family CAMEROBIIDAE

Genus *Neophyllobius*

guajavae

Family CHEYLETIDAE

Genus *Acaropsis*

docta, sollers

Genus *Chelacaropsis*

moorei

Genus *Cheletacarus*

gryphus

Genus *Cheletogenes*

ornatus

Genus *Cheletomimus*

sp.

Genus *Cheletonella*

summersi, rugosa

Genus *Cheletonota*

sp.

Genus *Cheyletus*

aversor, eruditus, fortis, malaccensis, malayensis, trouessarti, sp., *strenuous*

Genus *Cheletonotus*

sp.

Genus ***Cheletopsis***

major

Genus ***Cheletomorpha***

lepidopterorum

Genus ***Eucheyletia***

reticulata, sp.

Genus ***Eucheletopsis***

sp.

Genus ***Grallacheles***

tulipi

Genus ***Hemicheyletia***

bakeri, indica, hisariensis, sp.

Genus ***Neoacaropsis***

grannulatus

Genus ***Paracheyletia***

pyriformes

Family **CUNAXIDAE**

Genus ***Armascirus***

taurus

Genus ***Cunaxa***

anacardae, bambusae, capreolus, crista, curassavica, cynodonae, mangiferae, myabunderensis, setirostris, womersley, sp.

Genus ***Cunaxoides***

croceus, nicobarensis

Genus ***Dactyloscirus***

bengalensis, machairodus, sp.

Genus ***Neocunaxoides***

andrei, cerassoides, pradhani, sp.

Genus ***Pseudocunaxa***

sp.

Genus ***Scirula***

sp.

Family **ERYTHRAEIDAE**

Genus ***Abrolophus***

delhiensis, ripicola, sp.

Genus ***Balaustium***

sp.

Genus ***Bochartia***

sp.

Genus ***Erythraeus***

plumosus, cinchoni

Genus ***Leptus***

giganticus, indicus, poonaensis, samsungensis, sp.

Genus ***Paraerythraeus***

delhiensis, serratociliatus

Genus ***Sphaerolophus***

delhiensis, gigas, minutes

Family **EUPODIDAE**

Genus ***Eupodes***

sigmoidensis, sp.

Family **PYEMOTIDAE**

Genus ***Acarophenax***

nidicolus, triboli, sp.

Genus ***Pyemotes***

herfsi, ventricosus, sp.

Family **PYGMEPHORIDAE**

Genus ***Pygmephorus***

sp.

Family **LINOPODIDAE**

Genus ***Linopodes***

sp.

Family **RAPHIGNATHIDAE**

Genus ***Exothorhis***

nadiaensis, justicia

Genus ***Raphignathus***

darjeelingensis, guajavae

Family **STIGMAEIDAE**

Genus ***Agistemus***

albae, aramatei, edulis, exsertus, fleschneri, gamblei, garrulus, hebarius, heterophylla, hystrix, industani, inflatus, javanicum, lakoocha, lobata, macrommatus, obscura, terminalis, unguiparvus, sp.

Genus ***Cheylostigmaeus***

sp.

Genus ***Eryngiopus***

coimbatorensis

Genus ***Indostigmaeus***

rangatensis

Genus ***Ledermuelleria***

parryorum, sp.

Genus ***Zetzellia***

languida, sp.

Family **TYDEIDAE**

Genus ***Lorryia***

africana, stricta

Genus ***Paralorryia***

fodderi

Genus ***Parapronematus***

acacia, cameliae, ferox, murshidabadensis, sp.

Genus ***Pronematus***

anconai, elongates, fleschneri, mcgregori, oryzae, sextoni, ubiquitus, sp.

Genus ***Tydeus***

cumini, gossabaensis, justicia, ornamentalicus, schusteri, wallachi

Order **MESOSTIGMATA**

Family **PHYTOSEIIDAE**

Subfamily **AMBLYSEIINAE**

Tribe **Neoseiulini** Chant & McMurty

Genus ***Neoseiulus*** Hughes

aceriae, bindrai, baraki, cucumeris, cynodonae, dhooriai, fallacis, ficusi, imbricatus, indicus, lablabi, longispinosus, neoghanii, rangatensis, paspalivorus, reticulatus, umbraticus

Tribe **Kampimodromini** Kolodochka

Subtribe **Kampimodromina** Chant & McMurty

Genus ***Okiseius*** Ehara

himalayana, sikkimensis, yazuliensis,

Genus ***Proprioseius***

kumaonensis

Subtribe **Paraphytoseiina** Chant & McMurty

Genus ***Amblyseiulella***

hyauliangensis, nucifera, heveae

Genus ***Paraphytoseius***

apocynaevagrans, bhadrakaliensis, horrifer, multidentatus, narayanani, nicobarensis, orientalis, scleroticus

Tribe **Typhlodromipsini** Chant & McMurty

Genus ***Typhlodromips*** De Leon

syzygii

Genus ***Scapulaseius*** Karg & Oomen - Kalsbeck

andamanicus, arecae, augusta, daturae, eucalypticus, hapoli, officinaria, polyantheae, sapienticola, sorghumae, suknaensis

Tribe **Amblyseiini** Muma

Subtribe **Amblyseiina** Muma

Genus ***Transeius*** Chant & McMurty

bangalorensis, tetranychivorus

Genus ***Amblyseius*** Berlese

adhatodae, aerialis, amitae, amtalaensis, andersoni (=potentillae), apocynae, channabasavannai, charui, crotalariae, cucurbitae, deleoni, eujenae, excelsus, fraterculus, giganticus, guajavae, hapoliensis, herbicolus, herbicoloides, indirae, ipomoeae, jarooa, kulini, largoensis, manipurensis, mcmurtryi, muraleedharani, neocrotalariae, neorykei, orientalis, paraaerialis, pseudorientalis, rhabdus, rosica, rubiae, rykei, shorae, sijiensis

Subtribe **Proprioseiopsina** Chant & McMurty

Genus ***Proprioseiopsis***

Keralaensis, peltatus, punicae, rosellus, synachattiensis

Subtribe **Arrenoseiina** Chant & McMurty

Genus ***Phytoscutus*** Muma

bakeri, salebrosus

Genus ***Paraamblyseius*** Muma

fragariae, mumai

Tribe **Indoseiulini** Ehara & Amano

Genus ***Gynaeseius*** Wainstein

eharai, ghaiae, ricini

Tribe **Euseiini** Chant & McMurty

Subtribe **Euseiina** Chant & McMurty

Genus ***Euseius*** Wainstein

ahaioensis, alstoniae, bambusae, chikmagalurensis, chitradurgae, coccineae, coccosocius, concordis, delhiensis, eucalypti, finlandicus, hibisci, indica, insanus, kalimpongensis, kodaikanalensis, macrospatulatus, mangiferae, meghalayensis, neococcineae, ovalis, prasadi (=pruni), rhododendronis, scutalis, sacchari, vignus

Genus ***Amlydromelus*** Chant & McMurtry

sowaga

Subfamily **PHYTOSEIINAE**

Genus ***Phytoseius*** Ribaga

bandipurensis, brevicrinis, coheni, corniger, crinitus, domesticus, indicus, intermedius, jaunpurensis, jujuba, kapuri, macropilis, macrosetosus, maldahaensis, meyerae, minutus, mixtus, namdaphaensis, neglecta, neocorniger, neoferox, nipponicus, punjabensis, rachelae, roseus, rugosus, swirskii, viscosum, wainsteini, woodburyi

Genus ***Platyseiella*** Muma

mumai

Subfamily **TYPHLODROMIINAE** Wainstein

Tribe **Paraseiulini**

Genus ***Paraseiulus*** Muma

soleiger

Genus ***Kuzinellus*** Wainstein

kuzini, neosoleiger

Tribe **Typhlodromini** Wainstein

Genus ***Neoseiulella*** Muma

celtis, nesbitti, prunus, transitans

Genus ***Typhlodromus***

Subgenus ***Anthoseius***

arunachalensis, bakeri, bambusicolus, channabasavannai, chrysanthemi, communis, dactylifera, dalii, darjeelingensis, denmarki, divergentis, eharai, fleschneri, garhwalicus, ghanii, gopali, hadii, kashmiricus, himalayensis, homalii, incasus, intermedius, kodaikanalensis, majumderi, manipurensis, meerutensis, meyerae, mori, neorhenanus, neotransvaalensis, nilgiriensis, orissaensis, persicus, pruni, rhenanus, rhododendroni, rickeri, sijiensis, sonprayagensis, tarbatejamae, umbratus, vinifera, zafari

Subgenus ***Typhlodromus***

confusus, roshanlali

STORED PRODUCT/MUSHROOM/WEED MITES

Order **ASTIGMATA**

Family **ACARIDAE**

Genus ***Acarus***

farris, griffithsi

Genus ***Caloglyphus***

berlesei, mycophagus, rhizoglyphoides, oudemansi, sp.

Genus ***Lardoglyphus***

konoi

Genus ***Rhizoglyphus***

echinopus, singularis, robini

Genus ***Sancassania***

sp.

Genus ***Tyrophagus***

berlesei, dimidiatus, longior, perniciosus, putrescentiae, palmarum

Genus ***Tyrolichus***

casei

Genus ***Tyroglyphus***

entomophagus

Genus ***Tyroborus***

lini

Family **CHORTOGLYPHIDAE**

Genus ***Carpoglyphus***

lactis

Genus ***Chortoglyphus***

arcuatus

Family **GLYCYPHAGIDAE**

Genus ***Austroglycyphagus***

geniculatus

Genus ***Aleuroglyphus***

ovatus

Genus ***Blomia***

freeman, tropicalis

Genus ***Glycyphagus***

domesticus, hughesi, ornatus

Genus ***Lepidoglyphus***

destructor, sp.

Family **ANOETIDAE**

Genus ***Histiostoma***

gracilipes, heinemanni, humidiatus, rostroserratum

Family **PYROGLYPHIDAE**

Genus ***Dermatophagoides***

farinae, pteronyssinus

Genus ***Euroglyphus***

maynei, longior

Family **SAPROGLYPHIDAE**

Genus ***Neosuidasia***

faini

Genus ***Suidasia***

medanensis, nesbilti

Order **CRYPTOSTIGMATA**

Family **GALUMNIDAE**

Genus ***Galumna***

flabellifera, chujoi

Genus ***Notogalumna***

nortoni

Family **MOCHLOZETIDAE**

Genus ***Unguizetes***

clavatus

Family **OPPIIDAE**

Genus ***Oppia***

nodosa

Family **XYLOBATIDAE**

Genus ***Acterozetes***

sp.

Genus ***Brachychthonius***

sp.

Genus ***Hydrozetes***

terrestris

Genus ***Monoschelobates***

sp.

Genus ***Orthogalumna***

terebrantis

Genus ***Punctoribates***

insignis

Family **ORIBATULIDAE**

Genus ***Scheloribates***

decarinatus, laevigatus, praeincibates, rufafulvus, sicula, sp.

Genus ***Trimalconothrus***

herotrichus

Genus ***Unguizets***

clavatus

Genus ***Xylobates***

seminudus

Order **MESOSTIGMATA**

Family **ASCIDAE**

Genus ***Arctoscius***

butleri

Genus ***Blattisocius***

dentriticus, keegani, mali, tarsalis

Genus ***Gamasellodes***

bicolor

Genus ***Lasioseius***

bengalensis, mcgregori, parberlesi, phytoseioides, quadrisetosus, terrestris, sp.

Genus ***Melichares***

fici, sp.

Genus ***Proctolaelaps***

pygmaeus, sp.

Family **AMEROSEIIDAE**

Genus ***Kleemania***

bengalensis, plumigera, plumosus

Family **EVIPHIDIDAE**

Genus ***Eviphis***

cultratellus, indicus

Family **LAELAPIDAE**

Genus ***Androlaelaps***

casalis

Genus ***Ololaelaps***

sellinicki

Genus ***Hypoaspis***

aculeifer, calcuttaensis, dubium, miles, vacua

Family **MACROCHELIDAE**

Genus ***Holostaspula***

sp.

Genus ***Macrocheles***

muscaedomesticae

Family **OTOPHEIDOMENIDAE**

Genus ***Hemipteroseius***

indicus

Family **PARASITIDAE**

Genus ***Parasitus***

bengalensis, consanguineus, primitivus

Genus ***Pseudoparasitus***

sp.

Family **PACHYLAELAPTIDAE**

Genus ***Pachylaelaps***

femoralis, sp.

FUNGIVOROUS

Family **UROPODIDAE**

Genus ***Fuscuropoda***

marginata

Genus ***Leiodinychus***

krumeri, sp.

Genus ***Trematura***

sp.

Genus ***Uroseius***

sp.

5. SELECTED REFERENCES

Adhikary, M., Tudu, B., Dhar, P.P. & Somchoudhury, A.K. 2010. Bioefficacy of different treatment schedules of CHA 2062 against broad mite of chilli, *Polyphagotarsonemus latus* Banks *Abst. Int. Symp-cum-Workshop, Acarology,* Kalyani : 98.

Agarwal, K. & Kapil, R.P. 1988. In : *Africanized honey bees and bee mites.* Ellis Horwood Pub., UK : 404-408.

Agarwal, K. & Kapil, R.P. 1989. In : *Progress in Acarology* (eds. G.P. ChannaBasavanna & C. A. Viraktamath), Oxford, IBH, New Delhi : 283-286.

Ananthakrishnan, T.N. 1984. *Biology of gall insects.* Oxford I.B.H. : 1-360.

Anil, K.N. & Shetty, K.P.V. 1995. *Polyphagotarsonemus latus* (Acari : Tarsonemidae) infestation on capsicum. *Abst. V Nat. Symp. Acarology* : 85-86.

Anon. 1979. *Abstract First All India Symp. in Acarology,* Bangalore, April 23-25, 1979. Dept. of Ent., UAS, Bangalore : 1-60 + 1-10.

Anon. 1983. *Abstracts Second All India Symp. Acarology,* Pune, May, 26-28, 1983. ASI. , Dept. of Ent., UAS, Bangalore : 1-71.

Anon. 1987. *Abstracts First Nat. Seminar on Acarlogy,* Kalyani, 29-31 Oct., 1987. BCKV, Kalyani : 1-51.

Anon. 1990. *Abstracts Fourth Nat. Symp. Acarology,* Calicut, Oct. 12-14, 1990. Div of Acarology, Dept. of Zoology Univ. Calicut, Kerala : 1-76.

Anon. 1992-93. *Progress report AICRP on Agril. Acar. UAS, GKVK, Bangalore* : 6-8.

Anon. 1994. *Pests of tea in northeast India and their control.* Tocklai Expt. Stn. Jorhat. Mem. No. **27** : 1-231.

Anon. 1995. *Abstracts, Fifth Nat. Symp. Acarology,* Bangalore, Sept., 20-22, 1993. Souvenir. UAS, Bangalore : 1-104.

Anon. 1997. Management of brown wheat mite, *Petrobia latens* (Muller) in Rajasthan, Final Report. ICAR. Ad-hoc. Project, RAU, Bikaner.

Anon. 1999. *Abstracts, Silver Jubilee Symp.,* Oct. 27-30, 1999, ASI, UAS, Bangalore : 1-36.

Anon. 2006. *Handbook of Agriculture.* ICAR (Revised 5th Ed.) : 1-1345.

Anon. 2009. Annual Rept. AINP on Agril. Acarology (Apirl 2007-March 2009). Directorate of Res., BCKV, Kalyani : 1-80.

Anon. 2010. *Abstracts. Int. Symp-cum-Workshop Acarology,* Kalyani, 8-10 April, Kalyani : 1-152.

Arjunan, G., Swamiyappan, R. and Reddy, M.V. 1989. Studies on red gram sterility mosaic disease and its vector. *Abst. Nat. Sem. Red gram,* February 1989, IRS, Gulbarga, Karnataka.

Atyeo, W.T. 1960. A revision of the mite family Bdellidae in North and Central America (Acarina : Prostigmata). *Univ. Kansas Sci. Bull.,* **XL**(8) : 345-499.

Atyeo, W. T. 1963. The Bdellidae (Acarina) of the Australian Realm. *Bull. Univ. Nebraska St. Mus.,* **4**(9) : 113-210.

Baker, J.T. & Neunzaig, H.N. 1968. *Hirsutella thompsonii* as a fungus parasite of the blue berry mud mite. *J. Econ. Entomol.,* **61** : 1117-1118.

Baker, E.W. & Wharton, G.W. 1952. *An introduction to Acarology.* The Macmillan Co., New York : 1-465.

Banerjee, B. 1989. *An Introduction to Agricultural Acarology, Biology and Control of mite pests in the Tropics.* Associated Pub. Co., New Delhi : 1-116.

Barma, P. & Jha, S. 2010. Incidence pattern of mite (*Tetranychus urticae* Koch) and their management with integration of chemical, botanical and microbial insecticides infesting pointed gourd. *Abst. Int. Symp-cum-Workshop Acarology, Kalyani* : 119.

Bhagat, K.C., Masodi, A.M., Bhat, O.K. & Koul, V.K. 1993. Incidence and varietal susceptibility of apple to *Panonychus ulmi* (Koch) (Acari : Tetranychidae) in Kashmir. In : *Contributions to Acarological researches in India,* BCKV : 341-346 (eds. Mukherjee, A.B., Somchoudhury, A.K. & Sarkar, P.K.).

Bharadwaj, S.P. & Bharadwaj, S. 2010. Susceptibility of European red mite *Panonychus ulmi* (Koch) on apple to petroleum derived oils in Himachal Pradesh. *Abst. Int. Symp-cum-Workshop Acarology,* Kalyani : 110-111.

Bharadwaj, S.P., & Sharma, S. 2010. Response of two spotted mite *Tetranychus urticae* (Koch) (Fam. Tetranychidae) to new acaricides in apple orchards of Himachal Pradesh. *Abst. Int. Symp-cum-Workshop Acarology* : 81-83.

Bhaskar, S. & Putanda, B.N. 1989. In : *Progress in Acarology,* **2** : 287-289.

Bhaskaran, E.V., Jeyarani, S. & Ramaraju, K. 2010. Estimation of yield loss due to *Tetranychus urticae* Koch on Okra under protected and unprotected conditions. *Abst. Int. Symp.-cum-Workshop Acarology* : 44.

Bhullar, M.B. & Dhatt, A.S. 2007. Occurrence of spider mite *Tetranychus urticae* Koch under different cultural practices under nethouse conditions. *J. Acarol.,* **16** : 52-54.

Bhullar, M.B. & Kaur, P. 2010. *Eriophyes cernuus* Massee : First record from Ber (*Zizyphus jujuba*) in sub-mountainous regions of Jammu and Himachal Pradesh. *Abst. Int. Symp-cum-Workshop, Acarology* : 14.

Bhullar, M.B. & Kaur, P. 2010. First record of false spider mite *Larvacarus transitans* (Ewing); on *Zizyphus* from Punjab, Jammu and Himachal Pradesh. *Abst. Int. Symp-cum-Works Acarology* : 14-15.

Bindra, O.S. 1970. Insecta. In : Chadha, K.L. *et al.*, p. 64-78. *Citrus decline in India–causes and control.* PAU and Ohio State Univ. (eds.).

Bindra, O.S. & Kittur, S.U. 1961. Two new records of tetranychids as crop pests in Madhya Pradesh. *Indian J. Ent.*, **23** : 71.

Bindra, O.S. & Singh, G.S. 1970. Mite pests of ornamental plants in India. *Pesticides* **4** : 17-24.

Bolland, H.R., Gutierrez, J. & Flechtmann, C.H.W. 1998. World Catalogue of the spider mite family (Acari : Tetranychidae). Leiden.

Capoor, S.P. 1950. Report on pigeonpea sterility with symptoms and transmission. *Proc. Ind. Sci. Congr.*, **22** : 270-274.

Capoor, S.P. 1952. Observation on sterility disease of pigeonpea in Bombay. *Ind. J. Agr. Sci.*, **22** : 270-274.

Chadha, K.L. 2010. *Handbook of Horticulture.* ICAR, New Delhi

Chakrabarti, S. 1999. Plant-Mite interaction with reference to gall formation. In : *Souvenir, Acarological Society of India, Silver Jubilee Symp.*, Bangalore, Oct. 27-30, 1999 : 11-12.

Chakraborty, A. 2010. Association of the predatory mites with *Aceria litchii* Keifer (Acari : Eriophyidae) under West Bengal condition. *Abst. V Int. Symp-cum-Workshop Acarology* : 41-42.

Chakraborty, G., Roy, S.K., Roy, A., Mukherjee, A. & Ghosh, S.K. 2010. Screening of *Olitorius* jute germplasm based on yellow mite (*Polyphagotarsonenus latus*) abundance. *Abst. Int. Symp.-Cum-Workshop, Kalyani* : 59.

Chander, R., Bhardawaj, S.P. & Kumar, R. 1995. Factors influencing population dynamics of European red mite in apple orchards in Himachal Pradesh, India. *Abst. V Nat. Symp. Acarology, Bangalore* : 31-32.

Chandrasekharappa, B., Mallik, B. & Harishkumar, M. 1995. Effect of temperature and humidity on the feeding potential of *Amblyseius longispinosus* and *Amblyseius tetranychivorus* (Acari : Phytoseiidae). *Abst. V Nat. Symp. Acar.* : 53.

Chandrashekarappa, B., Mallik, B. & Harishkumar, M. 1995. Effect of temperature and humidity on the biology of predatory mite *Amblyseius longispinosus* (Acari : Phytoseiidae). *Abst. V Nat. Symp. Acarology* : 32-33.

ChannaBasavanna, G.P. 1966. *A contribution to the knowledge of Indian eriophyid mites (Eriophyoidea : Trobidiformes, Acarina).* UAS, Bangalore : 1-153.

ChannaBasavanna, G.P. 1971. The present status of our Knowledge of Indian plant feeding mites. *Proc. 3rd Int. Congr. Acar., Prague* : 201-204.

ChannaBasavanna, G.P., Mallik, B. & Ghorpade, K.D. 1981. *Contributions to Acarology in India.* ASI, Bangalore : 256.

ChannaBasavanna, G.P. & Nageshachandra, B.K. 1971. *Bibliography of Indian Plant feeding mites.* UAS, Banglore : 1-46.

ChannaBasavanna, G.P. & Nangia, N. 1984. The biology of gall mites. In : *Biology of gall insects* (ed. T.N. Ananthakrishnan). Oxford IBH Pub. : 323-327.

ChannaBasavanna, G.P., Nageshachandra, B.K. & Mallik, B. 1979. *Bibliography of Indian plant feeding mites.* UAS, Bangalore : 1-46.

ChannaBasavanna, G.P. & Viraktamath, C.A. (Eds.) 1988. *Progress in Acarology.* Vol. 1. Oxford IBH Pub. New Delhi : 1-523.

ChannaBasavanna, G.P. & Viraktanath, C.A. 1989. (Eds.) *Progress in Acarology.* Vol. 2. Oxford IBH Pub., New Delhi : 1-483.

Chant, D.A. & McMurtry, J.A. 2007. Illustrated keys and diagnosis for the genera and subgenera of the Phytoseiidae of the world (Acari : Mesostigmata). Indira Pub. House. Michigan, USA : 1-220.

Chatterjee, K. & Gupta, S.K. 1995. Effect of feeding by *Tetranychus ludeni* on minerals, inorganic and organic compounds in leaves of sponge gourd (*Luffa acutangula* Roxb.). *Abst. V Nat. Symp. Acarology,* Bangalore : 39.

Chatterjee, K. & Gupta, S.K. 1995. Mites occurring on vegetables, fruit trees and ornamental plants in West Bengal with comments on their pest status. *Abst. V Nat. Symp. Acar. Bangalore* : 13.

Chaurasia, D.C. 1993. Comparison of strains of sterility of pigeonpea in Nepal and India. *Pigeonpea Newsl.,* : 17-34.

Chen, C.M., Cheng, C.C., & Hsiao, K.C. 1979. Bionomics of *Steneotarsonemus spinki* attacking rice plants in Taiwan. In : *Advances in Acarology,* Vol. 1 : 111-117. (ed. J.G. Rodriguez) Academic Press, New York.

Chillar, B.S., Gulati, R. & Bhatnagar, P. 2007. *Agricultural Acarology.* Daya Pub. House, Delhi : 1-355.

Chinnaiah, C. & Mohanasundaram, M. 1995. Evaluation of the efficacy of neem products and certain pesticides against *Aceria cajani* on pigeonpea. *Abst. V Nat. Symp. Acarology,* Bangalore.

Cicilykutty, A. & John, P.A. 1981. Host preference of the Fish mite *Suidasia medanensis* (Acari : Saproglyphidae). In : *Contributions to Acarology in India* : 130-135.

Cicilykutty, A.K. & John, P.A. 1981a. The hosts of adult fish mite, *Suidasia medanensis* (Acari : Saproglyphidae). In : *Contributions to Acarology in India* : 128-130.

Cunnington. 1965. *J. Appl. Ecol.*, **2** : 295-306.

Das, G.M. 1959. Binomics of tea red spider, *Oligonychus coffeae* (Nietner). *Bull. Ent. Res.*, **50** : 265-274.

Das, G.M. 1965. *Pests of tea in North-East India and their control. Tea Res. Assoc. Toklai Expt. Stn. Mem.* No., **27** : 1-115.

Das, G.M. & Das, S.C. 1963. Biology and control of spider mite, *Calacaras carinatus* (Green), a pest of tea in northeast India. *J. zool. Soc., India,* **14** : 64-72.

Das, G.M. & Das, S.C. 1967. Effect of temperature and humidity on the development of tea red spider mite, *Oligonychus coffeae* (Nietner). *Bull. Ent. Res.*, **57** : 433-436.

Das, G.M. & Sengupta, N. 1958. Observations on the pink mite, *Acaphylla theae* (Watt) of tea in North-East India *J. zool. Soc. India,* **10** : 39-48.

Das, P. 1986. Bionomics and control of mushroom mites. Ph.D. thesis. B.C. Agr. Univ., Kalyani : 1-196.

Das, P., Somchoudhury, A.K. & Mukherjee, A.B. 1987. Nature and habitat of mushroom mites. *Env. & Ecol.*, **5**(4) : 677-686.

Das, P., Somchoudhury, A.K. & Mukherjee, A.B. 1988. Source of mite infestration in mushroom. *Env. & Ecol.*, **6**(3) : 669-671.

Das, P., Somchoudhury, A.K. & Mukherjee, A.B. 1989. Seasonal incidence and assessment of loss caused by mite complex on some cultivated species of mushroom. *Progress in Acarology,* **2** : 215-221.

Das, P., Somchoudhury, A.K., Mukherjee, A.B. & Sarkar, P.K. 1987. Some aspects of feeding behaviour of mushroom mites. *Abst. First Nat. Sem. Acar, BCKV., Kalyani,* 29-31 Oct., 1987 : 24.

Das, P., Somchoudhury, A.K., Sarkar, P.K. & Mukherjee, A.B. 1987. Effect of artificial diets on the population development of mushroom mites. *Abst. First Nat. Sem. Acar.,* : 24-25.

Das, P., Somchoudhury, A.K. & Mukherjee, A.B. 1987. Rearing of mushroom mites on artificial diets, *Env. Ecol.*, **5**(4) : 685-687.

Das, P., Somchoudhury, A.K., Mukherjee, A.B. & Sarkar, P.K. 1993. Some aspects of feeding behaviour of mushroom mites. In : *Acarological Researches in India (Eds.* A.K. Somchoudhury, A.B. Mukherjee & P.K. Sarkar) : 271-282.

Das, T.K., Somchoudhury, A.K. & Sarkar, P.K. 1987. Effect of temprature and relative humidity on the development of predatory mite *Neocunaxoides* sp. found associated with *Dolichotetranychus floridanus* on pineapple leaves. *Env. & Ecol.*, **5**(4) : 674-676.

De, R.K., Dhar, V. Rathore, Y.S. 1996. Control of mosic in pigeonpea with insecticides and acaricides. *Indian J. Pulses Res.*, **9**(1) : 87-89.

De, S., Karmakar, K., Bandopadhyay, B. & Pramanik, A. 2010. Studies on phytophagous mite species assocaited with banana in West Bengal. *Abst. Int. Symp-cum-Workshop, Acarology* : 36.

De, S., Karmakar, K. & Roy, K. 2010. Predatory mite fauna in association with banana. *ibid,* : 34.

Debnath, M. & Baidya, P. 2010. Assessment of efficacy of (NSKE) in management of the yellow mite (*Polyphagotarsonemus latus*) of chilli (*Capsicum annuum* L.) in coastal saline zone of West Bengal. *Abst. Int. Symp-cum-Workshop Acarology* : 105.

Debnath, P., Ghosh, A., Goswami, T.N., Chattopadhyay, A. & Karmakar, K. 2010. Occurrence of red spider mite, *Tetranychus urticae* Koch on different Okra varieties. *Abst. Int. Symp.-cum-Workshop Acarology* : 62.

DeJong, D. *et al.* 1982. *Ann. Rev. Ent.*, **27** : 229-252.

Deepak, M.R., Puttaswami & Mallik, B. 1995. Biology of *Oligota oviformes* (Coleoptera : Staphylinidae) on *Tetranychus urticae* (Acari : Tetranychidae). *Abst. V Nat. Symp. Acarology* : 90.

Deepak, M.R., Puttaswami & Mallik, B. 1995a. Feeding prefernce and feeding potential of *Oligota oviformis* (Coleoptera : Staphylinidae) on *Tetranychus urticae* (Acari : Tetranychidae). *Abst. V Nat. Symp. Acarology,* Bangalore, Sept. 20-22, 1995 : 90.

Delfinado, M.D. & Baker, E.W. 1974. *J. Wash. Acad.Sci.*, **64** : 4-10.

Delfinado-Baker, M.D. & Baker, E.W. 1982. *Am. Bee. J.* 122:416-417.

Denmark, H.A. *et.al.* 1991. *Ento. Cir. No.* 347, pdf.

Dhooria, M.S. 1983. Studies on ovipositional preference, host-range and seasonal incidence of *Eutetranychus orientalis,* (Acari : Tetranychidae) in Delhi. *Indian J. Acar.*, **6** : 77-83.

Dhooria, M.S. 1985. Effect of different levels of red spider mite, *Tetranchus cinnabarinus* Boised on growth of brinjal and okra plants. *Acar. Newsl.*, **15** : 3.

Dhooria, M.S. 1999. Two spotted spider mites, *Tetranchus urticae* – a serious pest of roses in polyhouses and its control. *J. Acarol.*, **14**(1-2) : 84-87.

Dhooria, M.S. 1999. Observation on the status of phytophagous and predatory mites on different ornamental plants in Punjab. *J. Acarol.*, **14**(1-2) : 88-89.

Dhooria, M.S., Bhullar, M.B. & Mallik, B. 2005. *Mite pests of citrus and their management in India. AINP, UAS, Bangalore* : 1-28.

Dhote, V.W., Samanta, A. & Karmakar, K. 2010. Estimation of crop loss in some vegetable crops due to mite infestation. *Abst. Int. Symp-cum-Workshop, Acarology* : 45.

Ein, J. & Zhang, Z.Q. 1999. Tarsonemidae of China. (Acari : Prostigmata). An annotated and illustrated catalogue and bibliography. *Syst. Appl. Acar. Spl. Pub. London* : 1-73.

Ehara, S. 1963. A new mite of *Oligonychus* from rice, with notes on some Japanese spider mites. *Jap. J. appl. Ent. Zool.*, **7** : 228-231.

Evans, G.A., Comroy, H.L. & Ochoa, R. 1993. The Tenuipalpidae of Hondurus (Tenuipalpidae : Acari). *Fla. Ent.*, **76** : 126-155.

Evans, G.O., Sheals, J.G. & Macfarlane, D. 1961. *The terrestrial Acari of the British Isles. An introduction to their morphology, biology and classification. Vol-1. Introduction and Biology*. Brit. Museum (Nat. Hist.) : 1-219.

Evans, G.O. & Till, W.M. 1979. Mesostigmatic mites of Britain and Ireland (Chelicerata : Acari : Parasitiformes). An introduction to their external morphology and classification. *Trans. zool. Soc. London*, **35** : 139-270.

Garg, R. & Kashyap, N.P. 1998. In : *Perspectives in Indian Apiculture* (ed. R.C. Mishra) : 264-303.

Garg, R. & Sharma, O.P. 1988. *Indian Bee J.*, 50 : 65-66.

Genersch, 2010. *Appl. Microbiol. Biotechnol.*, **87** : 87-97.

Gerson, U. 1985, Webbing. In : *Spider mites, their biology, natural enemies and control.* (eds. Helle W.M. & Sabelis, M.W.), Elsevier Pub. Amsterdam, vol-1A : 223-230.

Gerson, U. & Smiley, R.L. 1990. *Acarine biocontrol agents. An illustrated key and manual.* Chapman & Hall. Pub. : 1-172.

Ghai, S. 1964. Mites. In : Pant, N.C. (ed.). *Entomology in India.* Entomological Society of India, New Delhi : 385-396.

Ghai, S. 1976. Mites associated with stored food in India. *Bull. Grain Tech.*, **14**(2) : 134-149.

Ghanekar, A.M., Shiela, V.K., Beniwal, S.P.S., Reddy, M.V. & Nene, Y.L. 1992. Sterility mosaic of pigeonpea. In : *Plant diseases of International importance. Vol.-1. (Disease of cereals and pulses).* Prentice Hall. Inc. Englewood Cliffs. New Jersey, USA : 415-428.

Ghosh, A., Nath, A., Debnath, P., Pramanik, A. & Karmakar, K. 2010. Field screening of chilli germplasms against chilli yellow mite (*Polyphagotarsonemus latus* (Banks) in West Bengal. *Abst. Int. Symp-cum-Workshop Acarology* : 61.

Ghosh, N.K., Das, B. & Chakrabarti, S. 1989. Injury by gall mites (Acari : Eriophyidae) to plants in northeast India. *Progress in Acarology*, **2** : 135-140.

Ghosh, S., Ahmed, M.M., Dey, P.K. & Somchoudhury, A.K. 2010. Bioefficacy of different treatment schedules of CHA-2062 against spider mite of tea, *Oligonychus coffeae* Nietner. *Abst. Int. Symp.-workshop Acarology* : 89-91.

Ghosh, S.K., Rao, J. & Prakash, A. 1999. Off-season inhibition of rice tarsonemid mite, *Steneotarsonemus spinki* Smiley and *Tarsonemus cuttacki* Iswari (Acari; Tarsonemidae) in the rice ecosystem. *Annals Pl. Prot. Ser.*, : 7.

Goel, N. & Sadana, G.L. 1995. Quantitative analysis of biochemical components in the leaves of host and non-host plants of *Brevipalpus phoenicis* (Acarina : Tenuipalpidae). *Abst. V Nat. Symp. Acarology, Bangalore* : 40.

Goel, N. & Sadana, G.L. 1995. Seasonal fluctuations in population of *Brevipalpus phoenicis* (Acarina : Tenuipalpidae) on Kaghzinimbu, *Citrus aurantifolio. Abst. V. Nat. Symp. Acarology, Bangalore* : 27.

Gonzalez-Rodriguez, R.H. 1965. A taxonomic study of the genera *Mediolata, Zetzellia* and *Agistemus. Univ. Calif. Pub. Ent.*, **41** : 1-64.

Goyal, N. P & Kandoria J.L.1988. *Indian Bee J.*, **50** : 85-86.

Griffiths, D.A. & Bowman, C.E. (Eds.) 1984. *Acarology VI*, Vol. 1 & Vol. 2. Ellis Horwood Ltd., London : 1-1296.

Grobov, O.F. 1976. In : *Symposium Sofia* : 46-90.

Gupta, A. & Chatterjee, M. 2004. Some new records of mites infesting stored grains in Kolkata and its neighbourhood. *Rec. zool. Surv. India*, **102** : 77-82.

Gupta, A., Gupta, S.K. & Banerjee, S. 1991. A report on mites infesting stored grains in West Bengal. *Bull. Grain Tech.*, **29** : 47-49.

Gupta, B.M. 1990. Occurrence of brown wheat mite, *Petrobia latens* (Muller) on cumin in Rajasthan. *Indian Coca, Arecanut and spices. J.*, **13** : 143.

Gupta, S.K. 1970. Preliminary note on plant mites (Acarina) from West Bengal. *Sci. & Cult.*, **36** : 98-99.

Gupta, S.K. 1974. Incidence of scarlet mite, *Brevipalpus phoenicis* (Geij.) on sesamum in West Bengal. *Curr. Sci.*, **43**(11) : 361.

Gupta, S.K. 1976. Contribution to our Knowledge of Tetranychid mites (Acarina) with descriptions of new species from India. *Oriental Ins.*, **10** : 327-351.

Gupta, S.K. 1985. *Handbook – Plant mites of India*, Zoological Survey of India, Calcutta. : 1-520.

Gupta, S.K. 1986. *Fauna of India (Acari: Mesostigmata) Family Phytoseiidae.* Zoological Survey of India, Calcutta : 1-350.

Gupta, S.K. 1989. Mites occurring on tea plants in India with a key for their identification. In : *Progress in Acarology,* **2** : 177-182.

Gupta, S.K. 1989a. Systematices of plant mites in the tropics, p. 153-171. In : ChannaBasavanna, G.P., & Viraktamath, C.A. (eds.). *Progress in Acarology,* Vol. **2** : 1-483.

Gupta, S.K. 1991. The mites of agricultural importance in India with remarks on their economic status. (pp. 502-522). In : Dusbabeck, F. & Bukva, V. (eds.) *Modern Acarology,* **1** : Academia, Prague, SPB.

Gupta, S.K. 1992. Arachnida : Plant mites (Acari). In : *Fauna of West Bengal, State Fauna Series,* **3**(Part-3) : 61-211.

Gupta, S.K. 2002. A monograph on plant inhabiting predatory mites of India. Part-I. Orders : Prostigmata, Astigmata and Cryptostigmata. *Mem. zool. Surv. India.* **19**(2) : 1-183.

Gupta, S.K. 2003. A monograph on plant inhabiting predatory mites of India. Part II. Order : Mesostigmata. *Mem. zool. Surv. India,* **20**(1) : 1-185.

Gupta, S.K. 2005. *Insects and mites infesting medicinal plants in India.* Ramakrishna Mission Ashrama, Narendrapur : 1-214 pp + plates.

Gupta, S.K. & Gupta, A. 1999. Progress of taxonomic research on Indian mites upto the end of twentieth century and prospect of research in the next millennium. *J. Acarol.,* **15**(1-2) : 80-83.

Gupta, S.K., Biswas, H. & Das, S.N. 2007. Bioeffectiveness of some plant extracts towards causing mortality of *Brevipalpus phoenicis* (Geij.) (Acari : Tenuipalpidae), a new pest of medicinal plant, Vasak, *Justicia adhatoda L.* Ness (Acanthaceae). In : *Bioprospecting and application of medicinal plants in common ailments* (eds. Gupta, S.K. & Mitra, B.R.), R.K. Mission, Narendrapur : 121-126.

Gupta, S.K., Dhooria, M.S. & Sandhu, G.S. 1973. Varietal susceptibility of wheat to brown wheat mite, *Petrobia latens* (Muller). *Sci & Cult.,* **39** : 312-314.

Gupta, S.K., Dhooria, M.S. & Sidhu, A.S. 1974. Effect of food and temperature on the rate of development, longevity and fecundity of sugarcane red spider mite, *Oligonychus indicus* (Hirst). *Acarologia,* **16**: 436-440.

Gupta, S.K., Dhooria, M.S. & Sidhu, A.S. 1975. Comparative evaluation of methods for sampling of *Tetranychus cucurbitae* Rahman & Sapra. *Ent. News,* **86** : 33-36.

Gupta, S.K., Dhooria, M.S. & Sidhu, A.S. 1975a. Development of sampling technique for estimating population of *Tetranychus neocaledonicus* André, infesting brinjal. *Acarologia,* **17** : 489-492.

Gupta, S.K., Dhooria, M.S. & Sidhu, A.S. 1976. Seasonal abundance of *Tetranychus telarius* (Linn.) on castor in the Punjab. *Oilseeds Jour.,* **6** : 16-18.

Gupta, S.K. & Gupta, Y.N. 1974. A taxonomic review of Indian Tetranychidae (Acari : Prostigmata) with description of new species, re-descriptions of known species and keys to genera and species. *Mem. zool. Surv. India,* **18**(1) : 1-196.

Gupta, Y.N. & Gupta, S.K. 1978. On a collection of Tetranychoid mites from Madhya Pradesh, India, with a description of a new *Eotetranychus* (Acari Trombidiformes). *Indian J. Acar.,* **3** : 87-91.

Guruswamy, G., Roy, S. & Nachimuthu, S. 2010. Biorational approaches for the management of tea red spider mite, *Oligonychus coffeae* Nietner (Tetranchidae : Acarina) and their effect on predatory coccinellid, *Stethorus gilvifrons* Mulsant. *Abst. Int. symp. Workshop Acarology,* 109.

Gutierrez, J. 1983. Mounting technique. In : *Spider mites, their biology, natural enemies and control.* Vol. 1A : 351-353 (eds. Helle & Sabelis, 1985), Elsevier Pub., Amsterdam.

Haq. M.A. 1995. Mite induced cecidiogeny on the tree spice *Cinnamomum zeylanieum. Abst. V Nat. Symp. Acarology, Bangalore,* 45.

Haq. M.A. & Ramani, N. (Eds.) 1992. *Man, mites and environment.* Anjengo Pub. Calicut : 1-179.

Helle, W.M. 1984. Aspects of pesticide resistance in mites. In : *Acarology,* VI, (eds. D.A. Griffiths & C.E. Bowman), Ellis Horwood Ltd. : 122-131.

Helle, W. & Overmeer, W.P.J. 1985. Techniques. In : *Spider mite, their biology, natural enemies and control.* Vol. 1A : 331-335.

Helle, W.M. & Overmeer, W.P.J. 1985a. Toxicological test methods : 391-395. In : *Helle & Sabelis* (Eds.) : 1-403.

Helle, W.M. & Sabelis, M.W. 1985. *Spider Mites, their biology, natural enemies and control.* Vol. 1A(1-403), Vol. 1B(1-457). Elsevier Pub., Amsterdam.

Henderson, C.F. & McBurnie, H.V. 1943. Sampling technique for determining population of the citrus red mite and its predators. USDA, Cir. No. **671** : 1-11. Washington DC.

Hossein, M., Mozaffari, J. & Saboori, A. 2010. Acaricidal effect of essential oils of Rue (*Rute graveolens* L.) and Galbanum (*Ferula gambosa* Boiss) against adults of two spotted spider mite *Tetranychus urticae* Koch. *Abst. Int. Symp.-Cum-Workshop Acarology, Kalyani* : 101.

Hudait, R. & Banerjee, H. 2010. HPCL analysis of flubendiamide 24% + thiacloprid 24% - 480 sc (W/V) in chilli and soil. *Abst. Int. Symp.-Workshop Acarology, Kalyani* : 80.

Huffaker, C.B. 1948. An improved cage for work with small insects. *J. econ. Ent.,* **41** : 648-649.

Huffaker, C.B., Van de Vrie, M. & McMurtry, J.A. 1970. Ecology of tetranychid mites and their natural enemies - A review. *Hilgardia*, **40**(11) : 331-458.

Hughes, A.M. 1976. *The mites of stored food and houses*. Min. Agr. Fish Food, London, Tech. Bull., **9** : 1-400.

Indulatha, T. & Mallik, B. 2007. Does *Neoseiulus longispinosus* (Acari : Phytoseiidae) respond to kairomones? *J. Acarol.*, **16** : 117-120.

Jagadish, P.S., Nagaraj, D.N. & Nangia, N. 1995. Predatory mite fauna of fruit crops around Bangalore. *Abst. V Nat. Symp. Acar.*, : 17-18.

Jain, P.C. & Yadav, S.P.S. 1986. Occurrence of brown wheat mite *Petrobia latens* on coriander. *Acar. Newsl.*, **16** : 9-10.

Jain, P.C. & Yadav, S.P.S. 1986a. Effect of date of sowing on the incidence of insect pests of coriander. *Indian J. Agric. Sci.*, **56** : 56-59.

Jeppson, L.R., Keifer, H.H. & Baker, E.W. 1975. *Mites injurious to economic plants.* Univ. Calif. Press : 1-614.

Jeyarani, S., Bhaskaran, E.V. & Ramaraju, K. 2010. Monitoring of acaricide resistance in field collected population of *Tetranychus urticae* Koch (Acari : Tetranychidae) on okra. *Abst. Int. Symp-Workshop Acarology* : 75.

Jhaveri, T.N. 1921. Notes on wooly mite (*Eriophyes gossypii*). *Proc. Ent. Meeting, Puna* : 96-97.

John, P.A. 1981. Some aspects of infestation of cured stored fishery products by the mite *Lardoglyphus konoi* (Acari : Acaridae) in Kerala. In : *Contributions to Acarology in India* : 144-146.

Jones, R.K. 1978. Control of banana silvering thrips and cotton mites and banana. *Citrus & Subtrop. Fruit J.*, **534** : 5-7.

Jose, V.T. & Shah, A.H. 1989. Bionomics of the spider mite *Tetranychus macfarlanei* injurious to cotton in Gujarat, India. *Progress in Acarology*, **2** : 23-28.

Jose, V.T. & Shah, A.H. 1989. Carryover of spider mite, *Tetranychus macfarlanei* through alternative host plants in cotton growing areas of south and central Gujarat, India. *Progress in Acarology*, **2** : 29-32.

Jose, V.T., Shah, A.H. & Patel, C.B. 1989. Feeding potential of some important predators of the spider mite, *Tetranychus macfarlanei*, a pest of cotton. *Progress in Acarology*, **2** : 357-360.

Kakar, K.L. & Chander, R. 1995. Pest management strategies against European Red mite, *Panonychus ulmi* on apple in Himachal Pradesh. *Abst. V Nat. Symp. Acarology, Bangalore* : 74.

Kalaemani, N., Nair, T.S. & Mohanasundaram, M. 1987. Incidence of arthropods in dried fish products etc. *Fish Technol.*, **24** : 93-95.

Kannaiyan, J., Nene, Y.L., Reddy, M.V., Ryan, J.G. & Raju, T.N. 1984. Prevalence of pigeonpea diseases and associated crop losses in Asia, Africa and in the America, *Tropical Pest Management,* **30**(1) : 62-71.

Kannaiyan, S. & Ramaswamy, K., 1980. *A handbook of edible mushroom.* Today & Tomorrow Printers & Pub., New Delhi : 1-123.

Kantaratanakul, S., Chaiwat, W. & Prayoonrat, P. 1989. Bionomics of the Dolichocybid mite, *Formicomotes* sp., as a pest of cultivated mushroom in Thailand. *Progress in Acarology,* **2** : 225-280.

Kane, E.C. & Ochoa,R. 2006. Detection and identification of the red palm mite *Raoiella indica* Hirst (Acari : Tenuipalpitae) available at : htttp// www.sel.bare.urda.gov/acari/pdf, India Guide.pdf.

Kapil, R.P. & Bhanot J.P. 1973. Biology of *Acaropsis docta* Berlese with notes on its bionomics and behaviour of developmental stages. *Acarologia,* **14** : 595-603.

Kapil, R.P. *et al.,* 1982-1984. *Report PL 480 Project.*

Kapil, R.P. & Agarwal, K. 1989. *Progress in Acarology* (eds. G.P. ChannaBasavanna & C. A. Viraktamath), Oxford, IBH, New Delhi : 277-282.

Karmakar, K. 2008. *Steneotarsonemus spinki* Smiley (Acari : Tarsonemidae)–a silent yield reducing mite of rice in West Bengal, India. *Internat. J. Acarol.,* **34** : 95-99.

Karmakar, K. 2009. Influence of different organic, nutrients on the occurrence of *Steneotarsonemus, spinki* Smiley (Acari : Tarsonemidae) and seed yield of rice under Bengal basin of West Bengal, India. *Presented in Int. Conf : Quality Seed Food Security, Bangladesh Agril. Univ. Mymensingh,* 17-19 Feb. 2009.

Karmakar, K., Das, B. K. & Talukdar, B. 2010. Destructive and beneficial acarine fauna associated with betelvine (*Piper betle* L., Piparaceae) from West Bengal, India. *Abst. Int. Symp-cum-workshop Acarology* : 39-40.

Karmakar, K. & Gupta, S.K. 2008. The yellow mite *Polyphagotarsonemus latus* (Banks) (Acari : Tarsonemidae), a major constraint in Jatropha cultivation. In : *Symposium on sustainable uses of natural resources from medicinal and aromatic plants, 24-25 December, 2009, R. K. Mission, Narendrapur* : 72-73 (eds. S.K. Gupta & B.R. Mitra).

Karmakar, K. & De, S. 2004. Relative susceptibility of banana cultivars to spider mite, *Oligonychus oryzae* (Hirst) (Acari : Tetranychidae). *Banana research in India* (B. Bandyopadhyay, S.K. Sarkar, D.K. Misra & F.K. Bauri eds.). BCKV, India : 222-226.

Karmakar, M., Gupta, S.K. & Ali, N. 2007. Evaluation of entomopathogenic fungi along with indigenously made and commercially available botanical pesticides against two spotted spider mite, *Tetranychus urticae* Koch (Acari :

Tetranychidae) infesting Ashwagandha (*Withania somnifera*) (Family Solanaceae) In : *The All India Seminar on recent trends in utilization of plants in human welfare,* R.K. Mission : 117-120 (eds. S.K. Gupta & B.R. Mitra).

Karmakar, S., Gupta, S.K. & Bhattacharya, D.K. 2010. Phytophagous and predatory mites (Acari) occurring on ornamental plants in South Bengal, with their economic importance. *Abst. Int. Symp. Workshop Acarology, Kalyani* : 40-41.

Katagihallimath, S.S. 1995. Effect of carbaryl on *Aceria gossypii* on cotton and *Aceria cajani* and *Tetranychus* sp. on red gram. Abst. *V Nat. Symp. Acarology,* Bangalore, Sept. 20-22, 1995 : 79-80.

Keifer, H.H., Baker, E.W., Kono, T., Delfinado, M. & Styer, W.E. 1982. *An illustrated guide to plant abnormalities caused by eriophyid mites in North America.* USDA, Agr. Handbook No. 573 : 1-178.

Khan, R.M., Doval, S.L. & Joshi, H.C. 1969. Biology of brown wheat mite, *Petrobia latens* (Muller). *Indian J. Ent.,* **31** : 258-264.

Kotwal, D.R. & Boni, S.K. 1999. Insect and non-insect pests of button mushroom *Agaricus bisporus. Abst. Souvenir, Silver Jubilee Symp. Bangalore* : 26.

Krantz, G.W. 1978. *A manual of Acarology,* 2nd edition, Oregon State University Book Stores, Corvallis, Oregon , USA : 1-508.

Kulkarni, N.K. 2003. *Studies on pigeonpea sterility mosaic disease, transmission, virus-vector relationships and identification of resistant sources.* Ph.D. Thesis, Univ. Agr. Sci., Bangalore : 1-120.

Kumar, P.L., Jones, A.T., Duncan, G., Roberts, I.M. & Reddy, D.V.R. 2001. Characterization of a novel mite transmitted virus associated with pigeonpea sterility mosaic disease. *Phytopathlogy,* **91** : 51.

Kumar, P.L., Jones, A.T., Fonton, B., Sreenivasulu, P. & Reddy, D.V.R. 2001a. Characterization of a virus from pigeonpea with affinities to species in the genus *Aureuvirus,* Family : Tombusviridae. *Pl. Desease,* **85** : 208-215.

Kumar, P.L., Jones, A.T. & Reddy, D.V.R. 2002. Mechanical transmission of pigeonpea sterility mosaic virus. *Jour. Mycology & Pl. Path.*

Kumar, P.L., Jones, A.T., Sreenivasulu, P. & Reddy, D.V.R. 1999a. Characterization of a virus associated with sterility mosaic disease of pigeonpea. *Abst. XI Int. Cognr. Virology,* 9-13 Aug. 1999, Sydney : 1-90.

Kumar, P.L., Jones, A.T., Sreenivasulu, P. & Reddy, D.V.R. 1999b. Isolation of a virus associated with sterility mosaic disease of pigeonpea (*Cajanas cajan*). *Ind. J. Pl. Prot.,* **26** : 164-166.

Kumar, P.L., Jones, A.T., Sreenivasulu, P. & Reddy, D.V.R. 1999c. Unfolding the mystery of the causal agent of pigeonpea sterility mosaic disease. *Abst. Int. Conf. Life Sci. in next millennium.* Univ. Hyderabad, India : 65-66.

Kumaron, N., Douressamy, S., Ramaraju, K. & Kuttalam, S. 2007. Estimation of damage and yield loss due to *Tetranychus urticae* Koch (Acari : Tetranychidae) on okra under artificial infestation. *J. Acarol.*, **17** : 4-6.

Kumud & Mathur, R.B. 1989. Influence of ultra violet radiation on the survival of the acarid mite, *Tyrophagus putrescentiae* (Astigmata : Acaridae). *Progress in Acarology*, **2** : 249-253.

Kumud, Mathur, R.B. & Yadav, A. 1987. Bioecology of acarid mite *Tyrophagus putrescentiae* (Schrank). *Abst. I Nat. Sem. Acarology*, Kalyani : 21.

Lal, L. & Mukherji, S.P. 1977. A contribution to the knowledge of phytophagous mites infesting medicinal plants. *Sci. & Cult.*, **43** : 313-316.

Lindquist, E.E. 1986. The World genera of Tarsonemidae (Acari : Heterostigmata). A morphological, phylogenetic and systematic revision with a reclassification of family group taxa in the Heterostigmata. *Mem. Ent. Soc. Canada.* No. 136. 1-576.

Lindquist, E.E. 1996. Phylogenetic relationships. In : Eriophyid mites – their biology, natural enemies and control : 301-327. (eds. E.E. Lindquist, M.W. Sabelis & J. Bruin), Elsevier Pub., Amsterdam.

Maitra, S. & Gupta, S.K. 2006. Efficacies of some botanical pesticides for control of four mite pests infesting medicinal plants in West Bengal. In : *Herbs for health care and nutritional benefits.* (eds. S.K. Gupta & B.R. Mitra), R.K. Mission, Narendrapur : 191-195.

Malaviya, M.D. & Rai, A.B. 1995. Laboratory evaluation of conventional acaricides/ pesticides against *Tetranychus ludeni. Abst. V Nat. Symp. Acarology* : 80.

Mallick, P., Tudu, B., Dey, P.K. & Somchoudhury, A.K. 2010. Bio-efficacy of different treatment schedules of spiromesifen 24% SC (W/W) against red spider mite of brinjal. *Abst. Int. Symp-cum-Workshop Acarology* : 89.

Mallik, B. & ChannaBasavanna, G.P. 1983. Life history and life table of *Tetranychus ludeni* and its predator, *Amblyseius longispinosus* (Acari : Tetranychidae, Phytoseiidae). *Indian J. Acar.*, **8** : 1-12.

Mallik, B., Chinnamade Gowda, C.K. Srinivasa, N., Onkarappa, S., Jayappa, J. & Guruprasad, H. 2004. *Cocconut mite.* AINP, USA, Bangalore : 1-39.

Mallik, B., Krishnaswamy, H.S. & ChannaBasavanna, G.P. 1989. Mathematical models for the interaction between *Tetranychus ludeni* and its phytoseiid predators (p. 343-355). In : ChannaBasavanna, G.P. & Viraktamath, C.A. (eds.) *Progress in Acarology*, **2**, Oxford IBH : 1-483.

Mallik, B., Srinivasa, N. & Chinnamade Gowda, C. 2003. *Bibliography of plant feeding mites of India.* UAS, Bangalore : 1-56.

Mallikarjunappa, S. & Nageshchandra, B.K. 1990. Ovicidal action of pesticides against *Eotetranychus hicoriae* (McGregor) (Acari : Tetranychidae) infesting guava. *Abst. IV Nat. Symp. Acarology, Calicut* : 67.

Malaviya, M.D. & Rai, A.B. 1995. Studies on biology of red spider mite *Tetranychus ludeni* on Indian bean. *Abst. V Nat. Symp. Acarology, Bangolore* : 43.

Mani, M.S. 1964. *Ecology of Plant galls.* W. Junk. (Pub.). The Hague : 1-434.

Mani, M.S. 1973. *Plant galls of India.* The Macmillan Co. : 1-354.

Manjunatha, M. & Puttaswamy, 1990. Influence of nitrogen fertilization to brinjal plant on population development of *Tetranychus neocaledonicus. Acar. Newsl.,* 17-18 : 4-5.

Manjunatha, M., Bhat, N.S. & Puttaswamy. 1989. Morphology, histopathology, histochemistry and biochemical constituents of mite (*Aceria pongamiae*) induced galls and healthy leaves of *Pongamia glabra.* In : ChannaBasavanna, G.P. & Viraktamath, C.A. (eds.), *Progress in Acarology,* **2** : 141-146.

Manjunatha, M. & Lingappa, S. 1995. Chemical control of thrips and mite induced leaf curl in chilli. *Abst. V Nat. Symp. Acarology* : 84-85.

Manjunatha, M., Puttaswamy, Holihosur, S.V. & Lingappa, S. 1995. Acaricidal value of plant extracts against sorghum mite *Oligonychus indius* (Acari : Tetranychidae). *Abst. V Nat. Symp Acarology,* Bangalore : 84.

Manzoor, A. Rangrez & Rather, A.Q. 2010. Efficacy of various entomopathogenic fungi against the European Red Mite, *Panonychus ulmi* Koch on apple, *Malus domesticus* Borkh. *Abst. Int. Symp. Workshop Acarology* : 113-114.

Mathur, R.B. & Mathur, S. 1983. Mites associated with stored grains/products in Haryana, India. *Indian J. Acar.,* **7** : 44-52.

Mathur R.B. & Minocha, A. 1981. Effect of host stage density on cannibalism in *Acaropsis sollers* (Acaridae : Cheyletidae). In : *Contribution to Acarology in India* : 123-128.

Mathur, S. & Mathur, R.B. 1981. *Hemicheyletia hissariensis,* a new species of cheyletid mite from India. *Internat. J. Acarol.,* **7** : 69-70.

Mazumder, D., Karmakar, K., Hazra, P., Chattopadhyay, A. & Banerjee, A. 2010. Varietal resistance of cowpea germplasms against yellow mite, *Polyphagotarsonemus latus* Banks (Acari : Tarsonemidae) and its population dynamics in respect of prevalent weather parameters. *Abst. Int. Symp-cum-Workshop Acarology,* Kalyani : 52.

Mazumdar, D., Karmakar, K., Sreeramakumar, P., Banerjee, A. & Ghosh, D.K. 2010. Efficacay of different formulations of *Hirsutella thompsonii* against coconut perianth mite *Aceria guerreronis* Keifer under gangetic plains of West Bengal. *Abst. Int. Symp-cum-Workshop, Acarology* : 112-113.

Mehen, U.K. & Reddy, M.V. 1990. Diseases of pigeonpea and chickpea and source of resistance. In - *Country training course on legumes production, Sri Lanka,* 9-17 July, 1990, ICRISAT, Pantancheru, Andhra Pradesh, India.

Menon, R.M.G. & Ghai, S. 1968. Further records and distribution of *Petrobia latens* (Muller) (Acarina : Tetranychidae), a pest of wheat in India together with a description of a new species of predatory mite on the same. *Indian J. Ent.,* **30** : 77-79.

Meyer, M.K.P. 1979. The Tenuipalpidae (Acari) of Africa with keys to world fauna. *Ent. Mem. Dept. Agr. Tech. Ser. Repub. S. Afr.* **50** : 1-135.

Meyer, M.K.P. 1987. African Tetranychidae (Acari : Prostigmata) with reference to world genera. *Ent. Mem. Dept. of Agr. & Water Supply. Repub. S. Afr. No.,* **69** : 1-175.

Meyer, M.K.P., Loots, G.C., Pletzen, P. van, Engelbrich, C.M. & Walker, J.B. 1978. Acari of the Ethiopian region. *Ent. Mem. Dep. Agr. Tech. Ser. Repub. S. Africa* **29** : 1-45.

Misra, B.C. & Israel, P. 1968. Studies on the bionomics of paddy mite *Oligonychus oryzae* (Acarina : Tetranychidae). *Oryza J. Ass. Rice Res. Workshops,* **5** : 32-37.

Misra, C.S. 1920. Some pests of cotton in North Bihar. *Rept. Proc. 3rd Ent. Meeting Pusa, Calcutta* : 547-561.

Misra, H.P. 2010. Bioefficacy of Fenazaquin 10 EC against two spotted spider mite, *Tetranychus urticae* Koch (Acari : Tetranychidae) in tomato. *Abst. Int. Symp-cum-Workshop Acarology,* Kalyani : 94.

Mohanasundaram, M. 1987. Studies on the genus *Aceria* (Acari : Eriophyidae) from South. *Indian J. Acar.,* **12** : 15-88.

Mohanasundaram, M. 1995. A new genus and species of eriophyid mite on tea from South India. *Abst V. Nat-Symp. Acarology,* Bangalore : 16.

Mohanasundaram, M. 1999. Diversity of Acari. *Souvenir, Silver Jubilee Symp.* ASI, Bangalore : 9-10.

Mohanasundaram, M. & Manjunatha, M. 1995. Eriophyid mites (Eriophyidae : Acari) associated with mango trees in Dharwad, Karnataka. *Abst. V Nat. Symp. Acarology, Bangalore* : 17.

Mohanasundaram, M. & Parameswaram, S. 1991. Record of four mites associated with decaying or rotting agricultural crops in Tamil Nadu. *Mad Agr. J.,* **78** : 88.

Mohanasundaram, M., Parameswaram, S. & Natarajan, K. 1989. A note on the occurrance of *Phyllocoptruta musae* Keifer (Eriophyidae : Acari) on banana in South India. *Ind. Hort.,* **37**(5) : 300.

Mondal, S. & Chakrabarti, S. 1983. Studies on the eriophyid mites (Acarina : Eriophyidae) of India. 9 New species of *Calepitrimerus* with a key to Indian species. *Acarologia*, **24**(4) : 417-424.

Mozaffari, F., Abbasipour, H., Saboori, A. & Jabaleh, I. 2010. Ovicidol action of essential oil vapours of *Mentha pulegium* L. (Labiatae) and *Cinnamomim zelanicum* (Lauracea) plants against two spotted spider mite, *Tetrarychus urticae* Koch (Acari : Tetranychidae). *Abst. Int. Symp.-Cum-Workshop, Acarology, Kalyani* : 102.

Mukherjee, A.B., Sarkar, P.K., Somchoudhury, A.K. & Roy, K. 1989. Relative abundance of *Oligonychus oryzae* on nine varieties of paddy and its control. *Progress in Acarology*, **2** : 53-58.

Mukherjee, A.B. & Somchoudhury, A.K. 1972. Mite pests of mushroom. *FAO Pl. Prot. Bull.*, **22**(2) : 51.

Muraleedharan, N. 1991. *Pest management in tea.* UPASI, Valparai : 1-130.

Murthy, K.S.R. 2010. Studies on bioefficacy of fenpyroximate 5% EC (Mitigate) for the management of eriophyid mite (*Aceria lycopersici* Wolff.) and tetranychid mite (*Tetranychus neocaledonicus* Andre) on certain vegetable crops. *Abst. Int. Symp-cum-Workshop, Acarology, Kalyani* : 104.

Nagarjan, K.R. 1957. A short note on *Paratetranychus oryzae* Hirst, the paddy mite. *Mysore Agr. J.*, **44** : 480.

Nahar, S.C. & Gupta, S.K. 1980. A preliminary report on stored grain mites of Bihar. *Bull. Grain Tech.* **18**(2) : 130-134.

Nair, M.R.G.K. 1975. *Insects and mites of crops in India.* ICAR, New Delhi : 1-403.

Nakat, R.V., Power, V.M & Jadhav, R.G. 1995. Betel vine, a new host for *Brevipalpus phoenicis*. *Abst. V Nat. Symp. Acarology* : 44.

Nangia, N. 1986. Studies on mites associated with stored products and evaluation of different methods of control of acarids. (Astigmata : Acaridae), Ph. D. Thesis, UAS, Bangalore : 1-253.

Nangia, N. & ChannaBasavanna, G.P. 1984. The biology of *Typhlodromips tetranychivorus* Gupta on selected plant feeding mites of economic importance. In : *Acarology* VI (eds. Griffiths, C.A. & Bowman, C.F.). Chichester, England **2** : 725-732.

Nangia, N. & ChannaBasavanna, G.P. 1989a. Acarines associated with stored products in Karnataka, India. *Progress in Acarology*, **2** : 241-248.

Nangia, N. & ChannaBasavanna, G.P. 1990. The biology of *Cheyletus malaccensis* (Acari : Prostigmata) a predator of primary Acariformes. *Abst. IV Nat. Symp. Acarology, Calicut* : 15-16.

Nangia, N. & ChannaBasavanna, G.P. 1991a. Survey of acarines occurring in thrashing yards of Bangalore : In : *Advancement and conservation of soil fauna* (eds. Veeresh, G.K., Rajagopal, D. & Viraktamath, C.A.), Oxford IBH, New Delhi : 755-761.

Nangia, N. & ChannaBasavanna, G.P. 1995. Trend of *Amblyseius tetranychivorus* and its prey *Tetranychus ludeni* (Acari : Phytoseiidae : Tetranychidae) in response to release of predators at two intervals. *J. Acarol.*, **13** : 45-48.

Nangia, N. & ChannaBasavanna, G.P. 1995a. Interaction between *Amblyseius tetranychivorus* (Acari : Phytoseiidae) and its prey. *Tetranychus ludeni. J. Acarol.* **13** : 49-54.

Nangia, N. & ChannaBasavanna, G.P. 1995b. Evaluation of some plant materials as repellents of some astigmatid mites associated with stored products. *Abst. V Nat. Symp. Acar., Bangalore* : 50.

Nangia, N. & ChannaBasavanna, G.P. 1995c. Effect of infestation of astigmatid mites on fat acidity, seed germination and microflora in stored wheat. *Abst. V, Nat. Symp. Acarology*, Bangalore : 49.

Nangia, N., Jagdish, P.S. & Nageshachandra, B.K. 1999. Biochemical changes in different varieties of mulberry infested by *Eotetranchus suginamensis. J. Acarol.*, **15**(1-2) : 29-31.

Narayanaswamy, C.A. 2004. Studies on *Aceria cajani* ChannaBasavanna (Acari : Eriophyidae) mite vector of pigeonpea sterility mosaic disease with special reference to varietal screening and its interplant distribution. M.Sc. Agr. Thesis, UAS, Bangalore : 1-90.

Narayanaswamy, P. & Ramakrishnan, K.I. 1965a. Sutides on sterility mosaic disease of pigeonpea. III. Nitrogen metabolism of infected plants. *Proc. Ind. Acad. Sci.*, (B) **63** : 288-296.

Nassar, O.A. & Ghai, S. 1981. Taxonomic studies on tetranychoid mites infesting vegetables and fruit crops in Delhi and surrounding areas. *Oriental Ins.*, **15**(4) : 333-396.

Natarajan, E. & Beevi, D. 1992. Control of *Aceria cajani* (Eriophyidae : Acarina) on *Cajanas cajan* (L.) Millsp. *Internat. Pigeonpea Newsl.*, **16** : 22-24.

Navia, D., Mendonea, R.S. & DeMelo, L.A.M.P. 2005. *Steneotarsonemus spinki*—an invasive tarsonemid mite threatening rice crop in South America : In : *Plant Protection and plant health in Europe, introduction and spread of invasive species.* Humboldt University, Berlin, Germany, 9-11 June, 2005.

Nayak, U.S., Baral, K. & Senapati, K. 2010. Efficacy of certain acaricides against chilli mite (*Polyphagotarsonemus latus*). *Abst. Int. Symp.-cum-Workshop, Acarology* : 95.

Nene, Y.L. 1972. A survey of viral diseases of pulse crops in Uttar Pradesh. *Res. Bull.*, **4** : G.B. Pant. Univ. of Agr. & Tech. Pantnagar, Uttar Pradesh : 1-191.

Nene, Y.L. 1995. Sterility mosaic of pigeonpea : the challenge continues. *Indian J. Mycology & Plant Pathology*, **25** : 1-11.

Nene, Y.L., Beniwal, S.P.S., Reddy, M.V., Deena, E., Sithanantham, S. & Rameswara Rao, V. 1983. Nature and extent of pigeonpea sterility mosaic under field conditions. *Abst. 2nd All India Symp. Acarology*, Pune : 29-30.

Nene, Y.L. & Rathi, Y.P.S. 1972. Diseases of (Sterility mosaic and yellow mosaic) Viral diseases of pulse crops in Uttar Pradesh. *Final Tech. Rept. G.P. Pant Univ. of Agr. & Tech. Pantnagar* : 151-162.

Nene, Y.L. & Reddy, M.V. 1976b. A new technique to screen pigeonpea for resistance to sterility mosaic. *Tropical grain Legume Bull.*, **5** : 23.

Nene, Y.L., Hall, S.D. & Sheila, V.K. 1990. *The pigeonpea.* CAB International. Wallingford, Oxon Ox 1080, UK.

Nirula, K.K. 1955. Investigation of the pests of coconut palm. *Indian Coconut J.*, **8** : 101-130.

Oldfield, G.N. 1970. Mite transmission of plant viruses. *Ann. Rev. Ent.*, **15** : 343-380.

Oldfield, G.N. & Michalska, K. 1996. Spermatophore deposition, mating behaviour and population mating structure. In : *Eriophyoid mites, their biology, natural enemies and control* : 185-198. (eds. G.G. Lindquist *et al.* Elsevier, B.V. Amsterdam).

Onkarappa, S. & Ashok Kumar, C.T. 1995. Influence of synthetic pyrethroids on reproduction of red spider mite, *Tetranychus urticae. Abst V Nat Symp. Acarology* : 78.

Onkarappa, S., Srinivasa, N., Mallick, B. & Chinnamade Gawda, C. 2007. Chemical control of two spotted spider mite, *Tetranychus urticae* Koch (Acari : Tetranychidae) on brinjal. *J. Acarol.*, **17** : 81-83.

Pal, P.K., Somchoudhury, A.K., Sarkar, P.K. & Mukherjee, A.B. 1989. Approaches to integrated control of *Tetranychus cinnabarinus* on egg plant. *Progress in Acarology*, **2** : 453-459.

Pandit, R.K. & Chakrabarti, S. 2010. Eriophyoid mites on *Mangifera indica* in West Bengal, India. *Abst. Int. Symp-cum-Workshop Acarology, Kalyani* : 20.

Panja, B.N., Karmakar, K., Ghosh, A., Sahoo, A., Singh, A.S., Saha, J. & De, D.K. 2010. Is there any role of rice sheath mite *Steneotarsonemus spinki* Smiley on the occurrence of sheath rot disease caused by *Sarocladium oryzae.* Gams & Hawks? *Abst. Int. Syst-cum-Workshop, Acarology*, Kalyani : 46.

Papadoulis, G. Th., Emmanouel, N.G. & Kapaseidi, E.V. 2009. *Phytoseiidae of Greece and Cyprus (Acari : Mesostigmata).* Indira Pub House, West Broomfield, USA, : 1-200.

Patel, C.B., Patel, J.R., Patel, M.B., Patel, A.J. & Rai, A.B. 1995. Evaluation of pesticides including plant products against red spider mite, *Tetranychus macfarlanei* (Acarina : Tetranychidae) on Okra. *Abst. V Nat. Symp. Acarology* : 81.

Patel, K.A., Purohit, M.S. & Patel, K.G. 2010. Screening of rice varities for resistance to rice sheath mite, *Steneotarsonemus spinki* Smilley in South Gujarat. *Abst. Int. Symp. Workshop Acarology, Kalyani* : 59.

Patel, J.R., Patel, C.B., Patel, M.B., Desai, H.R., Patel, J. & Rai, A.B. 1995. Some ecological studies on eriophyid mite, *Acaria cajani* infesting pigeonpea in south Gujarat. *Abst. V Nat. symp. Acarology, Bangalore* : 29-30.

Patel, L.C., Mondal, B., Mondal, C.K., Mondal, P., Karmakar, K. & Roy, S.K. 2010. Management of leaf curl complex, a malady of summer chilli of Sundarban region of West Bengal. *Abst. Int. Symp-cum-Workshop, Acarology* : 97.

Patel, V.N., Thakur, A.V. & Yadav, S.P.S. 1989. Bioefficacy of certain acaricides against mite, *Tetranychus macfarlanei* on okra. *Indian J. Ent.,* **50** : 32-39.

Patil, R.S. & Nandihalli, B.S. 2007. Ovicidal and acaricidal action of biorationals against red spider mite *Tetranychus macfarlanei* Baker & Pritchard under laboratory conditions. *J. Acarol.,* **17** : 100-102.

Pillai, P.R.P. 1955. A new glycyphagid mite *Glycyphagus hughesi* sp. nov. from stored wheat. *J. zool. Soc. India,* **7** : 141-144.

Prabheena, P. & Ramani, N. 2010. Assessment of feeding symptoms and nature of damage induced by *Brevipalpus phoenicis* Geijskes (Acari :Tenuipalpidae) on the medicinal shrub, *Ocimum gratissimum* Linn. *Abst. Int. Symp. Workshop Acarology* : 68-69.

Prabhuswamy, H.P., Srinivasa, N. & Gupta, S.K. 1995. Population fluctuation of eriophyid mite *Aceria cajani* vector of pigeonpea sterility mosaic disease. *Abst. V Nat. Symp. Acar.,* Bangalore : 29.

Pradhan, S.K. & Pandit, N.C. 1982. Incidence of eriophyid mite *Eriophyes (Aceria) crotalariae* Chann. (Acari : Eriophyidae) on sunnhemp (*Crotalaria juncea* L.) from West Bengal. *Sci. & Cult.,* **48** : 391-392.

Prakash, A. & Rao, J. 1988. Occurrence of flour mite *Acarus siro* Linn. in rice mills. *Int. Rice Res. News.,* **13**(3) : 39.

Prasad, A., Singh, H. & Sukla, T.N. 1965. Present status of the mango malformation disease. *Indian J. Hort.,* **22** : 254-265.

Prasad, V. 1974. *A catalogue of mites of India*. Indira Acarology Pub. House, Ludhiana, : 1-320.

Pritchard, A.E. & Baker, E.W. 1955. A revision of the spider mite family Tetranychidae. *Mem. Pacific coast Ent. Soc.*, **9** : 1-472.

Pritchard, A.E. & Baker, E.W. 1958. The false spider mites (Acarina : Tenuipalpidae). *Univ. Calif. Pub. Ent.* **14**(3) : 175-274.

Putatunda, B.N., Mathur, S. & Mathur, R.B. 1999. Mites associated with some stored products in Haryana. *J. Acarol.* **15** : 64-67.

Putatunda, B.N. 2001. *Pl. Prot. Bull.*, 54 :

Puttarudriah, M. & ChannaBasavanna, G.P. 1955. Beneficial coccinellids of Mysore II. *Indian J. Ent.*, **17** : 1-5.

Puttarudriah, M. & ChannaBasavanna, G.P. 1956. Some beneficial coccinellids of Mysore-III. *J. Bomb. nat. Hist. Soc.*, **54** : 156-159.

Puttaswamy & ChannaBasavanna, G.P. 1981. Influence of host plants, on the development, fecundity and longevity of *Tetranychus ludeni* Zacher (Acari Tetranychidae). *Indian J. Acar.*, **5**(1-2) : 80-84.

Rahman, S. & Khan, M.R. 2010. Screening of popular jute (*Corchorus* sp.) varieties against yellow mite *Polyphagotarsonemus latus* Banks. *Abst. Int. Symp.-workshop-Acarology* : 68.

Rai, A.B., Malaviya, M.D. & Patel, C.B. 1995. Toxicity of pesticides including neem products on *Amblyseius alstoniae* (Acari : Phytoseiidae), an important predator of *Tetranychus ludeni* (Acari Tetranychidae). *Abst. V. Nat. Symp. Acarology* : 81.

Rai, A.B., Malaviya, M.D., Desai, H.R. & Patel, J.R. 1999. Impact of date of sowing, weather factors and natural enemies on the incidence of *Tetranychus ludeni* and role of botanicals in its control and safety to the predatory mite. *J. Acarol.*, **14** : 105-108.

Rai, A.B., Sejalia, A.S., Patel, C.B. & Shah, A.H. 1991. Studies on okra mite, *Tetranychus macfarlanei* (Acari : Tetranychidae) and its control. *Modern Acarology*, **1** : 571-580.

Rai, A.B., Vora, V.T. & Patel, C.B. 1995. Investigations on the integrated control of *Tetranychus urticae* (Acari : Tetranychidae) infesting brinjal in south Gujarat. *Abst. V Nat. Symp. Acarology* : 76.

Ramaraju, K., Velusamy, R. & Mohanasundaram, M. 1995. Laboratory evaluation of various plant products against *Tetranychus ludeni* infesting egg plants in Tamil Nadu. *Abst. V Nat. Symp. Acarology* : 81.

Ramaraju, K., Velusamy, R. & Mohansumdaram, M. 1995a. Evaluation of plant products for the management of carmine spider mite, *Tetranychus cinnabarinus* on bhendi. *Abst. V Nat. Symp. Acarology*, Bangalore : 82.

Ramos, M. & Rodriguez, H. 1999. Development of *Steneotarsonemus spinki* Smiley (Acari : Tarsonemidae) in laboratory. *Revista de-Protection-Vegetel,* **15** : 130-131.

Rao, J. & Prakash, A. 1984. Occurrence of grain mite *Tarsonemus* sp. in stored rice. *Ind. Rice Res. Newsl.,* **9**(2) : 17-18.

Rao, J. & Prakash, A. 1992. Infestation of rice tarsonemid mite, *Steneotarsonemus spinki* Smiley in rice in Orissa. *J. Appl. zool. Res.,* **3** : 103.

Rao, J. & Prakash, A. 1995. Bio-deterioration of paddy seed quality due to insects and mites and its control using botanicals. *Final Report of ICAR Ad. hoc. Scheme (1992-1995), CPRI, Cuttack (India)* : 1-76.

Rather, A.Q. 1989. Studies on mites (Acari) associated with stone fruits in subtropical, temperate and cold arid zones of Jammu & Kashmir. In : *Progress in Acarology,* **2** : 183-190.

Rather, A.Q. 1995. Carry over of red spider mite *Tetranychus cinnabarinus* (Boisduval) alternate host plants in field crops of Kashmir. *Abst. V Nat. Symp. Acarology,* Bangalore : 36-37.

Rather, A.Q. 1995a. Host preference of European red mite, *Panonychus ulmi* (Koch) (Acarina : Tetranychidae) in Kashmir. *Abst. V Nat. Symp. Acarology, Bangalore* : 35-36.

Rather, A.Q. & Haq. Z. 2010 Ecofriendly management of mite infesting button mushroom *Agaricus bisporus* cultivated on commercial scale in Kashmir Valley. *Abst. Int. Symp-cum-Workshop Acarology* : 142.

Rathi, Y.P.S. 1979. Temick treatment of pigionpea seeds for prevention of sterility mosaic. *Acta Botanica India,* **7**(1) : 90-91.

Rathi, Y.P.S. 1983. Studies on sterility mosic disease of pigeonpea (*Cajanas cajan* (L.) Millsp.). *Final Tech. Rept. G.P. Pant. Univ. of Agr. & Tech., Pant Nagar, Uttar Pradesh,* India.

Raut, S.K. & Bhattacharya, S.S. 1989. Ecology of predatory mite *Tencateia* sp. (Prostigmata : Anystidae) in betelvine orchards in West Bengal, India. *Progress in Acarology,* **2** : 191-194.

Raut, S.K. & Bhattacharya, S.S. 1999. Pests and diseases of betelvine (*Piper betle* L.) and their natural enemies in India. *Expt. Appl. Acarol.,* **23**(4) : 319-325.

Ravi, K.C. & Puttaswamy. 1995. Effect of feeding by mites on histology and histochemistry of *Cassia,* chilli and jasmine leaves. *Abst. V Nat. Symp. Acarology* : 38-39.

Ravi, K.C. & Puttaswamy, 1995a. Reaction of some groundnut genotypes to *Tetranychus urticae. Abst V Nat. Symp. Acarology* : 38.

Razvyazkina, G.P., Kopkova, E.A. & Belyanchikova, Y.V. 1963. Wheat streak Mosaic. *Lashchita Rastot Vreditelei Bolenzei,* **8** : 54-55.

Reddy, M.V., Beniwal, S.P.S., Shiela, V.K., Sithanatham, S. & Nene, Y.L. 1989a. Role of eriophyid mite *Aceria cajni* (Acari : Eriophyidae) in transmission and spread of sterility mosaic of pigeonpea. In : ChannaBassavanna, G.P. & Viraktamath, C.A. (eds.). *Progress in Acarology,* **2** : 121.

Reddy, M.V., Nene, Y.L., Raju, T.N., Sheila, V.K., Kanaiyan, J. & Beniwal, S.P.S. 1989a. Evaluation of pegeonpea lines for resistance to wilt, sterility mosaic and phytopthora blight. *International Pigeonpea Newsl.,* **10** : 22.

Reddy, M.V. & Raju, T.N. 1993. Some clues to increased incidence and seasonal variation of pigeonpea sterility mosaic in peninsular India. *Int Pigeonpea Newsl.,* **16** : 18-22.

Reddy, M.V., Raju, T.N. & Lenne, J.M. 1998. Diseases of pigeonpea. In : *The pathology of food and pasture legumes* (eds. D.J. Allen & J.M. Lenned). CAB International ICRISAT : 517-518.

Reddy, M.V., Reddy, D.V.R. & Sacks, W.R. 1984. Epidemiology and management of sterility mosaic disease of pigeonpea. In : *Proceeding of the Int. Symp. on Rose Rosette and other eriophyid mite transmitted plant disease agents of uncertain etiology.* 19-21 May 1994, Iowa St. Univ. Ames, Iowa, USA : 29-32.

Reddy, M.V., Sheila, V.K. & Nene, Y.L. 1993. *Cajanas scara* baeoides an alternate host of pigeonpea sterility mosic pathogon and its vector *Aceria cajani. Internat. Pigeonpea Newsl.,* : 18-24.

Reddy, M.V., Sharma, S.B. & Nene, Y.L. 1990b. Pigeonpea : Disease management. In : Nene, Y.L., Susan, D., Hall & Sheila, V.K. (eds.). *Pigeonpea.* CAB Int. UK and ICRISAT, India : 303-316.

Roy, I., Gupta, S.K. & Saha, G.K. 2006. A preliminary observation on the occurrence of phytophagous and predatory mites on maize in Kolkata, India. *Sci. & Cult.,* **72** : 213-215.

Roy, I., Gupta, S.K. & Saha, G.K. 2008. New reports of predatory mites (Acari : Prostigmata, Mesostigmata) from medicinal plants of Darjeeling district, West Bengal, India with description of a new species. *Entomon,* **33**(2) : 119-128.

Roy, I. & Saha, G.K. 2010. Two new predatory mites (Acari : Bdellidae, Phytoseiidae) collected from medicinal plants from West Bengal, India. *Jour. Asia Pacific Ent.,* **13** : 124-126.

Roy, K., Karmakar, K., Majumder, D., Khan, S.A., Gunri, S. & Bandopadhyaya, P. 2010. Population dynamics of yellow mite, *Polyphagotarsonemus latus* Banks (Acari : Tarsonemidae) on popular jute cultivars (*Corchorus* sp.,). *Abst. Int. Symp. cum-workshop. Acarology, Kalyani,* 8-10 April, 2010 : 53.

Sabelis, W.M. 1985. Sampling technique, pp. 337-349. In : *Spider mites their biology, natural enemies and control.* (Eds. Helle & Sabelis) : 1-403.

Sadana, G.L. & Gupta, B.K. 1982. Distribution of new host records of phytophagous mites (Acarina : Tetranychoidea). *Ind. J. Ent.*, **1** : 65-68.

Sadana, G.L. 1985. *Plant feeding mites of India.* Kalyani Pub., New Delhi : 1-99.

Sadana, G.L., Chhabra, S.C. & Gupta, B.K. 1982. Tetranychid mites infesting fruit trees in Punjab together with records of some new hosts and discriptions of new species. *Entomon.*, **7** : 397-401.

Sadana, G.L. & Gupta, B.K. 1983. *Sci. & Cult.*, **49** : 184-186.

Sadana, G.L., Singh, S.P. & Kumari, M. 1990. Phytoseiid mites associated with fruit trees in Punjab, India. *Acar. Newsl.*, **17** & **18** : 16.

Sadanandan, M.A. & Ramani, N. 2010. Developmental biology of *Amblyseius (Neoseiulus) longispinosus* (Evans, 1952) (Acari : Phytoseiidae). *Abst. Int. Symp.-cum-Workshop, Acarology,* Kalyani : 57.

Sadhukhan, R., Karmakar, K., Chattopadhaya, P. & Somchoudhury, A.K. 2010. Field evaluation of indigenous rice genotypes against rice sheath mite *Steneotarsonemus spinki* Smiley (Acari : Tarsonemidae) under Bengal basin. *'Abst. Int. Symp.-cum-Workshop'*, Kalyani : 63-64.

Sandhu, G.S., Kaushal, S.K. & Gupta, S.K. 1976. Mites associated with maize and their predators in the Punjab. *Sci. & Cult.*, **39** : 226-227.

Santhosh, P.P. & Haq, M.A. 2010. Developmental biology of *Dolichotetranychus cocos* Flechtmann & Fernando, 2000 (Acari : Tenuipalpidae) from Kerala, India. *Abst. Int. Symp. Workshop, Acarology,* Kalyani : 56-57.

Sarkar, P.K. & Somachoudhury, A.K. 1989. Influence of major abiotic factors on the seasonal incidence of *Raoiella indica* and *Tetranychus fijiensis* on coconut, 59-65 pp. In : *Progress in Acarology* : 1-483.

Saradamma, K., Pillai, K.S., Ambikadevi, D. & Das, M.N. 1983. Control of *Tetranychus neocaledonicus* (Acari : Tetranychidae) on brinjal using some safer pesticides. *Abst. Second All India Symp. Acarology,* Pune, May 26-28, 1983 : 64.

Selvanarayanan, V. 1999. Neem formulations and castor oil-a safe way to manage okra red spider mite. *J. Acarol.*, **14** : 77-79.

Senapati, A.K., Maiti, A.K. & Chatterjee, M.L. 2010. Effect of few new acaricides against yellow mite of chilli. *Abst. Symp. Workshop Acarology* : 95.

Seth, M.L. 1962. Transmission of pigeonpea sterility by a eriophyid mite. *Indian Phytopathology,* **15** : 225-227.

Sharma, A. 1992. Chemical control of ber mite, *Larvacarus transitans* (Ewing) in Rajasthan, In : *Man, mites & environment,* Anjengo Pub., Kerala : 15-17.

Sharma, A. 2001. *Amblyseius alstoniae* Gupta, a mite predator of *Petrobia latens* (Muller). *Abst. Nat. Conf. Pl. Prot. – New horizons in the millennium*, Feb. 23-25, 2001 : 57.

Sharma, A. & Bhatnagar, K.L. 1992. Observations on brown wheat mite *Petrobia latens* (Muller) on barley in semiarid regions of Rajasthan. *Sci. & Cult.*, **58** : 168.

Sharma, A. & Kushwaha, K.S. 1983. Natural enemy of *Larvacarus transitans* (Acari : Tenuipalpidae). *Abst. 2nd All India Symp. Acarology, Pune* : 75.

Sharma, A. & Pareek, R.K. 2000. First record of the occurrence of *Petrobia latens* (Muller) on oilseed crops from India. *J. Appl. Ent.*, **14** : 77.

Sharma, A. & Sharma, M. 1998. Effect of nutrients and salintly on the incidence of *Petrobia latens* (Muller) (Prostigmata, Tetranychidae). In : Halliday *et al.* (eds) *Acarology X, CSIRO Pub., Australia* : 349-351.

Sharma, A. & Srinivasa, N. 2004. Brown wheat mite *Petrobia latens* (Muller) (Acari : Tetranychidae). *AINP, UAS Bangalore* : 1-12.

Sharma, N.K. & Sadana, G.L. 1985. Influence of temperature on the development of the predatory mite, *Amblyseius finlandicus* (Acari : Phytoseiidae). *Indian J. Acar.*, **9** : 57-62.

Sharma, N.K. & Sadana, G. L. 1989. Development of *Amblyseius finlandicus* (Acari : Phytoseiidae) on its prey *Eutetranychus orientalis* (Acari : Tetranychidae). *Indian J. Acar.*, **11** : 51-54.

Sharma, N.K. & Sadana, G.L. 1990. Influence of temperature on the predator prey interaction between *Amblysius finlandicrus* and its prey, *Eutetranychus orientalis*. *Acar. Newsl.*, **17** & **18** : 15.

Sheeba, S., Roseleen, J. & Ramaraju, K. 2010. Evaluation of profenophos 50 EC and abamectin 1.8 EC against eriophyid mite, *Aceria guerreronis* on coconut. *Abst. Int. Symp.-Workshop Acarology* : 77.

Shivaraju, B. & ChannaBasavanna, G.P. 1995. Studies on bioecology of the citrus rust mite *Phyllocoptruta oleivora* (Acari : Eriophyidae). *Abst. V Nat. Symp. Acarology, Bangalore* : 30.

Siebold, G.R. von. 1950. Bemerkungen uber Bychiden. Fahresber S chfer. *Ges Kult.* **28** : 84-89.

Singer, G. 1964. A simple aspirator for collecting small arthropods directly into alcohol. *Ann. Ent. Soc. Amer.*, **57** : 796-798.

Singh, A.P. & Khan, R.M. 1979. A new pest of wheat in India. *Ent. Mon. Mag.*, **115** : 207-208.

Singh, A.P. & Singh, R.N. 2010. Population trend and biology of Yellow-mite *Polyphagotarsonemus latus* (Banks) (Acari : Tarsonemidae on chilli crop at Varanasi, Uttar Pradesh. *Abst. Int. Symp-cum-Workshop, Acaralogy* : 51.

Singh, A.R., Rathi, Y.P.S. & Agrawal, K.C. 1999. Sterility mosaic of pigeonpea a challenge of 20th Century, *Ind. J. Virology*, **15** : 85-92.

Singh, G..S., Kaushal, S.K. & Gupta, S.K. 1976. Mites associated with maize and their predators in Punjab. *Sci. & Cult.*, **39** : 226.

Singh, H. 1972. Host preference and population dynamics of *Acaropsis docta* (Berlese) in relation to some important wheat pests. M.Sc. Thesis, HAU, Hisar.

Singh, L.B. 1960. *Insects, mites and other pests in mango (Monograph)*. London, Leonard Hill : 292-337.

Singh, L.B., Singh, S.M. & Nirvan, R.S. 1961. Studies on mango malformetion. I. Review, symptoms, extent in intensity and causes. *Hort. Adv.*, **5** : 1-197.

Singh, M. & Mathur, S. 1995. Effect of infestation by *Suidasia nesbitti* (Acari : Acaridae) on germination of some stored crop seeds. *Abst. V Nat. Symp. Acarology, Bangalore* : 48.

Singh, R.N. & Mukherjee, I. 1995. Evaluation of insecticides/acaricides against *Tetranychus cinnabarinus* and *Amblyseius* (*Neoseiulus*) *longispinosus*. *Abst. V Nat. Symp. Acarology, Bangalore* : 83-84.

Sithanantham, S., Muthuswamy, S.K. & Bhaskaran, T.L. 1972. A note on the role of the eriophyid mite, *Aceria sacchari* ChannaBasavanna (Eriophyoidea : Acarina) in the transmission of streak virus disease of sugarcane (*Saccharum*). *Sci. & Cult.*, **38** : 248-250.

Smith-Meyer, M.K.P. & Ueckermann, E.A. 1987. A taxonomic study of some Anystidae (Acari : Prostigmata). *Ent. Mem. Dept. Agr. & Water Supply.*, : 1-37.

Solomon, M.E. 1945. Tyroglyphid mites in stored products. Methods for the study of population density. *Ann. appl. Biol.*, **32** : 71-75.

Solomon, M.E. 1946. Tyroglyphid mites in stored products. Ecological studis. *Ann. appl. Biol.*, **33** : 280-289.

Solomon, M.E. 1962. Ecology of the flour mite *Acarus siro* L (=*Tyrophagus farinae* D.C.). *Ann. appl. Biol.*, **50** : 178-184.

Solomon, M.E. 1969. Experiments on predator-prey interaction of storage mites. Symp. on population dynamics. *Acarologia*, **11** : 484-503.

Somchoudhury, A.K. 1983. *Adv. Acar. Res.*, : 283-289 (1993).

Somchoudhury, A.K., Das, P., Sarkar, P.K. & Mukherjee, A.B. 1987. Distribution of mites associated with mushrooms. *Abst. First Nat. Sem. Acarology* : 10.

Somchoudhury, A.K., Dey, P.K., Sengupta, A. & Tudu, B. 2010. Bio-agent in forecasting on bearing pattern of mango. *Abst. Int. Symp-cum-Workshop Acarology* : 64-65.

Somchoudhury, A.K. & Mukherjee, A.B. 1971. Observations on the seasonal abundance of some common stored grain mites in India. *Indian J. Ent.*, **33** : 350-351.

Somchoudhury, A.K., Singh D.K. & Mukherjee, A.B. 1989. Interrelationship between *Aceria litchii* (Acari : Eriophyidae) and *Cephaleuros virescens*, parasitic alga in the formation of erineum-like structure on litchi leaf. *Progress in Acarology*, **2** : 147-152.

Sonenshine, D.E., 1984. Pheromones of Acari and their potential use in control strategies. *Acarology VI* (eds. D.A. Griffiths & Bowman, C.E.) : 100-108.

Srinivasa, N., Mallik, B. & Chinnamade Gowda, C. 2004. *Aceria cajani* (Acari : Eriophyidae) transmitted pigeonpea sterility mosaic disease. AINP, UAS, Bangalore : 1-24.

Srinivasa, N. & Mallik, B. 2010. Botanical acaricides—a viable alternative to synthetics. Abst. *Int. Symp-Cum-Workshop Acarology*, 8-10 April, 2010, Kalyani : 106-108.

Srinivasa, N. & Sugeetha, G. 1999. Bioeffectiveness of some botanical and synthetic pesticides against okra red spider mite, *Tetranychus macfarlanei*. *J. Acarol.*, **15** : 1-5.

Srinivasa, N., Prabhakar, H. & Mallik, B. 2004. Rice sheath mite *Steneotarsonemums spinki* Smiley (Acari : Tarsonemidae). *AINP, UAS, Bangalore* : 1-24.

Srinivasa, N., Prabhuswamy, H.P. & Gupta, S.K. 1995. Influence of sowing time on the incidence of pegeonpea sterility mosaic disease and the associated mite vector, *Aceria cajani*. *Abst V Nat. Symp. Acarology, Bangalore* : 28.

Summanwar, A.S. 1967. Mango malformation : serious economic consequences. *Indian Hort.*, **2** : 12.

Summanwar, A.S. & Raychaudhuri, S.P. 1968. The role of eriophyid mite (*Aceria mangiferae*) in the causation of mango malformation. *Indian Phytopath*, **21** : 463-464.

Sumangala, K. & Haq, M.A. 1995. Chlorophyll depletion in *Eichhornia crassipes* due to feeding and colonisation by *Eutetranychus orientalis*. *Abst. V Nat. Symp. Acarology* : 40.

Summanwar, A.S., Raychaudhuri, S.P. & Phatak, S.C. 1966. Association of the fungus *Fusarium moniliforme* Shld., with the malformation in mango (*Mangifera indica*). *Indian Phytopath.*, **19** : 227-228.

Summers, F.M. 1962. The genus *Stigmaeus* (Acarina : Stigmaeidae). *Hilgardia,* **33** : 491-537.

Thaker, B.T. & Desai, M.M. 1929. Wooly mite (*Eriophyes gossypii*) on cotton : its status and commercial importance in Gujarat. *Agr. J. India,* **24** : 175-182.

Thangaraju, D., Gajendran, G. & Mohanasundaram, M. 1995. Insectides inducing resurgence of carmine spider mite, *Tetranychus cinnabarinus* on brinjal, *Abst. V Nat. Symp. Acarology* : 79.

Trivedi, T.B. 1988. Occurrence of mites in the beds of cultivated mushroom. *Univ. Agr. Sci. Bangalore, Curr. Res.,* **17**(9) : 125.

Umamaheswari, T., Sharmila Bharathi, C., Kanagarajan, R., Arivudainambi, S. & Selvenarayanan, V. 1999. Neem formulations and castor oil - a safe way to manage okra spider mite. *J. Acarol.,* **14** : 77-79.

Veeravel, R., Narayanaswamy, P. & Baskaran, V. 1995. Relative toxicity levels of certain plant products against red spider mite, *Tetranychus telarius* in brinjal. *Abst. V Nat. Symp. Acarology* : 83.

Veeravel, R., Raghuraman, M. & Chandrasekharan, M. 1995. Effect of intercroping on ecology and population dynamics of brinjal mite, *Tetranychus telarius. Abst. V Nat. Symp. Acarology,* Bangalore : 31.

Vijayambika, V., Cicilykutty, A. & John, P.A. 1981a. Host of adult fish mite *Lardoglyphus Konoi* (Acari : Acaridae), a pest of dried stored fish. In : *Contributions to Acarology in India* : 139-141.

Vijayambika, V. & John, P.A. 1974. Internal morphology and histology of the fish mite, *Lardoglyphus konoi* (Sasa & Asanuma). 4. Digestive system. *Acarologia,* **16** : 709-718.

Vijayambika, V. & John, P.A. 1974a. Observations on the environmental regulation of hypogeal formation to the fish mite, *Lardoglyphus konoi. Acarologia,* **16** : 160-165.

Vijayambika, V. & John, P.A. 1975. Functional morphology of the alimentary canal of the fish mite *Lardoglyphus konoi,* forma et Function. *Acarologia,* **8** : 387-394.

Vijayambika, V. & John, P.A. 1975a. Internal morphology and histology of the fish mite, *Lardoglyphus konoi* (Sasa & Asanuma) (Acarina : Acaridae). 3 : Nervous system. *Acarologia,* **17** : 114-119.

Vijayambika, V. & John, P.A. 1975b. Internal morphology and histology of the post embryonic stages of the fish mite, *Lardoglyphus konoi* (Sasa & Asanuma). (Acarina : Acaridae). Larva. *Acarologia,* **17** : 745-750.

Vijayambika, V. & John, P.A. 1977. Digestive system of *Aleuroglyphus ovatus* (Acarina : Tyroglyphidae). *Indian J. Acar.,* **2** : 24-29.

Vijayambika, V. & John, P.A. 1977a. Nervous system of *Aleuroglyphus ovatus* Troupeau (Acarina : Tyroglyphidae). *Indian J. Acar.*, **2** : 33-36.

Vijayambika, V. & John, P.A. 1978. Reproductive system of *Aleuroglyphus ovatus* (Acari : Tyroglyphidae). *Indian J. Acar.*, **2** : 42-47.

Vijayambika, V. & John, P.A. 1981. Histochemistry of the adult *Lardoplyphus konoi* (Acari : Acaridae), a pest on dried stored fish. In : *Contributions to Acarology in India* : 141-144.

Vishwakarma, R., Ghatak, S.S. & Mondal, S. 2010. Bioefficacy of some organic formulations and novel pesticides against chilli mite, *Polyphagotarsonemus latus* (Banks) (Tarsonemidae, Acari). *Abst. Int. Symp.-cum-Workshop Acarology* : 78.

Vitzthum, H.G. 1940-43. Acarina in 'Bronns' Klassen und Ordnungen *des Tierreich* Leifzig, **5**(4) : 801-902.

Vora, V.T. & Rai, A.B. 1995. Bioefficacy of different synthetic and botanical pesticides against *Tetranychus urticae* (Acari : Tetranychidae) on brinjal. *Abst. V Nat. Symp. Acarology* : 82.

Vora, V.T. & Rai, A.B. 1995a. Susceptibility of different brinjal cultivars to two spotted spider mite, *Tetranychus urticae* (Acari : Tetranychidae). *Abst. V Nat. Symp. Acarology* : 40.

Walter, D. & Proctor, H. 1999. Mites. In : *Ecology, evolution and behaviour.* CAB, Publishing, UK : 174-313.

Weinan, W., Lairong, L. & Wenming. L. 1997. *Economic insect fauna of China. Acari : Phytoseiidae.* Sci. Press, Beijing : 1-223.

Westphal, E. 1996. *Marcellia,* **39** : 193-375.

Xu, G.L., Wu, H.J., Huen, Z.L., Mo, G. & Van, M. 2001. Study on the reproductive characteristics of rice mite, *Steneotarsonemus spinki.* Smiley (Acari : Tarsonemidae). *Syst. Appl. Acarol.*, **6** : 45-49.

Yathiraj, B.R. & Jagadish, P.S. 1999. Plant extracts-future promising tools in the integrated management of spider mites, *Tetranychus urticae* (Acari : Tetranychidae). *J. Acarol.*, **15**(1-2) : 40-43.

Zhang, F.P. & Fu, Y.G. 2004. The occurrence of banana leaf mite and its control. *South China Fruits,* **6**(44) : 47.

Zhao, S. & Amrine, J.W. 1997. Investigation of snow borne mites (Acari) and relevancy to dispersal. *Internat. J. Acarol.*, **23** : 209-213.

6. INDEX OF SCIENTIFIC NAMES

C

M

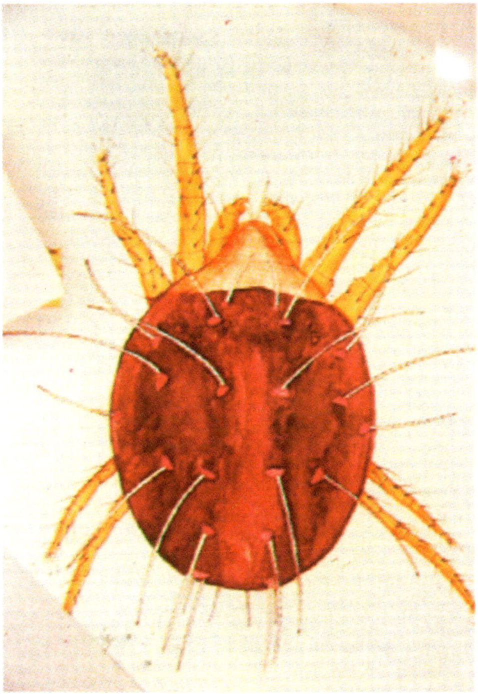

A common red spider mite (Tetranychidae)

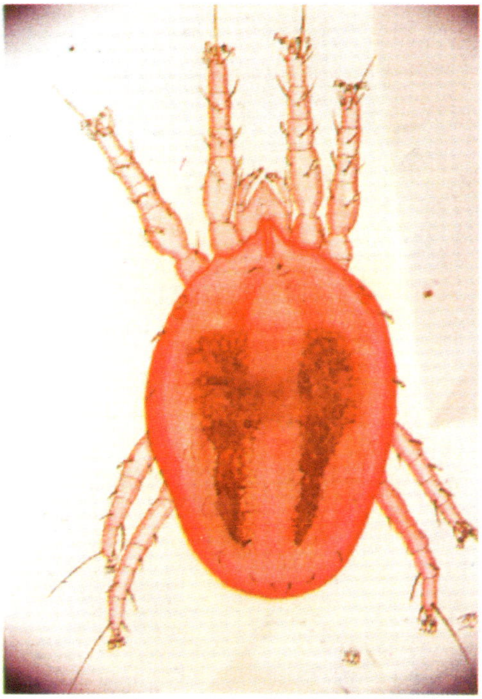

A common false spider mite (Tenuipalpidae)

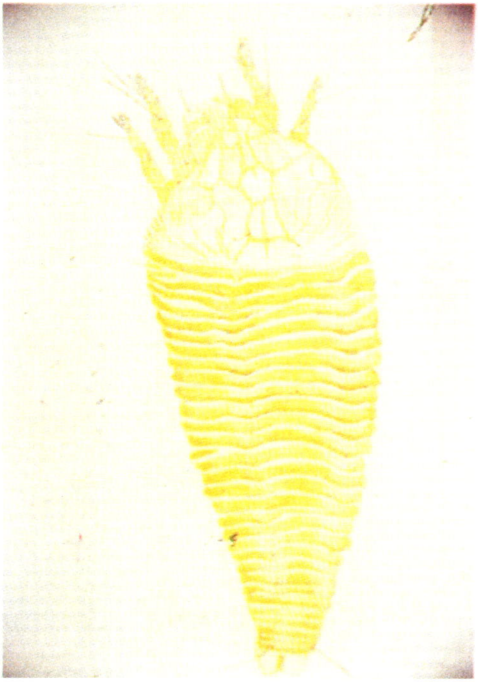

A common erineum mite (Eriophyidae)

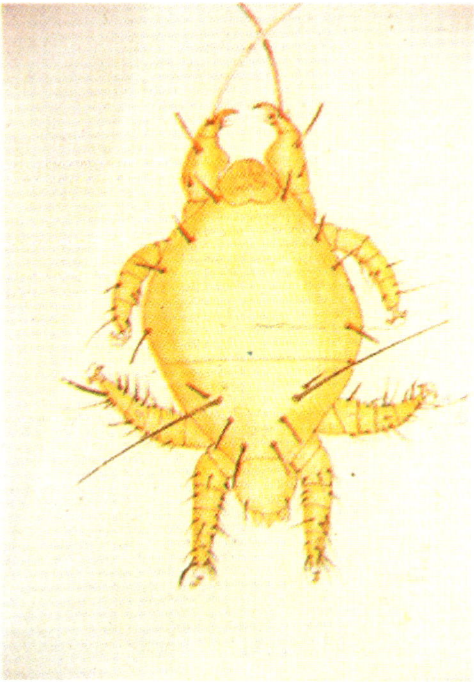

A common broad/yellow mite (Tarsonemidae)

SEM of Eriophyid mite

SEM of Eriophyid mite

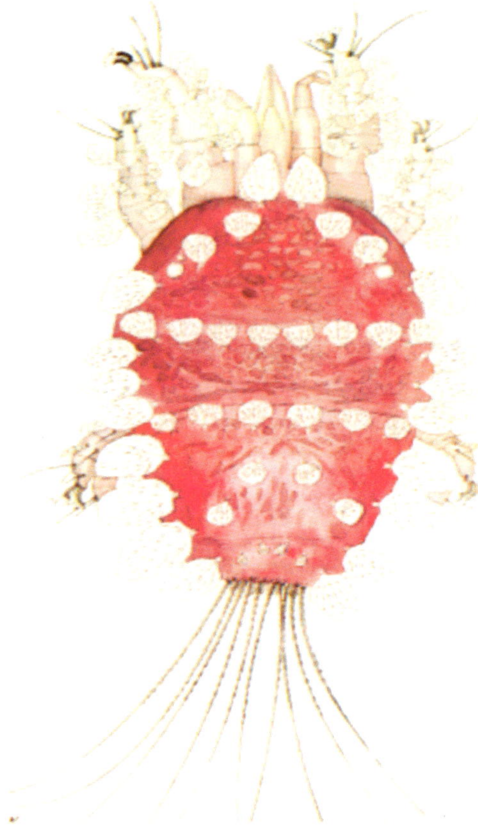

Tuckerellid mite, after Meyer, 1981

Anystid mite (Source Dr. K. Karmakar, BCKV)

Cunaxid mite (Source Dr. K. Karmakar, BCKV)

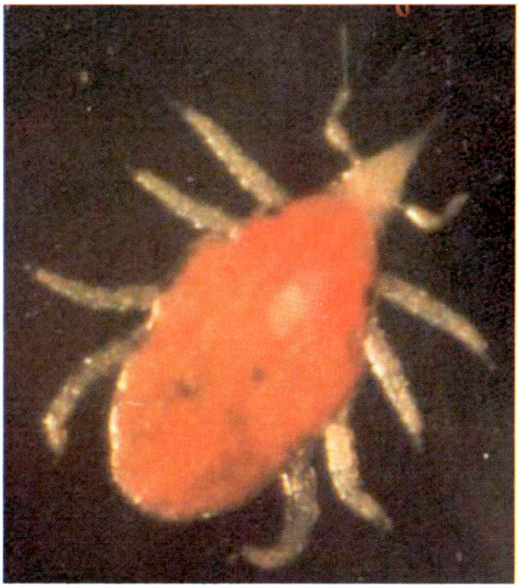

Bdellid mite (Source Dr. K. Karmakar, BCKV)

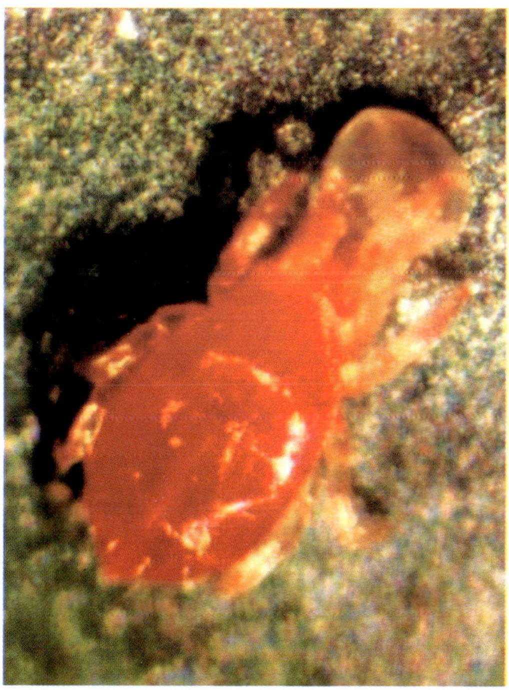

Stigmaeid mite (Source Dr. K. Karmakar, BCKV)

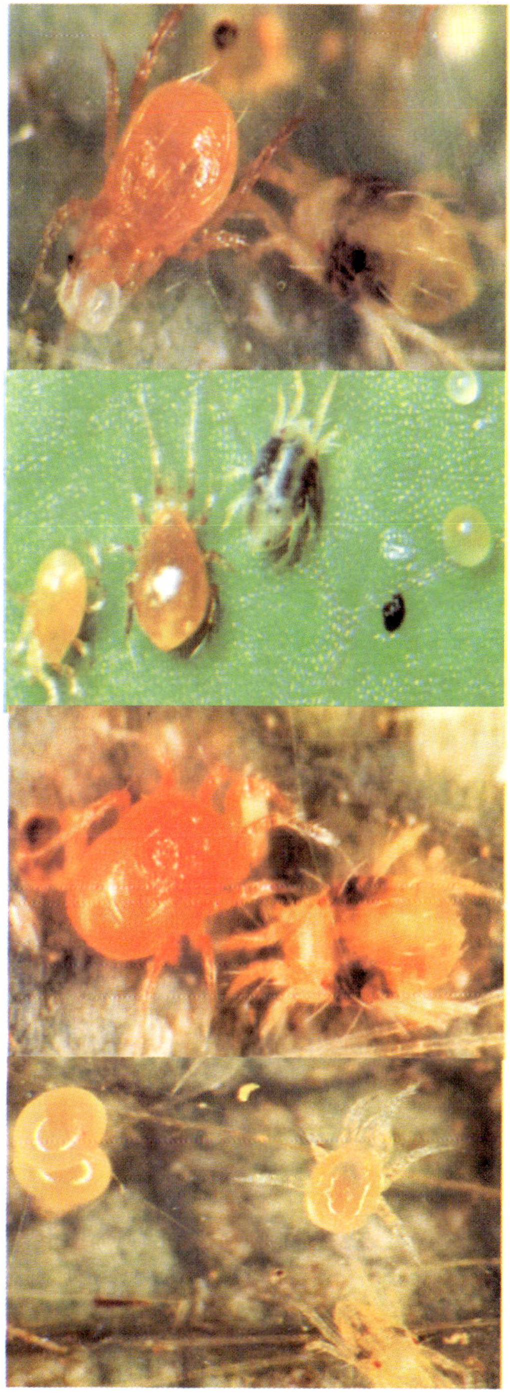

Phytoseiulus persimilis with two spotted spider mite as prey

Balooning of spider mites

Damage symptoms due to rice sheath mite, *Steneotarsonemus spinki* (Source Dr. K. Karmakar, BCKV)

Balooning of spider mites

Petrobia latens feeding on wheat leaves (a and b) and spikes (c)
Source: Sharma and Srinivasa, 2004

a & b : Damage symptoms in Jatropha due to yellow mite, *Polyphagotarsonemus latus* (Source Dr. K. Karmakar, BCKV)

Damage symptoms in Betelvine due to *Brevipalpus* sp. (Source : Dr. K. Karmakar, BCKV)

Tea leaf damaged by *Oligonychus coffeae*

Tea leaf damaged by *Brevipalpus phoenicis*

Mite colony & damage symptoms by coconut perianth mite, *Aceria guerreronis*
(Source Dr. K. Karmakar, BCKV)

Mite colony & damage symptoms by Jute yellow mite, *Polyphagotarsonemus latus*
(Source Dr. K. Karmakar, BCKV)

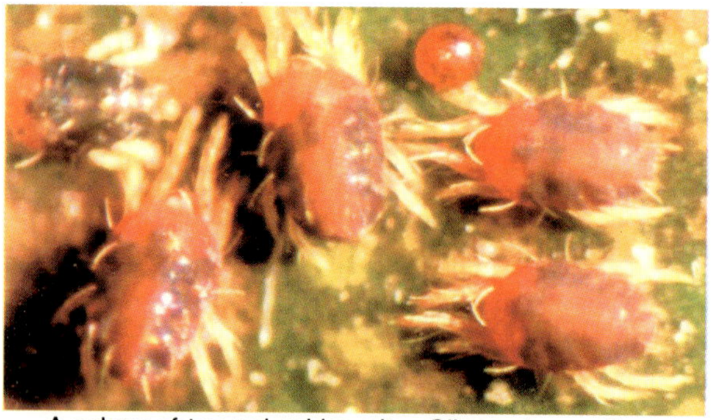

A colony of tea red spider mite, *Oligonychus coffeae*
(Source : Dr. K. Karmakar, BCKV)

Tydeid mite

Phytoseiid mite, *Neoseiulus longispinosus*
(Source : Dr. K. Karmakar, BCKV)

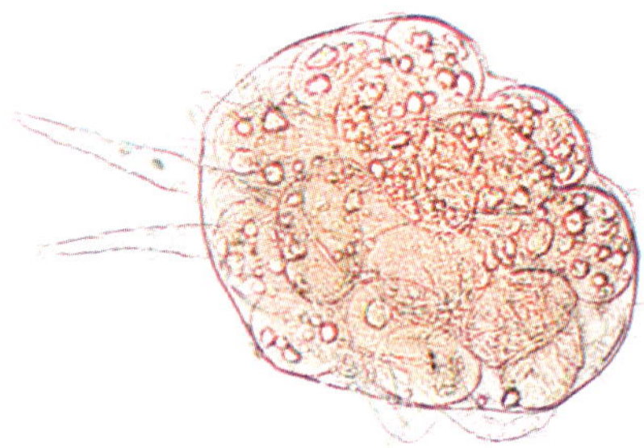

Lorryia sp., after Roy, 2010

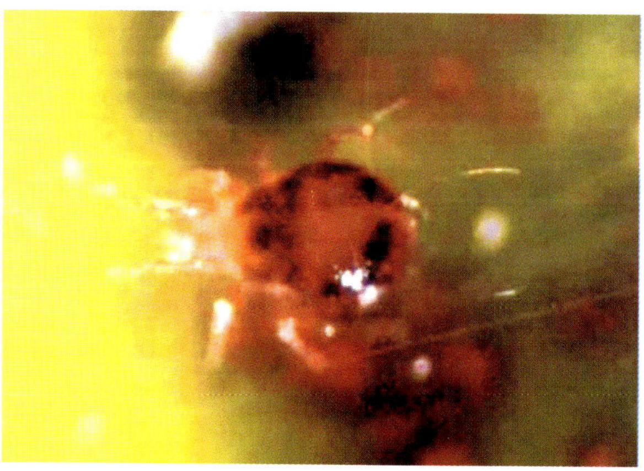

Phytoseiid mite, *Amblyseius largoensis*
(Source Dr. K. Karmakar, BCKV)

Citrus fruit damagod by
Phyllocoptruta oleivora

Stigmaeid mite under feeding condition
(Source : Dr. K. Karmakar, BCKV)

Citrus Brown Mite, Source : Meyer, 1981

Damage on pineapple leaves due to infestation of pinapple tenuipalpid mite, *Dolichotetranychus floridanus*

Damage on chilli plant showing crinkling/curling of leaves due to yellow mite infestation, *Polyphagotarsonemus latus* (both healthy and damaged plants)

Litchi leaves showing velvety brown erineum associated with an eriophyid mite, *Aceria litchii*

a

c

c

a. Citrus mite, *Brevipalpus californicus* (after Smith-Meyer, 1981)
b. Citrus Fruit browning by *Brevipalpus californicus* (after Smith-Meyer, 1981)
c. Browning of tea leaf by Citrus flat mite (after Smith-Meyer, 1981)

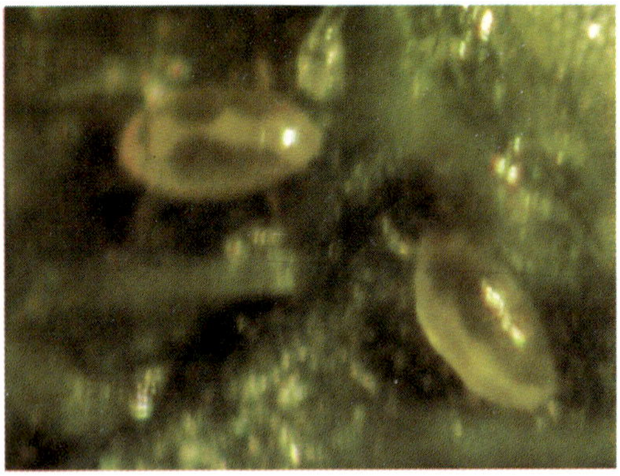

Mite colony & damage symptoms by chilli yellow mite, *P. latus* (Source : Dr. K. Karmakar, BCKV)

Mite colony and damage symptoms by garlic mite, *Aceria tulipae* (Source : Dr. K. Karmakar, BCKV)

Damage on *Cymbopogon* leaves by *Schizotetranychus cajani*

Damage on *Oxalis corniculata* leaves by *Petrobia harti*

Damage on Neem leaves by
Schizotetranychus hindustanicus

Mango web mite, *Cisaberoptus kenyae*

Damage on brinjal leaf by
Tetranychus neocaledonycus

Severe browning of leaves by two
spotted spider mites, *Tetranychus urticae*

Damaged bhendi leaf by *Tetranychus urticae*

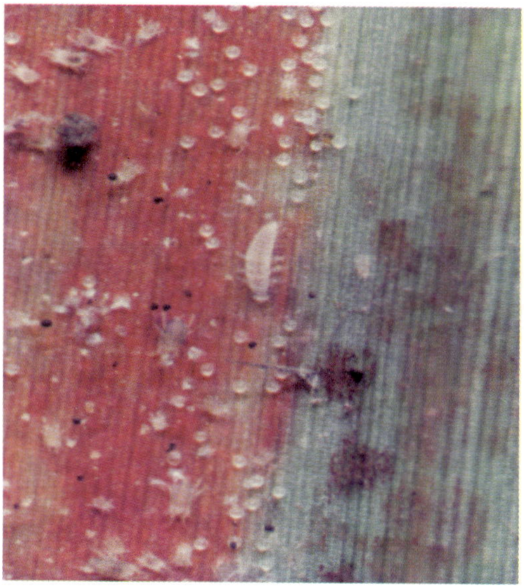

Reddish patches on sugarcane leaf by *Oligonychus indicus*

Mite webbing on leaves of ornamental plant

Leaf damaged by the pink mites, unattacked leaf on the right (Source : Muraleedharan, 1991)

Acaphylla theae, the pink mites of tea (Source : Muraleedharan, 1991)

Leaf damaged by the purple mites, unattacked leaf on the right (Source : Muraleedharan, 1991)

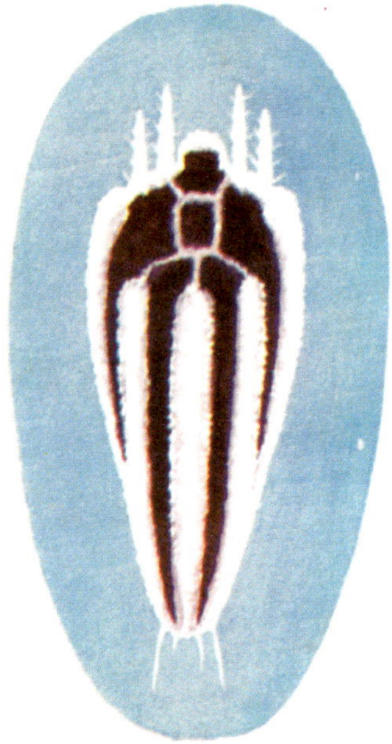

Calacarus carinatus, the purple mite of tea (Source : Muraleedharan, 1991)

Brevipalpus australis, the scarlet mite of tea (Source : Muraleedharan, 1991)

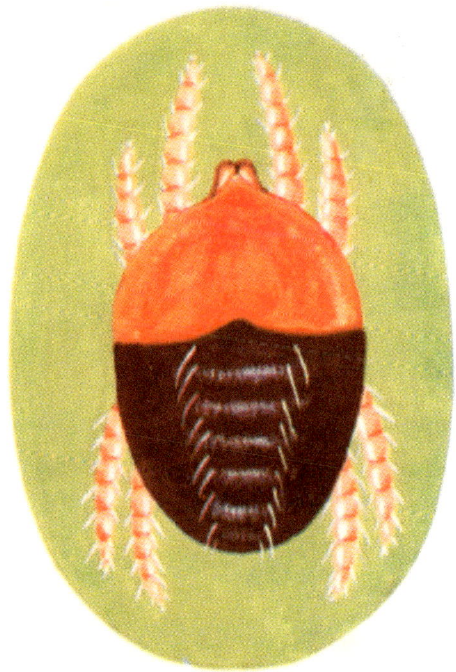

Oligonychus coffeae, the red mite of tea (Source : Muraleedharan, 1991)

Leaf and bud injury of cotton by *Acalitus gossypii* (Source : Keifer *et al.,* 1982)

Pear leaf blister mite, *Phytoptus pyri* (Source : Keifer *et al.*, 1982)

Russeting of Tomato foliage by *Aculops lycopersici* (Source : Keifer *et al.*, 1982)